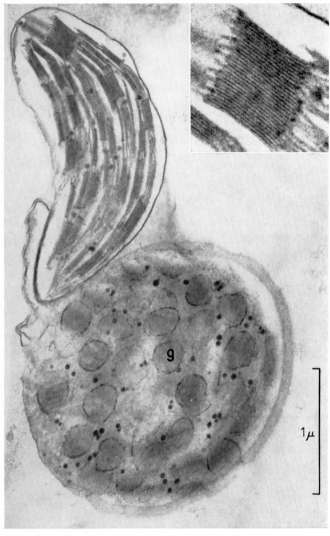

Chloroplasts from a cell of a broad bean leaf. The upper chloroplast shows grana cut transversely. The lower chloroplast is cut in the plane of the surface of the grana (g), and the wall of the chloroplast is cut obliquely. × 33,000. Inset: a single granum enlarged 100,000 times

AN INTRODUCTION TO
PLANT
PHYSIOLOGY

BY

W. O. JAMES, F.R.S.

*Professor of Botany, Imperial College
London*

SIXTH EDITION

OXFORD
AT THE CLARENDON PRESS

Oxford University Press, Amen House, London E.C.4

GLASGOW   NEW YORK   TORONTO   MELBOURNE   WELLINGTON
BOMBAY   CALCUTTA   MADRAS   KARACHI   LAHORE   DACCA
CAPE TOWN   SALISBURY   NAIROBI   IBADAN   ACCRA
KUALA LUMPUR   HONG KONG

FIRST EDITION 1931
SECOND EDITION 1933
THIRD EDITION 1936
FOURTH EDITION 1943
FIFTH EDITION 1955
SIXTH EDITION 1963
REPRINTED 1965

PRINTED IN GREAT BRITAIN

PREFACE TO THE SIXTH EDITION

VERY extensive rewriting has been found necessary for this edition, especially in those chapters dealing with metabolism, which is considered from a physiological and not only biochemical angle. The great advance of biochemistry during the past decade has given it a degree of pre-eminence which, at the moment, somewhat threatens the study of the integrated organism so that it seems the more important to preserve a due balance at this elementary level.

The gap between physiological knowledge and possible practice in class laboratories becomes greater every year and the question must be asked whether the time devoted to simple experimentation is well spent. If the study is not to become wholly unscientific it seems essential that the student should learn the right attitude towards physiological inquiry by performing and interpreting such experiments as lie within his competence and opportunities, however humble the latter may be. For this reason the simple experimental sections have been retained at the ends of the chapters.

I wish to thank my colleagues in the Imperial College botany department who have helped me in the preparation of this edition; particular thanks are due to Dr. S. E. Jacobs, Dr. J. W. Hannay, Mr. A. D. Greenwood, and also to my wife.

PREFACE TO THE FIRST EDITION

THIS book is written for readers of senior school or junior university status, and seeks to give a balanced account of the more elementary aspects of plant physiology. Recent research has not been eschewed, where fundamental principles are involved, but controversial matter has been as far as possible avoided. The aim has been to give an all-round account of the subject as it presents itself to the author, not to fulfil the requirements of any formal syllabus. Nevertheless, while writing was in progress the botany schedules of a number of representative bodies were examined, and found to contain nothing of a physiological nature which it was not proposed to include in the text.

In compiling the experimental work set out at the end of each chapter the needs of small laboratories of limited means have been kept in mind. Experiments involving special apparatus of an elaborate kind have generally been avoided, being indeed unnecessary for the purpose in view, since a very limited skill in manipulating glass vessels and tubing may be made to accomplish much. The directions given err, perhaps, on the side of too detailed a description, but the success or otherwise of an experiment depends so often upon apparent trifles that the risk has been taken. This part of the book owes much to the co-operation of my wife, formerly botany mistress at Roundhay High School.

The majority of the illustrations are original; where other sources have been drawn upon acknowledgement is made in the text. Those marked with the initials M.S. are from drawings by Miss Marie Solari, B.A., to whom I am greatly indebted.

My sincere thanks are also due to Professor A. G. Tansley, F.R.S., for reading the manuscript, and to Mr. G. R. S. Snow, M.A., for reading that of Chapter VII,[1] and to both of them for making valuable suggestions concerning the subject-matter.

[1] Now Chapter X.

CONTENTS

CHAPTER X. IRRITABILITY

PLATES

Frontispiece and Plates I (facing p. 32), II (facing p. 33),
III-V (between pp. 168 and 169), and VI (facing p. 230)

I

MATERIAL AND ENERGY

INTRODUCTION

The Nature of Plant Physiology. Since Theophrastus first collected and described the common plants of Greece, mankind has been interested in plant studies in many different ways, and very different points of view have been brought to bear on them. Even before Theophrastus' time, and in all ages since, herbs have been gathered for their real or supposed healing powers, but there has often been but little science in the matter. For a few hundred years now, botanists have studied plants for their own sakes, and have investigated their variety, form, structure, life-processes, and the societies which individual plants form, without any other motive than the increase of knowledge. Each of these aspects of the knowledge of plants has been given a distinctive name, since each may be a study in itself. The study of life-processes, or functions, and the development which results from them, is called *plant physiology*, and is the subject dealt with in this book.

Divisions such as the foregoing are made for convenience only. It is not possible to isolate a single body of facts, and study them satisfactorily, without reference to any other subject. Natural phenomena are linked together in such complex and often unexpected ways that subjects which might seem at first sight to be quite unrelated have to be considered together. It will easily be realized that plant functions cannot be properly understood unless something is known of the structures with which they are associated, and a knowledge of plant anatomy is, therefore, one of the tools with which the physiologist works. He presses many others into his service as well, and the most important of these are provided by chemistry and physics. Modern developments in these subjects have enabled plant physiologists to push forward their inquiries to an extent which would have been quite impossible before, while, on the other hand, discoveries made by the physiologists have started chemists on new and fruitful lines of investigation; the discovery of osmosis by the botanist de Vries was an example.

The methods used by plant physiologists at the present day are mainly derived from various branches of chemistry and physics; that is to say, they are similar to the methods employed in the study of non-living matter. The use of these methods has proved extraordinarily fruitful, and our knowledge of plant activities is still increasing so rapidly that it is becoming difficult to keep oneself informed of all the advances that are being made. It might, indeed, seem to an optimistic observer that the use of such methods must eventually reveal to us all the secrets of plant life; but this is not a logical conclusion, though some people believe it, because they like to think that knowledge can be thus unified. Since such a belief implies that living matter is not radically different from non-living, but is subject to the same natural laws and no others, such people may be described as *materialists*. *Vitalists*, on the other hand, are those who feel confident that sooner or later such methods will reach the end of their usefulness, leaving much still unexplained, or, in other words, that living matter is subject to special laws of its own. The strictly scientific attitude, however, is to believe neither of these things, since neither can be shown to be true at present. Meanwhile, whether either belief is held, or none, much may certainly be learnt concerning life processes by physico-chemical methods of inquiry; it is to such methods that the whole of our existing knowledge is due.

Living and Not Living. There is little difficulty in deciding whether common objects are alive or not, but the actual borderline between all living and all non-living things is very difficult to trace. No formal definition can be given which will include all living organisms and exclude all inanimate objects. Nevertheless, matter which we recognize as being alive possesses a number of properties which, taken all together, are characteristic of it, even though each individually may be shared with other things. These properties may be summarized as follows. *Continuous internal change* goes on in protoplasm, or living matter. Even seeds which seem to remain unchanged for years are usually undergoing slow maturation. *Irritability*, or the power to respond to outside changes, is very marked. Some inanimate substances react to particular external effects; selenium, for example, reacts to alterations of light intensity, but none respond to so many influences as protoplasm. The after-effects upon living matter may also be very prolonged. In some seeds, exposure to light for only 30 seconds brings them into a suitable condition for germination, when, without the light, they would not germinate at all. *Growth* by the assimilation of new matter and *reproduction* without outside interference are perhaps the most characteristic features of organic material, though they also can be imitated by the growth of crystals in saturated solutions and the behaviour of emulsions under the influence of external forces.

The Plant and its Surroundings. In spite of their special property of life, plants cannot be studied apart from their environment. Even animals, with their powers of free movement, cannot escape from dependence upon their surroundings; they must feed. In plants, although the connexion is not more real, it is certainly more obvious, because the great majority of plants spend their lives rooted to a single spot. They can only grow if suitable substances enter their roots from the soil, and it is not surprising to find that differences of soil and other surroundings exert easily noticed effects upon them. In a field of wheat, for example, the plants growing in the centre, in the full sun, are short and sturdy; they are bright green before ripening, and finally carry large ears of grain. If the planting has been carried close to a hedge, or under the shade of an overhanging oak or elm, the stalks run up to an unusual height, the colour of the leaves is much darker, but the ears are smaller; a trained observer, again, can tell a great deal about the soil of a field, and the cultivation it has undergone, by examining the crop growing on it. The state of adjustment which exists between plants and their environment is often very delicate, so that quite small changes of the latter will bring about corresponding changes in the living organism. This is strikingly illustrated by an observation made upon the sensitive leaves of the sunflower (*Helianthus annuus*). Hot, bright weather causes them to lose water rapidly, and as their cells become less turgid their area diminishes. Such shrinkages and corresponding recoveries are very rapid, and so easily brought about that it has been found possible to measure the leaf's changes as clouds pass across the sun.

The plant is not entirely the creature of its surroundings, however. High winds, shallow soil, and lack of soil-water will convert a holly-tree growing on the side of a chalk down into a stunted little bush, but no adversity of environment would change it into a juniper. Regarded in this way, plants may be said to be developed by two agencies, the chromosomes of the seed or spore, and the environment; and their physiology to consist of the results produced by external influences working upon materials provided by the plant's history and inheritance.

The influence between plant and environment is mutual.

Not only do the natural surroundings mould the plant, but they are themselves liable to be changed by it. Low-lying land, moist enough for sphagnum moss to become established upon it, may become covered with a thick layer of the plant, which grows at the tip as it dies away below. The mat of dead material blocks all drainage, and may eventually retain water over a wide area of land, turning it finally into a deep bog. The roots or underground stems of many plants growing in loose or sandy soils bind the particles together, and so prevent erosion by sea or wind. Marram grass (*Psamma arenaria*), growing on sand dunes, fixes them against the action of wind, while *Spartina townsendii* has proved a valuable agent in reclaiming tidal salt mud from the sea. These are a few instances of the many ways in which plants alter the physical features of a countryside, and they may also cause considerable changes in the atmosphere above. A covering of vegetation, for example, greatly reduces the temperature of the earth's surface and the lower layers of the atmosphere, owing to the evaporation constantly going on from the leaves. An entirely different case is that of yeast, a unicellular plant normally producing large quantities of alcohol, which pass out into the liquid in which the cells are growing, and so become part of their environment. From 4 to 10 per cent. of alcohol is fatal to most submerged organisms, but yeast is not injured at these concentrations, though if the medium is limited sufficient alcohol will accumulate to kill it in the end.

In studying the physiology of plants we are primarily concerned with things going on inside the plants themselves, but it will be clear that we also have to consider the ways in which these happenings depend on circumstances outside. In other words, we always have to take environment into account, the connexion between internal and external events being so close that no real separation can be made.

THE GREEN PLANT

The Plant as a Structure. All material structures, whether living, such as the plant, or non-living, such as a machine, can only be formed from stuff already in existence. The appearance and nature of the *raw materials* may be very much changed in the process, but there is at the end just as much matter by weight in the final product as there was in the original substances. To construct a machine there is also a second necessity; there must be *energy* to shape the materials and fasten them together in the required ways; and, finally, when the machine is complete, further energy must be supplied to drive it. This is not necessarily all of one kind; there is the mental energy of the designer and the muscular energy of the manufacturing engineers, besides electrical and other forms which they may have turned to their purpose. Finally there is the explosive or other energy which is used to drive it. Similarly, the formation of a plant from inorganic materials can only go on when energy is brought to bear upon them, and the plant's life can only continue if there is a certain amount continuously available. The essential requirements, material and energy, for formation and operation are thus the same, both for the living and non-living.

The Ability to Grow. One of the most important ways in which the living structure differs from the non-living lies in its ability to grow. Machines are formed by various agencies, usually under human control, and once formed remain unchanged except for wear and tear. Plants, on the other hand, have a steady development, and are subject to continuous change throughout their existence. Each individual has a definite history, called its *life-cycle*, which is repeated more or less closely by its successors. More important still, once the cycle is initiated by the formation of a spore or seed it continues automatically to its close without human interference. In this sense, the structure manufactures itself. It is constructed, that is to say, by the play of natural forces, those which we have named the hereditary tendencies of·the seed, together with the forces of the environment. This spontaneous development of the living organism is called its *growth*, and the fashion in which matter and energy are assimilated into the plant body in growth is one of the most important studies of plant physiology. It forms the subject of this chapter.

The Green Plant and Others. Plants containing chlorophyll are unique in their method of adding to themselves material and energy. The raw materials that they use are entirely inorganic and are converted by the plants to organic forms, resembling in their complexity and content of energy the foodstuffs of animals. Green plants may thus be said to manufacture their own food; a foodstuff being defined as any substance from which an organism derives transformable energy and material for maintenance and growth. The inorganic compounds do not provide the transformable energy; they may be called the raw materials of plant food, and they are sometimes called plant nutrients. When this is done it is necessary to keep the distinction from foodstuffs in mind.

The organic foodstuffs of animals are all derived, directly or indirectly, from those of green plants. Colourless plants resemble animals in this, and are called *heterotrophic* to distinguish them from the self-supporting, or *autotrophic*, green plants. A few bacteria, which possess a bacteriochlorophyll similar to the higher plant chlorophylls, are to be included among the autotrophes. Since they are the only organisms that convert inorganic to organic materials on any large scale, green plants are in plain fact the mainstay of the living world. The only colourless organisms known to synthesize organic matter from wholly inorganic sources are the chemosynthetic bacteria (p. 36).

The variations of structure and function in the entire range of green plants are very wide, but in the essential features of the assimilating process they resemble one another to a remarkable degree. The sources of inorganic material are few and almost always the same, and the energy drawn upon is invariably direct radiation from the sun. The essential property which distinguishes green from other plants and gives them their unique powers is their possession of the mixture of pigments called *chlorophyll*.

THE RAW MATERIALS OF GROWTH

Ten elements, carbon, hydrogen, oxygen, nitrogen, potassium, calcium, magnesium, iron, phosphorus, and sulphur, as well as others in minute amounts, are essential to the growth of the great majority of plants, and are derived in various compounds from the surrounding air and soil. Of the solid material in the plant remaining after all water has been driven off, about 90 per cent. is composed of compounds containing only carbon, oxygen, and hydrogen. On this account these three elements are of particular importance, but their significance is still further increased by the fact that the assimilation of energy is associated exclusively with their entrance into the plant. The assimilation of the remaining elements has little or no association of this kind.

PHOTOSYNTHESIS

It is indeed now clear that photosynthesis consists fundamentally of a breaking of one O—H bond in the water molecule by means of energy absorbed from sunlight by chlorophyll. The 'reducing power' represented by the hydrogen released is then used to reduce carbon dioxide. The carbon dioxide molecule is not split and the oxygen released comes from the water not from the carbon dioxide (*see* p. 22). In consisting mainly of a series of hydrogen transfers, photosynthesis resembles most other metabolic (i.e. synthetic and breakdown) processes.

Atmospheric Carbon Dioxide. The atmosphere surrounding plants contains only a very low percentage of carbon dioxide, much lower, for example, than its percentage of the inert gas argon. The average proportion in the lower atmosphere is about three parts in ten thousand, but this decreases at high levels. Even near the earth's surface the proportion is anything but constant, and there are considerable daily and seasonal variations. It has been shown, for instance, that by day the value is usually about 12 per cent. lower than at night. This is mainly due to the removal of carbon dioxide by assimilating plants, which ceases at nightfall, and measurements made in mid-Atlantic showed no fluctuations of this kind.

It has been calculated that vegetation assimilates about 1/35th of the atmosphere's carbon dioxide each year; but, in spite of this fact, the percentage has not altered appreciably during the past century. It is clear, therefore, that there must be agencies which release carbon dioxide into the atmosphere. The principal of these are the activity of volcanoes, combustion, and the respiration of plants and animals, including the so-called 'soil respiration' due to respiration and fermentation by organisms in the surface layers of the soil. As a result of all these changes, carbon is kept in continuous circulation, and its principal transformations are shown in fig. 1.

These various agents operate in different places and to some extent at different times. Winds and convection currents, especially over hot places, bring about a certain amount of mixing, but it is by comparison a slow process and local differences of concentration are continually being set up. During an eruption in Guadeloupe, the carbon dioxide content of the neighbouring atmosphere rose to 2 per cent., and measurements made in the centre of London on a bank holiday, when factory fires and human respiration would be much less than usual, showed a carbon dioxide content of about half the normal value. These

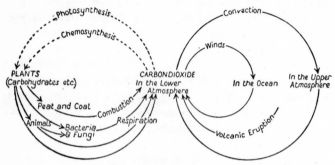

FIG. I. THE CARBON CYCLE

Diagram to show the principal natural transformations and movements of the element. On the left-hand side the broken lines indicate endothermic reactions (energy taken in), and the continuous lines exothermic reactions (energy set free)

are probably extreme examples, and the most significant fact is that the natural CO_2-concentration of the atmosphere is always very low. It follows that there must be a very high chemical affinity between carbon dioxide and the substance in assimilating cells with which it reacts.

Combustion, human respiration, and volcanic eruption occur mostly at a distance from areas covered by vegetation, so that the air of such districts usually holds a comparatively small amount of carbon dioxide. At a distance from the above sources, the carbon dioxide produced by the respiration of the plants themselves, by grazing animals, and by the organisms of the soil are of great importance.

Carbon Dioxide from the Soil. The soil population consists of many unicellular plants and animals, but by far the most numerous and important are the bacteria. When plant or animal remains fall upon the ground or are buried in it, various bacteria break down their materials, and carbohydrates, such as starch, cellulose, etc., which were present in the original material, are split up and oxidized, eventually giving rise to gaseous carbon dioxide. These changes are carried out in many stages, and often many different organisms take part. Free oxygen is not always necessary, since *anaerobic bacteria*, so named because they are able to exist in an atmosphere which is entirely devoid of gaseous oxygen, can cause changes of oxygen distribution among the organic compounds themselves. In this way, oxidized and reduced substances are formed at the same time, in the process which is called *fermentation*. When cellulose, which is very abundant in plant remains, is fermented or decomposed in the absence of oxygen, a number of organic acids, such as formic, acetic, and butyric, are produced. These contain a relatively high amount of oxygen, but hydrogen and methane also appear simultaneously. In the presence of free oxygen, methane and the acids are completely oxidized to carbon dioxide and water, various organisms being concerned. The hydrogen also becomes oxidized to water, and combustible gases are never given off by ordinary soils.

The changes going on are thus very complex, since many substances are being acted upon by a host of bacteria, fungi, and other organisms. Of the gaseous carbon dioxide which is always being formed, a great deal escapes into the lower layers of the air. For example, an unmanured and fallow field was found to give off about 250 c.c. of free carbon dioxide per hour for every square metre of its surface. The carbon dioxide thus produced by the soil is liberated near the position of carbon dioxide removal, i.e. near the leaves of plants growing upon it, and so tends to prevent the concentration from falling.

The process has been increased artificially by what is called 'carbon dioxide manuring'. Fermenting manures are added to the soil in order to increase its output of carbon dioxide. Near towns an attempt has also been made to utilize waste furnace gases, which are very rich in carbon dioxide, by laying pipes to deliver them over the surface of farm fields. In favourable years, when light and warmth have been sufficient, increased harvests have been secured by this means.

Dissolved Carbon Dioxide. Natural waters contain a great deal of carbon dioxide, but only about one-fiftieth of it is dissolved gas. The rest is associated with calcium and other bases as carbonates, bicarbonates, and the ions which arise from them, by far the most plentiful of these forms being the bicarbonate ion HCO_3^-. Such a solution is said to be 'buffered' in respect to carbon dioxide, since, whenever pure carbon dioxide is removed, it is at once replaced from the stores present in its compounds. An equilibrium is set up between the combined and free carbon dioxide in solution, and again with the gaseous carbon dioxide of the overlying atmosphere. If the latter is increased, some of it goes into solution, in which one-fiftieth part of the carbon dioxide remains as dissolved gas, and the remainder passes into the combined forms. Conversely, if the atmospheric pressure of carbon dioxide is reduced, free gas is given off from solution, the bulk of it being derived from the dissolved compounds. The oceans contain enormous quantities of such substances and therefore act as regulators of the carbon dioxide in the atmosphere above them. These adjustments are very slow, however, and do not prevent minor alterations occurring in the atmosphere from day to day.

Other Sources of Carbon. Vast quantities of carbon exist as the bicarbonate ion, HCO_3^-, and both fresh and salt water contain a great deal more bicarbonate than dissolved carbon dioxide. Various opinions have been held as to whether submerged plants assimilate this source of carbon direct. It is now believed that they do not; probably because the HCO_3^- ion enters cells too slowly to maintain observed rates of carbon assimilation. Uncharged molecules, like the carbon dioxide in solution, are likely to reach the reacting centres more rapidly. The hydration of carbon dioxide to carbonic acid and its ions is also slow unless catalysed; and carbonic anhydrase, the appropriate catalyst, has not been commonly found in assimilating cells. In other words, there is no indication that the entering carbon dioxide is converted to bicarbonate ions before it reacts with the assimilating apparatus. There are also other possible sources of carbon supply to the plant, such, for example, as the *humus*, or decayed vegetable matter, which is reached by roots penetrating the soil. It was originally believed that carbon compounds from this source were the green plant's main supply, but it has since been shown that this is not so. It appears, in fact, that the sole source of carbon for the typical green plant consists of carbon dioxide. Land plants depend upon the gaseous carbon dioxide of the atmosphere, while water plants absorb dissolved carbon dioxide, but not its derivatives.

The Entry of Carbon Dioxide. By examining a leaf section it can readily be seen that the green pigment, which is essential for the assimilation of carbon, is limited to certain plastids or small bodies differentiated from the general cytoplasm. These are called *chloroplasts* and occur in the cortical cells of green stems and aerial roots as well as in the inner tissues of leaves. Photosynthesis goes on only in the chloroplasts, so their distribution is a matter of importance.

Fig. 2 (p. 14) shows the position of the chloroplasts in

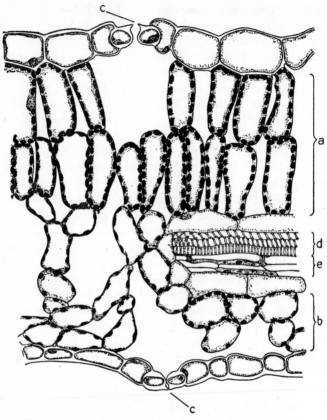

FIG. 2. VERTICAL SECTION OF A SMALL PIECE OF RHUBARB LEAF
(*Rheum officinale*)

a. palisade; *b.* spongy mesophyll; *c.* stomata, which in this leaf occur on both surfaces; *d.* xylem of a small vascular bundle; *e.* phloem. Chloroplasts shown in solid black. Highly magnified

the leaf of a land plant, and fig. 6 their position in the submerged ribbon-shaped leaf of *Sagittaria sagittifolia*. In the land plant, chloroplasts are most abundant in the elongated cells of the *palisade tissue* (fig. 2 *a*), but they also occur in the more scattered cells of the *spongy mesophyll* (*b*). There are few chloroplasts in the outermost layer of cells, or *epidermis*, except in the *guard cells* of stomata (*c*). The cells which contain the chloroplasts are always vacuolated, and the plastids occur in the thin layer of cytoplasm lining the cell wall. The walls are thin and are composed of cellulose; they are never lignified or suberized.

The Diffusion Stage. In many leaves, the stomata are confined entirely to the lower surface, and advantage has been taken of this fact to show that carbon dioxide enters the leaf only through their open pores. A small glass chamber was fitted to each surface of a leaf and a separate stream of air passed through each. The air which was passed through the upper chamber did not lose any of its carbon dioxide, but the stream passing through the lower chamber did. For another experiment the water plantain (*Alisma plantago*) was used. This has stomata on both surfaces of its leaves, the upper surface having 135 stomata for every 100 on the lower. When the experiment was carried out with this leaf it was found that the upper gas-stream lost 146 parts of carbon dioxide for every 100 lost by the lower. In other words, the amount of carbon dioxide which entered the leaf was approximately proportional to the number of stomata, and it seems clear from these experiments that, in the main, carbon dioxide gets into the leaf through the stomatal openings. A certain amount may penetrate the epidermal cells, but in the ordinary way this is quite negligible.

A sunflower (*Helianthus annuus*) leaf in bright light assimilates about 13 c.c. of carbon dioxide per hour for every 100 sq. cm. of its surface. Only about 1 per cent. of this area is occupied by stomatal openings (fig. 3), and at first sight it seems surprising that the low proportion of carbon dioxide in the atmosphere is sufficient to ensure such a supply. A careful examination of the diffusion of gases through small openings provided the solution of the mystery. It was found that a single large opening in a surface does not let nearly as much gas diffuse through it as a number of small openings set at a few diameters apart,

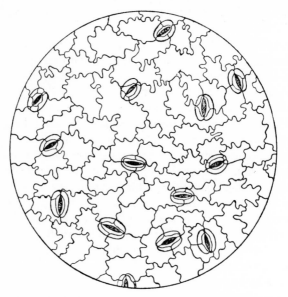

Fig. 3. Surface view of the epidermis of *Hypericum calycinum* with stomatal pores shaded. Highly magnified. (M.S.)

and having the same total area. Following up this observation, the number, size, and distribution of the stomata on sunflower leaves were examined. From the figures obtained it was calculated that no less than 258 c.c. of carbon dioxide might diffuse each hour through every 100 sq. cm. of leaf surface under normal atmospheric conditions. This is enormously in excess of the highest value observed for this species, which is only about 15 c.c., and it is, therefore,

evident that it is not the smallness of the stomatal aper-
tures which restricts photosynthesis.

In the air spaces inside the leaf there are no air movements or draughts, and the carbon dioxide travels only by
diffusion. This is a physical process depending upon the
spontaneous movements of molecules. The molecules of all
gases and of all substances in solution are supposed to be
in continuous motion. They travel in straight lines until
they collide with other molecules, when their course is
changed.

In any volume of gas the contained molecules are moving in all directions at random, and if, for example, two
equal volumes containing different numbers of molecules
are in connexion with one another, the final result of the
haphazard movements will be to equalize the two concentrations. This is called diffusion and takes place because
there will be more frequent invasions from the more
numerous molecules into the less numerous than vice versa.
It is important to notice that the pressure, i.e. number of
molecules, of other gases present will not affect this equaliz-
ing tendency, or, in other words, each gas diffuses according to its own pressure differences, and is not affected by
those of other gases. In solutions the situation is similar,
but diffusion is slower because of the obstacles afforded
by the closely packed molecules of the solvent.

The cellulose walls of the cells surrounding the air spaces
of the mesophyll are impregnated with water, indeed in
the natural condition water accounts for the greater part
of their weight. When carbon dioxide comes into contact
with these wet surfaces it goes into solution, and the final
stages of the journey to the chloroplast is performed by
diffusion in a watery medium. Gaseous diffusion is very
slow: if an opening to the atmosphere 1 sq. cm. in area
was made 1 cm above a surface of caustic soda, only
0·003 c.c. of carbon dioxide would enter the absorbent in

an hour. Diffusion through water is about ten thousand times slower, because the molecules of the gas meet with much more resistance from the closely packed water molecules to their free movement. Even though a very large area of contact is developed between the surfaces of the mesophyll cells and the intercellular air spaces through which the invasion may go on, the passage from this surface to the chloroplasts usually provides the principal resistance to carbon dioxide entry. A similar resistance has to be overcome even in submerged unicells.

Movements of Stomata. It is well known that the guard cells of stomata alter their shape from time to time and so change the area of the opening between them. A partial closing of the stomata might be expected to hinder the diffusion of carbon dioxide into the leaf and so slow down the rate of assimilation. It has been shown that this does happen; but only when the stomata are almost closed. Variations when the stomata are fairly widely open probably have little significance for photosynthesis.

The behaviour of stomata is very complex. In many plants, such as the cereals, they open widely only for a comparatively short part of the day. The stomata of some species close in the early afternoon, bringing photosynthesis to a standstill long before sundown. Potato stomata remain open all day and much of the night (fig. 4), and *Hydrangea* stomata are said never to close. There is usually a well-marked diurnal rhythm of opening and closing; but the degree of opening at any particular time may also be affected by factors among which light, humidity, and the carbon dioxide concentration inside the leaf are conspicuous.

The guard cells of the stomata have osmotic pressures usually much higher than those of the surrounding epidermal cells, and therefore tend to take up water from their neighbours until they are fully turgid. In this state they are rigid like two sausage-shaped balloons blown up with air, and they stretch their walls to their fullest extent.

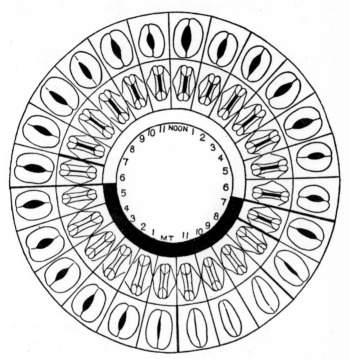

FIG. 4. DIAGRAM TO SHOW THE DAILY OPENING AND CLOSING OF STOMATA
Inner circle maize; outer circle lower surface of potato. Hours of darkness are shown by the black band. (After Loftfield, modified. M.S.)

They then appear as shown on the right-hand side of fig. 5. When their osmotic pressure is reduced, they lose water and rigidity and collapse together as the balloons would when deflated. Guard cells of open stomata commonly have osmotic pressures of about 20 atm., which drop to about 10 atm. during closure.

Water Plants. The movement of carbon dioxide towards the chloroplasts of submerged plants is simpler in some respects than the corresponding movement in aerial plants. The carbon dioxide is in solution at all stages and the leaf

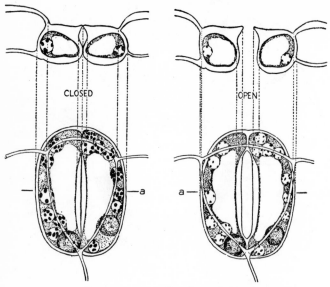

FIG. 5. STOMA OF *Hypericum calycinum*

On left-hand side the stoma is shown closed and on the right open. Surface views below, with sections along the line a a above. Chloroplasts are left white and their starch grains shown in solid black. Highly magnified

structure is usually simpler also. A typical example is shown in fig. 6. There are no stomata and the dissolved gas diffuses through the epidermis, which has thin and unmodified outer walls. The path of diffusion inside the leaf is much shorter than in aerial leaves, but diffusion is so slow in solution that it may still retard the rate of photosynthesis considerably. If the plant were submerged in a solution of carbon dioxide alone, diffusion through the water layers outside would also cause a delay, and under these conditions water currents would play a great part as accelerators of the process, because they would continually bring fresh carbon dioxide to the plant. Actually, however, most natural waters, and especially 'hard' ones, contain a good deal of carbonates and bicarbonates, and

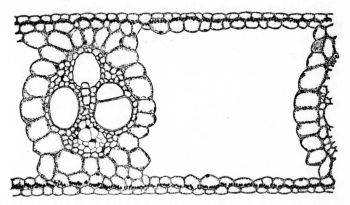

Fig. 6. TRANSVERSE SECTION OF PART OF A SUBMERGED RIBBON LEAF OF *Sagittaria sagittifolia*

The chloroplasts are shown in solid black. A large air-space appears between the two vascular bundles. Such air-spaces appear in many submerged leaves, and accumulate carbon dioxide from respiration as well as other gases. Highly magnified. (M.S.)

only about a fiftieth of their carbon dioxide supply is ever present as dissolved gas. The result is that, as plants remove carbon dioxide, it is spontaneously replaced from the bicarbonates owing to the chemical equilibrium which exists in solution (*see* p. 12). When a molecule of calcium bicarbonate releases a molecule of carbon dioxide to maintain this equilibrium, it also forms a molecule of the normal carbonate (chalk) which is very insoluble,

$$Ca(HCO_3)_2 \rightarrow CaCO_3 + CO_2 + H_2O.$$

This is why the surfaces of plants growing in hard water often develop an incrustation of chalk as carbon dioxide is removed by their assimilation. The breakdown of bicarbonate goes on rapidly at the point where carbon dioxide is removed, so that the retarding influence of diffusion is not felt, and the rate of assimilation remains fast.

Unicellular Algae. Although submerged leaves are simpler than aerial ones they still present a number of structural difficulties to the investigator of photosynthesis. These can be more successfully evaded by experimenting with unicellular green algae such as *Chlorella* species. Besides being structurally much simpler, they are easier to cultivate under carefully standardized conditions giving much less variation among cells than occurs on leaves. They are also much easier to handle accurately in experimental apparatus. For such reasons most of the great progress that has been made recently in the study of photosynthesis has depended on the use of unicells. For certain purposes the photosynthetic bacteria (p. 23) have also been invaluable.

The Source of Hydrogen. The essential feature of photosynthesis lies in the fact that carbon (absorbed into the plant as CO_2) is reduced by hydrogen to the redox level of a carbohydrate. This can be summarized as

$$O=C=O\ldots+4H \rightarrow HCOH+H_2O.$$

The dots separating the carbon dioxide and hydrogen are put in to indicate that these substances do not interact directly, but only after the CO_2 has already undergone initial transformations. Among the higher plants, the source of hydrogen is always water, so the overall equation becomes

$$CO_2+2H_2O \rightarrow HCOH+H_2O+O_2.$$

According to this mechanism, all the free oxygen released should come from the water, none from the carbon dioxide; and this has been verified by the use of water and carbon dioxide containing heavy oxygen ^{18}O. The proportion of ^{18}O in the oxygen liberated by the photosynthesis of *Chlorella* was found to be proportional to the amount in the water and independent of the amount in the carbon dioxide.

Some photosynthetic bacteria utilize other sources of hydrogen. The green and purple sulphur bacteria, Thiorhodaceae, use H_2S, and sulphur is formed instead of oxygen. The Athiorhodaceae may even use free hydrogen, and the green alga, *Scenedesmus*, has been trained to do the same. This corresponds with the first equation above, and no oxygen or other oxidized component is formed. These variations emphasize the transfer of hydrogen as the fundamental feature of photosynthesis. The transfer may involve considerable increase of free energy, especially when the very stable union of hydrogen to oxygen in water is broken. The additional energy is acquired from the incident light.

The Action of Light. Some chemical reactions, such as the liberation of free iodine from a solution of potassium iodide, only go on in the presence of light. During their course light energy is absorbed which may provide the energy for the chemical change or be transformed to heat or emitted again as fluorescence. These are called photochemical reactions. The initial photochemical reaction is always followed by a series of 'dark' or 'thermal' reactions. Photosynthesis includes one or more photoreactions and numerous dark reactions (p. 30).

The Action Spectrum of Photosynthesis. Sunlight is not a single form of energy, but a mixture of radiations of various kinds, distinguished by their different wave-lengths. The power to bring about photosynthesis is not limited to any one wave-length, but is possessed in varying degrees by the whole visible spectrum. Before light can cause photosynthesis it must first be absorbed by the pigments in the chloroplasts. It has long been known that those wave-lengths which are most strongly absorbed cause most photosynthesis, though the yield is not strictly proportional to the amount of light absorbed.

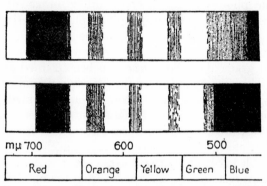

Fig. 7. Upper band: absorption spectrum of a colloidal solution of chlorophyll. Lower band: absorption spectrum of a stinging-nettle leaf. (After Willstätter)

It appears that a quantum of light absorbed by chlorophyll (the principal photosynthetic pigment) brings about the same amount of photosynthesis irrespective of its energy content, i.e. of its colour. But the quantum yield of photosynthesis in a green leaf or an algal suspension does vary to some extent with the colour of the incident light. It is lower in the blue-green region of the spectrum than in the red. The chlorophylls absorb light most strongly at the red end (wave-length about 650 to 700 mμ) as shown in the upper band of fig. 7. The lower band of the figure shows that there is a good deal of light absorption by a living leaf at the blue end of the spectrum which is not accounted for by the chlorophylls and which is, in fact, due to the carotenoids. Accurate determination of how much of the incident light goes into the chlorophylls and how much into the carotenoids at this end of the spectrum is extremely difficult; but the best results available seem to show that the light absorbed by the carotenoids is not wholly lost. They are probably acting as accessory sensitizers. Pigments dissolved in the cell sap, like the red pigments of copper beech and blood hazel leaves, cannot do this.

All the plastid pigments fluoresce; but when a suspension of algae is illuminated by monochromatic light primarily absorbed by a carotenoid, the only fluorescence observed is that of chlorophyll. Similar observations can be made with mixtures of extracted pigments. The explanation can only be that energy is transferred from the other pigments to chlorophyll. In a mixture of chlorophylls the transfer is from chlorophyll-b to chlorophyll-a, whose absorption and emission spectra lie a little more towards the red. The transfer is always towards the red, i.e. such that the quanta become smaller. It is now generally supposed that chlorophyll-a is the final acceptor of light energy towards which the energy absorbed by all the other pigments is funnelled.

Some Properties of Chlorophyll. Chlorophyll can be extracted from leaves, without changing its composition, by a mixture of 80 per cent. acetone and 20 per cent. water, and can afterwards be separated from various impurities by transferring it to petrol ether. It forms a rich green solution with a blood-red fluorescence. It is not a pure substance, but has been shown to be a mixture of pigments, chlorophyll-a and chlorophyll-b, which are always accompanied by carotins and xanthophylls. The chlorophylls give green solutions with a strong blood-red fluorescence, the carotins are orange-red, and the xanthophylls yellow.

They may be separated on a carefully prepared column of calcium carbonate or cellulose. When a mixed solution is poured on to the column, the solvent runs through, taking the carotin with it and leaving the other pigments adsorbed upon the carbonate. If the column is then developed by pouring through petrol ether, the remaining pigments separate from one another owing to their different adsorbabilities, with the xanthophylls farthest down, chlorophyll-*b* near the top, and chlorophyll-*a* in the middle (*see also* **exp. 12**). Separations can also be made by means of the different solubilities of the pigments in various organic solvents.

The chlorophylls can be completely extracted from leaves by boiling them with ethyl alcohol; but they are esterified by the hot alcohol to ethyl chlorophyllides. Chlorophylls *a* and *b* are closely related in their molecular structures which are built upon a complex porphyrin ring similar to that of the blood pigment haemoglobin; but, whereas the haem contains an atom of iron, the chlorophylls contain an atom of magnesium. Joined to the porphyrin ring there is a long phytyl side chain which is soluble in lipids. Carotins are long-chain hydrocarbons and xanthophylls are similar, but contain a little oxygen in —OH groups attached to their hydrocarbon chains.

Fine Structure of Chloroplasts. Although chloroplasts may take many shapes and sizes in the green algae they are fairly uniform in the cells of higher plants. They are bun-shaped and about 10 μ (0·01 mm) in diameter and about 5 μ thick. They are separated from the general cytoplasm by a continuous membrane. The stroma (ground substance) lying within the membrane consists of lipids and proteins and is itself without visible structure, but it encloses the grana, the pigment-carrying bodies, which are usually about 1 μ across. Grana can just be seen, given favourable material, under the light microscope. The electron microscope has revealed that grana consist of piles of thin circular lamellae stacked like piles of pennies (Plate I facing p. 32). The lamellae lie in the same plane as the main axis of the chloroplast itself. The number of grana in a chloroplast and the number of platelets in a granum are very variable with species. In the algae the lamellae extend continuously throughout the entire chloroplast forming, as it were, a single large granum. Even in the higher plants there are often some lamellae stretching through the stroma from one granum to another.

It is generally supposed that the lamellae revealed by the electron microscope are formed of layers of lipids (fats and phospho-lipids) and of protein to one or both of which the pigment molecules are attached. About one-third of the solids in a chloroplast consists of lipids and the rest is mostly protein. A conjugated chlorophyll-protein has been isolated from leaves with an absorption spectrum very similar to that of the intact leaf. Contrary to what was at first supposed the pigment molecule is probably not attached to the protein through its magnesium atom since the bond persists after the magnesium has been removed. It seems likely that the chlorophyll molecules may be anchored to the lipid layers by the fat-solubility of their phytol chains (p. 26). The pigments and fats are readily removed together (and without proteins) by fat solvents. The carotenoids which are able to transmit the energy they absorb at least partially to the chlorophylls are also probably dissolved in the lipid layers. The molecular pattern of the chloroplast lamellae is proving difficult to elucidate accurately. It is no doubt of great importance in securing the high efficiency with which light absorbed by the pigments is used in photosynthesis.

Function of Chlorophyll in Photosynthesis. Chlorophyll and the associated pigments absorb light which could not be absorbed by water. When a chlorophyll molecule absorbs a photon (a light quantum) it becomes excited, i.e. able to perform reactions or emit energy (as heat or fluorescence) which it could not perform in its normal ground state. At least three excitation levels of chlorophyll are known, but in none of them has a chlorophyll molecule acquired enough energy to split an O—H bonding. The lifetimes of excited states are exceedingly short and it is still uncertain how the energy of two or more photons is combined to bring about photolysis of the O—H bond. The least excited above the ground state has a mean lifetime of 10^{-2} seconds which would permit energy migrations between molecules, and this may indicate the significance of the close packing of chlorophyll molecules upon the chloroplast lamellae.

The action of the chlorophylls is catalytic and they are not used up. Neither the amount of chlorophyll in a leaf nor the proportions of the constituent pigments is changed during a prolonged period of photosynthesis. The reactions of the pigments during photosynthesis must therefore be readily reversible. Most of the known reactions of the extracted pigments are irreversible and therefore, do not help to indicate their photosynthetic role.

Other Internal Factors. Attempts have been made to synthesize sugars by bubbling carbon dioxide through chlorophyll solutions outside the plant. They have all failed under whatever conditions they were carried out, because chlorophyll is not the only part of the chloroplast which is engaged in the process. This has been shown by measuring the photosynthesis of young bean seedlings from the time they were a week old. At this period they were fully green, but could hardly assimilate at all. After a fortnight, however, assimilation was rapid, though there was no more chlorophyll than before. The increased photosynthesis must have been due to the development of some other factor or factors, such as enzymes, in the chloroplasts, whose formation in the bean plant is slower than that of the chlorophyll.

The growth of the plant depends upon an adequate supply of certain inorganic substances (*see* p. 8), and any deficiency of these has a very marked effect upon photosynthesis. Magnesium, for example, is necessary for the formation of chlorophyll, but other essential elements, such as potassium, do not enter into any of the known parts of the photosynthetic apparatus.

Water is also essential for photosynthesis, and is derived from the internal supply which reaches the leaves from the roots. It is always present in very considerable excess, the quantity of water used in photosynthesis being a very small proportion of that which passes through the plant.

The Interaction of Factors. The speed at which photosynthesis goes on depends upon the concentration of available carbon dioxide, the quantity of chlorophyll, the intensity of light, temperature, and other factors. Each of these exercises its effect upon the rate of the process, and an increase in any one of them may cause a faster rate. An increase of carbon dioxide concentration from 0·1 per cent. to 0·2 per cent. was found to accelerate the rate of photosynthesis of the water moss *Fontinalis antipyretica* by 42 per cent. An increase from 0·3 per cent. to 0·4 per cent. only caused an additional 35 per cent., while an increase from 3 per cent. to 4 per cent. caused no acceleration at all. If a brighter light was used, there was a greater response to increases in the concentration of carbon dioxide. Two things have to be remembered therefore: first, that the effect of an increase of any given factor is greatest when its intensity is low; and, second, that its effect is always modified by that of other factors. The interference of other factors can, however, be reduced to negligible proportions by making their intensities so high that further increases do not accelerate photosynthesis. In this way, the effect of single factors can be isolated, and studied in detail.

If all the controllable factors are increased, photosynthesis can be made to go on much faster than under normal outdoor conditions. There is a limit, however, above which the mechanism breaks down; too high a light intensity destroys the chlorophyll by oxidation, and too much carbon dioxide acts as an anaesthetic. Even before destructive intensities are reached, the mechanism becomes light-saturated, indicating that not only photochemical but also other and slower reactions are involved.

Thermal Reactions. When carbon dioxide and light are both abundant so that neither restrict the rate of photosynthesis, the rate is found to depend on temperature. This must be because ordinary 'dark' or thermal reactions are then controlling the rate. These reactions are collectively called the Blackman reaction from their discoverer. Their existence is confirmed in a striking way by the action of flashing light. It has been found that a given quantity of light causes more photosynthesis if it is given as a series of flashes, separated by short dark intervals, than if it is given continuously. The amount of photosynthesis per flash increases, as the dark intervals are lengthened, up to about an eighth of a second. This indicates further that the dark reactions must take about an eighth of a second to consume the photoproduct. The photoreactions themselves are virtually instantaneous, because flashes of extremely short duration give the full yield of photoproduct.

The dark reactions which consume the photoproducts are now known to be numerous. If the products of the photolysis of water are XH and YOH, there is on the one hand the series of reactions which leads to the release of oxygen from YOH, and on the other hand the series which utilizes the XH to reduce a CO_2-complex to the carbohydrate level.

The Carbon Path in Photosynthesis. Carbon dioxide is fixed without the assistance of light in chemical carboxylations, i.e. reactions of the type

$$RH + CO_2 \rightarrow RCOOH$$

in almost all living cells (p. 39). It is now supposed that photosynthesis is no exception to this rule. The discovery of the substance that accepts CO_2 in such a reaction during photosynthesis had to await two things; the provision of radioactive $^{14}CO_2$, capable of labelling small amounts of the compounds into which it is built, and the development of a method capable of separating the small amounts of nearly related compounds occurring in photosynthesizing cells.

It was then found that when $^{14}CO_2$ was fed to brightly illuminated suspensions of unicellular algae, the first substance to become labelled was 3-phosphoglyceric acid

$$H_2PO_3OCH_2CH_2OHCOOH.$$

This occurred very rapidly; detectable amounts of acid labelled in the carboxyl group were formed within a few seconds. Later the labelling spread to a wide variety of other materials as they were synthesized from the primary photosynthetic products.

Since carbon dioxide fixation in photosynthesis is a continuous process, the acceptor substance must be constantly renewed as it is converted to phosphoglyceric acid. This implies a cyclic series of reactions into which CO_2 is fed and from which an equivalent amount of carbon is passed to C_6 photosynthetic products for each turn of the cycle. It is now virtually certain that the cycle includes a number of sugar-phosphates (see p. 61) of C_4, C_5, and C_7 chain-lengths. Among these the C_5 compound, ribulose 1,5-diphosphate, is specially interesting because it appears to be the CO_2-acceptor. Its carboxylation differs from most carboxylations like the one mentioned above (p. 31) by being strongly exergonic. It releases 8000 cal per mole whereas most other carboxylations require a considerable input of energy. This difference is associated with the fact that the carboxylation of the C_5-compound does not give a stable C_6-compound, but two molecules of a C_3-compound, the phosphoglyceric acid. It therefore occurs readily in the dark independent of light or any other supply of energy.

The Reduction of 3-Phosphoglyceric Acid. It has been pointed out earlier that the effect of the photo-reactions of photosynthesis is to generate 'reducing power' as hydrogen (or electrons). The first reduced compound at present identifiable is reduced nicotinamide-adenine trinucleotide ($NADPH_2$, p. 62). It is this that reduces the 'fixed' CO_2 which we now recognize as phosphoglyceric acid. It can further be said that it is the phosphoglyceric acid itself (not some further derivative) which is reduced and that the product is initially phosphoglyceraldehyde which sets up an equilibrium mixture with the corresponding keto compound dihydroxyacetone phosphate. This mixture then leads on to the other products of the acceptor cycle.

The reduction of phosphoglyceric acid to phosphoglyceraldehyde is an endergonic reaction which only occurs under the 'electron pressure' generated by the photoreactions. Its opposite reaction is exergonic and occurs spontaneously during respiration (p. 97). The photosynthetic reaction is not, therefore, a unique biological reaction proceeding in reverse due to the special

PLATE I

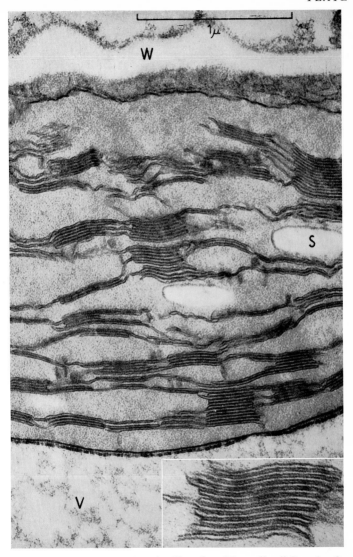

Portion of a transverse section of a chloroplast; W = cell wall, S = site of starch formation, V = cell vacuole. × 42,000. Inset: a single granum showing the double nature of the internal lamellae. × 80,000. The plastid has been treated with permanganate, causing partial oxidation of the constituents and leaving the lamellae more visible

PLATE II

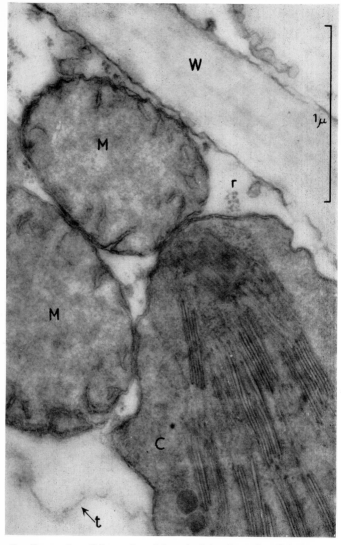

Small part of a cell from a broad bean leaf showing cell wall (W) with middle lamella; one end of a chloroplast (C) showing double membrane round the outside; two mitochondria (M) showing double wall and infoldings; tonoplast (t) and ribosomes (r). ×47,000

energy conditions. The opposite photosynthetic and respiratory phases of the reaction do not tangle, because the photosynthetic reduction occurs only within the chloroplasts and the respiratory oxidation only in the cytoplasm. They are catalysed by two different enzymes located in the two different sites and associated with two different coenzymes. Both enzymes are called triosephosphate dehydrogenases; the chloroplast enzyme operates with $NADPH_2$ (p. 32) as explained above and the respiratory enzyme with $NADH_2$ (p. 104).

Isolated Chloroplasts. It is possible to isolate chloroplasts from the other fragments of broken-up cells by careful centrifuging. It has been known for some time that if a suspension of isolated chloroplasts is illuminated in the presence of a strong oxidizing agent such as a ferric salt, or even a redox dye, they continue to evolve oxygen. This reaction can also be carried on by grana isolated from broken chloroplasts. It requires the same wave-lengths of light as photosynthesis, becomes saturated at moderate light intensities, and has other characteristics relating it to normal photosynthesis.

It was more difficult to show that isolated chloroplasts would reduce oxidized NADP which now appears to be the substance that the artificial oxidizing agents were replacing. More recently this has been achieved by more careful preparation of the chloroplast suspensions and by adding back cofactors presumed to have been lost from the chloroplasts during isolation. One of the most important of these is ADP (p. 61) which is phosphorylated to ATP simultaneously with the reduction of the NADP. The energy-rich ATP so formed is used in promoting the dark reactions leading to sugar formation, so emphasizing once more the similarity of photosynthetic and respiratory reactions. Photophosphorylation (ADP $\rightarrow$ ATP) in chloroplasts is, however, associated with reduction whereas respiratory phosphorylation depends on oxidation. When chloroplasts are finally purified from other cell fractions by recentrifuging in a density gradient it can be shown that they contain none of the respiratory oxidizing systems.

The Primary Products of Photosynthesis. All the substances of which a plant is composed contain carbon which has been fixed in photosynthesis. When $^{14}CO_2$ is fed to an illuminated plant the labelling is distributed by degrees to all the new compounds synthesized. It has been traditional to consider the sugars, especially glucose, fructose, and sucrose, the end products of photosynthesis as such, and their subsequent changes and interactions as opening a further stage in metabolism.

In the experiments in which illuminated algae were fed with $^{14}CO_2$, phosphoglyceric acid could be detected after about 5 seconds. Within the first minute there was also detectable triosephosphate (phosphoglyceraldehyde and dihydroxyacetone phosphate); and hexosephosphates. The hexosephosphates were labelled on the two middle carbon atoms of their carbon chain, consistent with the idea that they had been formed by the fusion of two triosephosphate molecules end to end. About this stage some labelled sucrose appeared and a little later glucose and fructose. The free sugars are probably formed secondarily from their phosphate esters but still within the chloroplasts. It has long been known that even starch, a more complex product, is formed within the chloroplasts themselves. It is further interesting that some amino-acids, and others such as succinic and citric acids, were found to be labelled as rapidly as the sugars. This is considered further on p. 128.

The oxygen set free during photosynthesis escapes into the intercellular spaces of leaves. From submerged plants

FIG. 8. STARCH GRAINS IN CHLOROPLASTS

Left from assimilating cells of *Pellionia deveauana*, right from potato plant. The chloroplasts are shaded and the starch grains left white. In *Pellionia* the starch is precipitated in a single large grain, but in the potato plant each chloroplast forms several grains, which do not reach so large a size. The latter arrangement is much more frequent than the former. Highly magnified

it may go into solution in the surrounding water; but if it is given off rapidly, or if the water is saturated, it comes off as small bubbles which form at the surface of the plant, or escape from the intercellular spaces through any breaks. When photosynthesis is proceeding at a steady rate, the volume of oxygen liberated is equal to the volume of carbon dioxide consumed. This means that the number of molecules of oxygen released equals the number of CO_2

molecules reduced, and is in agreement with the equation on p. 22. It does not, as is often assumed, mean that the number of water molecules utilized is necessarily the same also.

The Energy Transformed in Photosynthesis. Vast quantities of sunlight are transformed every year by green plants. It has been calculated that about $2 \cdot 5 \times 10^{10}$ tons of carbon are fixed by land plants every year and an equal amount by the seaweeds and plankton of the oceans. This represents an energy income from the sun of about 5×10^{17} kcal per year.

Not all the sunlight falling on a leaf is fixed by photosynthesis, but only a very small proportion. The remainder is converted into heat or lost by reflection or transmission. The following table represents in round figures the partition of light energy falling upon the leaf of a land plant; but it must be remembered that the numbers vary within fairly wide limits according to circumstances.

Incident energy (light)	.	.	.	100
Light fixed by photosynthesis		.	.	1
Light reflected or passing through leaf	.			30
Heat absorbed by transpiration		.	.	49
Heat radiated into atmosphere		.	.	20

In the unicellular green algae there is no transpiration and less grey matter to absorb light and transform it to heat, and it has been found accordingly that *Chlorella*, a member of this class, fixes a much greater proportion of the incident light than do aerial leaves.

CHEMOSYNTHESIS

Green plants and the organisms, such as animals, fungi, and bacteria, that depend upon them all derive their energy directly or indirectly from sunlight. There are however a few bacteria that live and grow quite independently of light and of the compounds formed by green plants under its influence. They resemble photosynthesizing plants in the source of their carbon which is still carbon dioxide; but the necessary energy is not derived from sunlight, as these organisms are able to assimilate in complete darkness. The

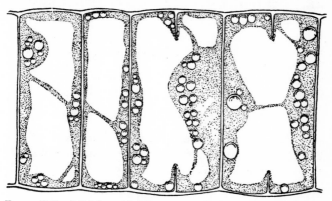

FIG. 9. Cells of *Beggiatoa mirabilis* showing sulphur grains in the protoplasm. (Redrawn after Hinze.) × 750

energy that they utilize is the product of chemical reactions, and various oxidizable substances present in soils or stagnant pools are made to release energy by oxidation. Very little is known about the means by which this energy is harvested, or how the carbon dioxide is reduced, or into what compounds it is converted. Examples of chemosynthetic bacteria are *Beggiatoa*, oxidizing hydrogen sulphide; *Leptothrix*, oxidizing ferrous salts; *Hydrogenomonas*, oxidizing hydrogen; *Nitrosomonas*, oxidizing ammonium ions; and *Nitrobacter*, oxidizing nitrites.

The Sulphur Bacteria. The *Beggiatoa* group of bacteria is found in sulphur springs or bogs, and can exist in the mud saprophytically upon decaying organic matter. If carbon dioxide and hydrogen sulphide, from putrefying material, are present, it becomes independent of the organic matter and carries out its own primary synthesis. The sulphuretted hydrogen is oxidized to sulphur and water:

$$2H_2S + O_2 \rightarrow 2H_2O + S_2 + 65 \text{ kcal.}$$

Particles of solid sulphur (fig. 9) are formed inside the bacterium, and may eventually be further oxidized to sulphuric acid:

$$S_2 + 2H_2O + 3O_2 \rightarrow 2H_2SO_4 + 283 \cdot 6 \text{ kcal.}$$

Free sulphuric acid does not accumulate, but reacts immediately with carbonates from the external water:

$$H_2SO_4 + CaCO_3 \rightarrow CaSO_4 + CO_2 + H_2O.$$

Energy becomes available in the oxidations represented by the first two equations, and is used to assimilate dissolved carbon dioxide. When *Beggiatoa* is kept in tap-water it dies if deprived of either carbon dioxide or sulphuretted hydrogen.

Thiobacillus denitrificans is also able to oxidize sulphur; but, unlike *Beggiatoa*, does not use free oxygen but potassium nitrate as the oxidizer. The sulphur is oxidized to potassium and calcium sulphates, and the nitrogen of the nitrate is released as gas.

Iron Bacteria. *Leptothrix* and similar organisms possess the power of oxidizing ferrous compounds into ferric hydrate. They occur in ditches and other swampy places, and their presence becomes apparent owing to the rusty-red deposit of ferric hydrate, which may be very considerable. A large proportion of the world's iron deposits are thought to have originated in this way.

Nitrifying Bacteria. A very important class of chemo-synthetic bacteria are those which oxidize reduced nitrogenous compounds. Ammonia is produced as a final product of putrefaction and gives rise to ammonium ions in the soil. Their oxidation provides the bacterium *Nitrosomonas* with the energy necessary for sugar formation:

$$(NH_4)_2CO_3 + 3O_2 \rightarrow 2HNO_2 + CO_2 + 3H_2O + 148 \text{ kcal.}$$

The nitrites which are formed by the nitrous acid are further oxidized to nitrates by a second bacterium, *Nitrobacter*, which is thus able to synthesize organic compounds in its turn:

$$Ca(NO_2)_2 + O_2 \rightarrow Ca(NO_3)_2 + 22 \text{ kcal.}$$

Nitrosomonas and *Nitrobacter* are plentiful in all fertile soils, and the oxidations from which they derive their synthesizing energy have important effects upon the nitrogen contents of such soils. This aspect of their activity is dealt with in the fourth chapter.

CARBON DIOXIDE ASSIMILATION IN THE DARK

It has been discovered that practically all types of organisms are capable of assimilating carbon dioxide to some extent in the dark and without the oxidation of simple inorganic materials. The amount of fixation may not be great and its functional significance, if any, is not very clear. The usual product of the fixation is a carboxylic organic acid. Among plants, this kind of carbon dioxide assimilation is greatest in the succulent leaves of the Crassulaceae, where it may lead to the accumulation of considerable amounts of malic acid. The reaction is not inhibited by light; but usually ceases under illumination because photosynthesis reduces carbon dioxide to a very low concentration in the tissues. The dark carboxylation of ribulose diphosphate that occurs during photosynthesis can take place at very low carbon dioxide concentrations such as the 0·03 per cent. in the air. The carboxylation that leads to malic acid formation in the dark is less efficient and is suppressed when the two are in competition. If the carbon dioxide concentration is raised to about 5 per cent. and the leaves are kept cool, malic acid continues to accumulate in the light. The CO_2-acceptor in this reaction is either pyruvic acid or phosphoenolpyruvic acid and the product is oxaloacetic acid:

$$CH_3COCOOH + CO_2 \rightarrow COOHCH_2COCOOH$$

$$CH_2COH_2PO_3COOH + CO_2 + H_2O \rightarrow$$
$$COOHCH_2COCOOH + H_3PO_4.$$

When phosphoenolpyruvic acid is the reactant the carboxylation becomes exergonic owing to the simultaneous release of phosphate. If the reactant is pyruvic acid itself about 8 kcal of energy has to be supplied by respiration for each mole of malic acid formed.

EXPERIMENTAL WORK

The value of experimental work is always increased if careful notes and, whenever possible, diagrams are made.

Exp. 1. REDUCING SUGARS IN A LEAF EXTRACT

Cut up a lily, turnip, or other leaf which has been exposed to bright light, and crush it well with a little water. Filter the liquid into a test-tube, which should be about one-third filled. Add about 3 ml of Fehling's solution (p. 317) and then boil for a minute.

Fehling's solution is strongly alkaline and contains cupric hydrate, which is deep blue in colour. Substances such as reducing sugars (glucose, fructose, etc.) can reduce the copper in an alkaline medium to cuprous oxide, which is bright red and insoluble. If a reducing sugar was present in your leaf, the blue colour of the Fehling's will become fainter on boiling, and be replaced by a bright red or brick-red precipitate.

Exp. 2. Reducing Sugars in a Leaf Section

Fill a watch-glass with Fehling's solution, and then cut some transverse sections of a fresh onion leaf. The razor and sections should be moistened with alcohol during the cutting. The sections should be just thin enough to be translucent when mounted. Transfer several sections to the Fehling's solution, place the watch-glass on a water-bath, and allow it to heat slowly. The solution must not be allowed to dry up, and as the volume in the watch-glass shrinks distilled water should be added a few drops at a time from a pipette. While the heating is going on, mount a freshly cut section in water, or dilute glycerine, and keep for comparison. When the watch-glass has been on the water-bath for 5–10 minutes, remove a section with a brush, mount in the same way, and examine under a microscope. The precipitate of cuprous oxide will be visible as minute spherical particles, which appear shiny or black, and not red, owing to their minute size. If some sugar has escaped from the sections, the colour of the precipitate may become visible to the naked eye in the external solution.

Exp. 3. The Presence of Non-reducing and Combined Sugars in Leaves

Take several leaves of one of the species named below, and grind them up thoroughly with about 50 ml of water in a mortar. Filter some of the liquid into a flask and bring to the boil. Add Fehling's solution a few drops at a time, until there is no further precipitation and the blue colour remains. Allow the precipitate to settle and filter off the bulk of the clear liquid. Boil this with a few drops of strong sulphuric acid for several minutes. Then make neutral to litmus by adding a few drops of caustic soda. Add about 10 ml of Fehling's solution and boil again. A red precipitate will be formed once more, due to the formation of reducing sugars by the hydrolysis, through the agency of the sulphuric acid, of sucrose, a non-reducing sugar, and of various glycosides, i.e. sugar compounds.

Suitable plants are garden nasturtium (*Tropaeolum*) and beet. In the winter, greenstuffs: cabbage, brussels sprouts, etc., will be found useful.

Exp. 4. THE FORMATION OF STARCH FROM SUGARS

Sterilize two beakers by washing them with 1 per cent. formalin, and rinsing out the last traces of the fluid, first with freshly boiled water and finally with the experimental liquids. These are a 5 per cent. sucrose solution and pure distilled water, both previously sterilized by boiling. Take two destarched *Pelargonium* leaves (from a plant kept for 2 days in the dark), cut a new surface to the stalk close to the lamina and float one on each liquid. Cover each beaker with a loose piece of glass, and put aside in a dark cupboard for several days. It is necessary during this time that the leaves shall receive plenty of air, so a tight joint between the beakers and their covers must not be made; a cover is necessary to prevent bacterial and fungal spores from entering the solutions. At the finish mark the leaf which has been floating on glucose by cutting a notch in it. Dip both leaves into a beaker of boiling water. After 1 minute, transfer them to a second beaker containing 70 per cent. alcohol, and allow to stand until the colour is completely extracted. This is greatly hastened by placing the beaker in a water-bath which has been brought to the boil and the flame then extinguished. The beaker should hang into the water, being supported at the rim by the rings of the bath. When the leaves are colourless they will be hard and brittle. Place them on a white saucer and moisten them with tap-water until they are limp again, and then pour off the water. Immerse the leaves in a solution of iodine in potassium iodide, and, when there are no further colour changes, wash away the iodine with rinsings of water. The leaf which has been floating on sucrose will show a dark coloration (due to the presence of starch), especially near the veins along which the glucose has travelled. The leaf which has floated on water will show no coloration. Notice that no light is necessary for this reaction.

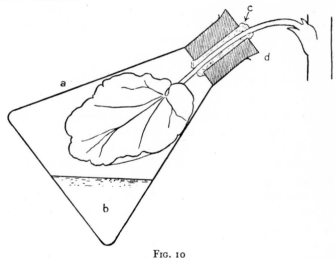

Fig. 10

Exp. 5. The Uptake of Carbon Dioxide during Starch Formation

Destarch a pot plant of *Pelargonium* by keeping it for 2 days in the dark. When it is brought back to the light, enclose one leaf in a conical flask (fig. 10 *a*) of suitable size containing about 50 ml of a strong solution of caustic soda (*b*).

Roll the lamina carefully to pass it through the neck of the flask. Wrap a piece of cotton-wool, soaked in lime-water (*c*), round the petiole, and close the flask with a holed and split rubber cork (*d*). This will make a joint sufficiently impermeable to carbon dioxide. If an ordinary cork has to be used, its surface should finally be smeared with grease or painted with wax. Support the flask by means of a retort stand, taking care not to crack the petiole or let the leaf touch the caustic soda. Place the whole in direct sunlight or about 9 inches from a 60 watt electric lamp for not less than 4 hours, and then test the enclosed leaf for starch as in experiment 4. Test an untreated leaf similarly. Both leaves should be young (near the apex of the plant), as old leaves are much slower in forming starch. The enclosed leaf will contain no starch as no carbon dioxide was available.

Exp. 6. The Connexion between Stomata and Air Spaces of the Leaf

Cut an onion leaf low down, and push the end of a piece of glass tubing into the cavity. Bind the leaf on firmly with wool or soft cotton. Immerse the leaf in water, and blow gently into the tube. Bubbles of air will be forced out of the stomata.

Rub one side of the leaf with a moistened finger, until the waxy bloom is removed. On further blowing, bubbles will no longer come out on the rubbed side. This is because its surface is now thoroughly wetted and the stomatal pores blocked by water.

If onion leaves are not available, other fistular organs, such as the flower stalks of *Narcissus*, may be used.

Exp. 7. Air-Space System of the Leaf

Fit a new rubber cork (fig. 11 A) having one hole, with a glass tube (B) drawn into a jet at the lower end. The cork

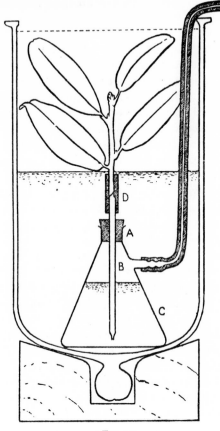

Fig. 11

is to be fitted into a small filter-flask (c) so that the tube reaches almost to the bottom. Fill the flask with tap-water almost up to the side tube, which is to be attached to a filter-pump by a long piece of pressure tubing. To the upper end of the tube (B) attach a piece of new pressure tubing (D) about 2 inches long. Unless the rubber used is new and springy, there will be difficulty in obtaining the necessary air-tight joints. Select a twig of cherry laurel (*Prunus laurocerasus*) and cut off a terminal piece with four or five leaves attached. Make sure that the surfaces of leaves and stem are unbroken. The stem of the piece selected must be straight, without leaves for the lowest inch, and about 4 mm diameter at the cut. The sprig must not be trimmed or cut in any way. Smear the sides of the straight stem above the cut with a little grease (avoid the cut surface), when it will be found easy to push it well into the upper end of the pressure tubing (D) without damaging the bark. Stand the entire apparatus in a large inverted bell-jar and connect with the filter-pump. Run water into the jar until the upper end of the pressure tubing is just immersed, then turn on the pump. Bubbles will at once begin to escape from the jet, showing that air is being drawn through the leaves and stem into the flask. Adjust the rate of bubbling by altering the rate of flow through the pump until the bubbles can easily be counted. Take several half-minute readings of the rate, which should remain fairly constant.

Pour further water into the bell-jar until the shoot itself is completely immersed. The rate of bubbling will greatly decrease, since air can no longer enter the stomata. It will not stop, because air in the internal air-spaces is slowly drawn out. After about half an hour, dark patches will be noticed on the under surfaces of the leaves, showing that water has entered through the stomata and is filling the spaces previously occupied by air.

Exp. 8. CARBON DIOXIDE ENTERS THE LEAF THROUGH THE STOMATA

Cut two leaves from a *Pelargonium* plant which has been destarched by keeping it for 2 days in the dark. These leaves have stomata on their lower surfaces only. Grease the under side of one leaf and the upper side of the other, and place both in a bright light with their petioles dipping into water. Leave for at least 4 hours and then wipe off with a soft rag as much grease as possible without damaging the leaf. Mark the leaf greased on top by cutting a notch in its lamina, and test both for starch by the iodine method.

The notched leaf will show a blue colour due to the starch which has formed from the carbon dioxide absorbed. The other, in which the stomata were blocked, will show none.

Exp. 9. The Closure of Stomata due to Plasmolysis of the Guard Cells

Strip a piece of epidermis from a lily, iris, or rhubarb leaf, and divide it into two pieces. Put one piece into a watch-glass containing a strong solution (about 33 per cent.) of calcium chloride, and the other into a watch-glass of dis-tilled water. After 5–10 minutes, transfer the pieces to a drop of the same medium on microscope slides, cover with coverslips, and examine. The stomata in the calcium chloride solution will be closed, whereas those in distilled water will be open.

Exp. 10. The Fixation of Light

Make an envelope of dull black paper just large enough to slip over and enclose the lamina of any selected leaf; it should be more than 3 inches square. Cut a simple design in one face of the envelope, and then fix it on to a destarched leaf with the stencil uppermost. Close the envelope with paper clips across its open end, and place further clips to keep the paper in close contact with the leaf, especially round the cut edges. No light must be allowed to get between the leaf and the paper.

The experiment is best performed with a young leaf

attached to a plant rooted out of doors, but a pot plant will do. Destarching may be carried out beforehand by enclosing the leaf in a black paper envelope with no stencil cut in it. Potato leaves require 12 to 24 hours' darkening followed by about 4 hours' exposure to light; *Pelargonium* leaves 48 hours and 4 hours respectively. At the end of the exposure cut off the leaf, and test for starch as described in experiment 4. It will be found that a dark-blue pattern, representing the cut-out part of the envelope, is formed on the colourless background of the leaf. Starch formation is thus seen to be limited to the region which received light. The formation of starch is so sharply limited that if a photographic negative is placed over a destarched leaf, a good print may be 'developed' on the leaf, after exposure to light, by the iodine treatment.

Exp. 11. THE NECESSITY FOR CHLOROPHYLL

Cut a variegated leaf of *Pelargonium* of a 'bicolor' variety from a plant that has been exposed for several hours to bright light. Soak the leaf thoroughly in tap-water, and place it on a dark background under a flat piece of glass. Lay transparent paper on the glass, and trace the outline of the leaf, and the divisions between the green and colourless portions. Decolorize the leaf and stain with iodine as in experiment 4. Finish by soaking the leaf in water until the outline again coincides with that originally traced on the paper. Compare the area stained blue-black with the area you have drawn as originally green. Notice that starch is only formed where chlorophyll is developed.

Exp. 12. EXTRACTION AND SEPARATION OF CHLOROPHYLL

Place a handful of chopped and air-dried grass cuttings or nettle leaves in a flask with about 100 ml 85 per cent. acetone. Shake round and allow to stand until the colour has passed into the acetone. The extraction can be made more rapid by placing the leaf material in a filter-funnel and drawing the acetone through several times. When the acetone has become a deep green, view the solution by reflected light. A characteristic blood-red fluorescence is visible.

Drop a spot of the solution on to a clean piece of filter paper. As it dries, add another and continue until a strongly coloured patch is obtained. Then add similarly drops of petrol ether. As the patch of colour spreads outwards, notice that the carotene travel fastest, forming a red circle round a pale zone of xanthophylls with chlorophylls at the centre.

Place about half a centimetre's depth of the chlorophyll extract in a small beaker and stand a fresh piece of black-board 'chalk' upright in it. After a few minutes, remove the solution from the beaker and replace with petrol ether. The pigments will be carried up the column of chalk, separating into similar zones as they go. The separation will be more effective if the chalk is dried in an oven just before use.

Exp. 13. The Chloroplast, the Site of Photosynthesis

a. Mount a moss leaf in a solution of chloral hydrate, and examine under the microscope. Notice that the green colour is confined in little granules, the chloroplasts. Put a second leaf into a watch-glass full of Schimper's solution. After 2–3 minutes transfer the leaf to a drop of the reagent on a slide, cover, and examine under the microscope. The iodine in the Schimper's solution will have stained the starch present in the leaf. Notice that it is confined to the chloroplasts.

b. Cut a transverse section of a leaf in a piece of split pith, and treat as above. Notice the distribution of the chloro-plasts and of the starch. Starch formation only goes on in the green plastids. Suitable leaves are those of cherry laurel and St. John's wort (*Hypericum calycinum*).

Exp. 14. The Formation of Free Oxygen

Put enough water-weed into a 500 ml flask to fill the bulb loosely. Enrich some tap-water with carbon dioxide. This may conveniently be done by bubbling carbon dioxide from a Kipp into a large flask about half-filled with the water. When bubbling has gone on for about 5 minutes stopper the flask and shake. Transfer this solution of carbon dioxide to the experimental flask, which must be com-pletely filled. Invert the flask, and place with the open end dipping into water in a trough. This need not neces-sarily contain extra carbon dioxide. Support the flask by means of a ring or clamp, and place the whole in a bright light.

Notice that gas-bubbles immediately begin to escape from the plants, especially at the broken ends of the stalks, and collect round the surface of the flask. When a sufficient quantity of the gas has been collected, stopper the flask under water, and place with the neck upwards to collect the gas. Bubbles which stick to the glass surface may be detached by rotating the flask rapidly while holding the bulb in one hand. There should be about an inch of gas down the neck of the flask. Uncork and put in a glowing splint to recognize the gas, which proves to be largely oxygen.

Suitable plants for this experiment are Starwort (*Calli-triche*), Water Buttercup (*Ranunculus aquatilis*), Canadian Pond Weed (*Elodea canadensis*), or Pondweeds (species of *Potamogeton*).

II

SUGARS AND THE PLANT MATERIALS FORMED FROM THEM

THE CHEMISTRY OF THE CARBOHYDRATES

A GREAT many substances containing carbon, hydrogen, and oxygen in their molecules occur in plants and are derived either directly or indirectly from the sugar formed by photosynthesis. In the first part of this chapter their most important chemical characters are described, and in the latter part their behaviour in plants.

The most important of these substances belong to the class called *carbohydrates*, which includes the sugars themselves and the substances which are formed by the union of two or more sugar molecules. The common carbohydrates can be arranged in the following scheme:

Monosaccharides:
Pentoses, e.g. arabinose, ribulose
Hexoses, e.g. glucose, mannose, fructose ⎫ Soluble in
Heptoses ⎬ water
Disaccharides, e.g. sucrose, maltose ⎭
Polysaccharides, e.g. starch, cellulose   Insoluble

Monosaccharides. The *pentoses* differ from the hexoses in possessing five carbon atoms linked together in a chain, whereas the hexoses have a chain of six. The general formula for all pentoses is $C_5H_{10}O_5$, and for all hexoses, $C_6H_{12}O_6$. Pentose sugars differ from one another in the way in which their hydrogen and oxygen atoms are grouped round the carbon chain. Like all other monosaccharides and disaccharides, they are readily soluble in water, and in this respect they differ sharply from the polysaccharides. Pentoses are rarely found free in plants except in very small quantities, but they give rise to polysaccharides and other compounds, which are the gums and mucilages of succulent plants, seaweeds, and others.

Hexoses include a large number of different substances, all of which are readily soluble and more or less sweet to the taste. In the majority of their properties they resemble one another closely, but differ among themselves in certain important respects. They are all fairly easily oxidized to organic acids, as, for example, by Fehling's solution, which they reduce under the conditions described on p. 40. Their complete oxidation by combustion yields carbon dioxide and water.

Glucose is called an aldehyde hexose (aldose), because its molecule may be represented with an aldehyde group $-C\underset{O}{\overset{H}{<}}$ at the end of a chain of carbon atoms which are numbered one to six, beginning at the aldehyde end. *Fructose*, a ketose, does not possess this group, but owes its reducing power to the presence of a ketone group $>C=O$ at the second carbon atom.

$$
\begin{array}{cc}
\text{CHO} & \text{CH}_2\text{OH} \\
(1) & (1) \\
\text{HO—C—H} & \text{C}=\text{O} \\
(2) & (2) \\
\text{H—C—OH} & \text{H—C—OH} \\
(3) & (3) \\
\text{HO—C—H} & \text{HO—C—H} \\
(4) & (4) \\
\text{HO—C—H} & \text{HO—C—H} \\
(5) & (5) \\
\text{CH}_2\text{OH} & \text{CH}_2\text{OH} \\
(6) & (6) \\
\text{glucose (aldehyde)} & \text{fructose (ketone)}
\end{array}
$$

These formulae are not capable of explaining all the properties of glucose and fructose, and it is believed that, in solutions and under biological conditions, the great majority of the molecules exist not as chains but as closed rings. These consist of five carbon atoms and one oxygen atom, the remaining carbon atom making a side chain. The flat hexagonal plate thus formed

D (+) glucose   D (−) fructose

is about $0.6 \times 0.5 \times 0.15$ mμ (millionths of a millimetre) in size. The fructose ring sometimes undergoes a further modification in which another carbon atom is pushed out on to a side chain and the ring itself thus has only five members, one oxygen atom and four carbon atoms. The molecule is then highly unstable or 'active' and cannot exist free for any appreciable time. It either reacts at once or relapses into the normal six-membered ring. The active form is called fructofuranose, and the normal form fructo-pyranose.

Fructofuranose

Substances such as glucose and fructose which possess the same atoms in the same numbers, but differ in the manner of their grouping, are called *structural isomers*. It is

impossible to understand the sugars without knowing another kind of isomerism called *stereoisomerism*, in which both
isomers have the same atomic groups and differ only in the
arrangement of them in space. The parent substance of all
sugars is the 'triose', glyceraldehyde,

$$\overset{(3)}{C}H_2OH . \overset{(2)}{C}HOH . \overset{(1)}{C}HO.$$

This exists in two forms and is actually two substances,
not one, due to the fact that the arrangement of the other
groups round carbon atom 2 (in heavy type) is asymmetrical. It is not possible to represent the differences between
the two isomers 'on the flat' because they are brought
about by differences of arrangement 'in the solid'. They
are, however, of such a kind that the molecule of one
isomer is the mirror-image of the other, and no rearrange-
ment of the molecules as a whole will make them coincide
(fig. 12). Substances with asymmetrical carbon atoms
always have the property of rotating the plane of polarized
light.[1] If one isomer causes dextro-, or clockwise, rotation,
the second isomer always causes laevo-, or counter-
clockwise, rotation. There is thus a d-glyceraldehyde
(dextro-glyceraldehyde) with dextro-rotatory powers and
a corresponding l-glyceraldehyde with laevo-rotatory
powers. All sugars lineally derived from d-glyceraldehyde
are named D-sugars and those from l-glyceraldehyde
L-sugars. Their own rotation, which may not coincide with
that of their parent triose, is indicated by the signs $(+)$ for
clockwise and $(-)$ for counter-clockwise rotation. The

[1] In a narrow beam the rays of light are supposed to be vibrating in all
planes. Certain prisms have the property of stopping all the rays except
those vibrating in one plane only, and the light which passes through them
is said to be polarized. If such light is passed through a sugar or other
similar solution, the plane of the vibration is rotated, as is shown by the
fact that a second prism placed in its path after leaving the solution must
be rotated from the original plane before it will allow the light to pass
through.

glucose which occurs in plants is always D(+) glucose and the fructose is D(−) fructose. When a glucose molecule passes from the aldehyde to the ring formation, another carbon atom (No. 1) becomes asymmetric. Another pair of stereoisomers thus arises, and D(+) glucopyranose gives α- and β-glucopyranose, the former having a strong dextro-

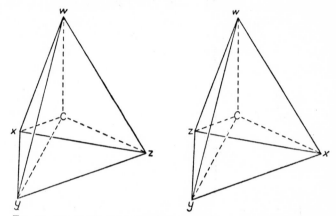

FIG. 12. THE SPACE ARRANGEMENT OF CARBON ATOMS AND ASSOCIATED GROUPINGS

Each carbon atom (C) is situated at the centre of a tetrahedron, and the linkages, shown by broken lines, run to the groups w, x, y, z, which are combined with it at the four corners of the figure. There are two possible arrangements of w, x, y, and z about the carbon atom, such that the two tetrahedra (molecules) do not coincide, however they are turned around.

There are in consequence two separate substances to correspond

rotation and the latter a weaker dextro-rotation. Both the α and β forms occur in plants and form two separate series of compounds. The D(+) glucose formula on p. 53 is that for α-glucopyranose. The reversal of the H and OH groups shown by the broken arrows would give β-glucopyranose.

Disaccharides. These are formed by the condensation of any two monosaccharide molecules with the elimination of one molecule of water. They are soluble and sweet, like the monosaccharides. At least one reducing group is involved in the condensation, sometimes both, and then the disaccharide has no powers of reduction. The natural disaccharides are all derived from hexoses and share the formula $C_{12}H_{22}O_{11}$.

Sucrose is the sugar of commerce, the only disaccharide that is commonly found free in plants and probably occurs in every living cell. It accumulates in concentrations up to 20 per cent. in the stem of sugar-cane and in the root of sugar-beet. It consists of a molecule of glucopyranose condensed with a molecule of fructofuranose. The linkage involves the reducing groups of both sugars, so that sucrose itself has no reducing powers. It is, however, very easily hydrolysed, like all compounds of the active (furanose) sugars.

Maltose only rarely occurs free in plants, but is found during the germination of starchy seeds such as barley, from the malt of which it gets its name. It is formed by the condensation of two glucose molecules. One of these is always α-glucopyranose and is linked by means of its reducing group at carbon atom (1). The other unit may be either α- or β-glucopyranose and is linked at C atom (4). Maltose thus retains one-half of the reducing power of an equivalent weight of glucose. Since both its constituents are pyranoses, it is much more difficult to hydrolyse than sucrose.

Polysaccharides. These differ from mono-, and disaccharides by being insoluble in water, or soluble only to a slighter extent. They are derived from monosaccharides in a similar way to disaccharides, that is to say, by condensation. A single polysaccharide molecule may contain many sugar molecules but the number is very variable, ranging from about six glucose molecules in a simple dextrin to about 500 to 2000 in cellulose. The solubility decreases with increasing size of the molecule. By far the commonest parent sugar is glucopyranose. The two most important plant polysaccharides which occur in almost every plant are starch (fig. 13) and cellulose.

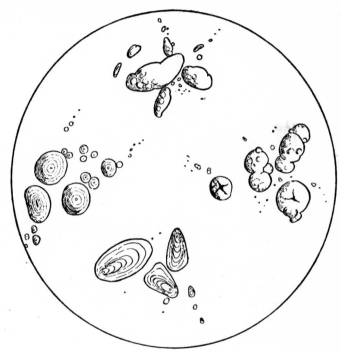

FIG. 13. STARCH GRAINS FROM THE RESERVE TISSUES OF VARIOUS SPECIES
Top from cotyledons of broad bean; left from endosperm of barley; bottom from tuber of potato; right from cotyledons of pea

Starch appears as granules inside living cells, the shape of the grains varying in different species and being to some extent characteristic. It is easily recognized by the blue colour it gives with iodine in the presence of water. In the absence of water, if, for example, an alcohol solution of iodine is used with dry material, there is no reaction. Like sucrose, starch may accumulate to very high concentrations in special tissues. The endosperms of some seeds end by being little more than a mass of starch grains held together by a minimum of cell structure. Each starch grain appears to have a surface pellicle which is more resistant than the interior of the grain. It can be broken down by boiling the starch into a paste or by abrasion or treatment with acid. The starch then becomes much more soluble and hydrolysable and is called 'soluble starch'.

Native starches consist of variable proportions of amylose, which gives a clear blue with aqueous iodine, and amylopectin, which gives a purplish blue. Amylose is formed of unbranched spiral chains of about 100 to 300 α-glucose molecules. In amylopectin there appear to be branches in the chain at about every twentieth α-glucose molecule, and a bushy macromolecule results. These differences of structure cause considerable differences in the relations of the two starch fractions with the enzymes that form and degrade them.

On boiling with dilute acids, both amylose and amylopectin are hydrolysed through a series of *dextrins* to glucopyranose. The higher dextrins give a purple colour with iodine and are precipitated by dilute alcohol. The lower members of the series give no iodine colour and are not precipitated by alcohol. The only disaccharide formed is maltose.

Cellulose is deposited round the outside of living protoplasts and forms the cell walls, and eventually a very large proportion of the plant. Notable examples of pure cellulose walls are afforded by the seed-coat hairs of the cotton plant. In older cell walls the cellulose often becomes impregnated or combined with various complex materials whose chemistry is little known; *lignin* and *suberin* are substances of this kind.

Pure cellulose is very insoluble and very resistant to hydrolysis or other chemical change. For this reason it has important uses as paper, cellophane, and rayon. Very few organisms can decompose cellulose, certain fungi and bacteria being the chief. On prolonged hydrolysis with strong acids, cellulose yields glucopyranose, like starch. The disaccharide formed is cellobiose, which differs from maltose only in being an anhydride of β-glucopyranose. Owing to this difference the cellulose molecule is a long straight chain instead of a spiral. Large numbers of these chains cohere laterally to form the colloidal particles of which a cell wall is built up.

Many other polysaccharides are formed in plants.

Hemicelluloses are mixed polysaccharides containing other sugars besides glucose. They are much less resistant to hydrolysis than cellulose and are broken down by the plants which form them. They occur as heavy thickenings of cell-walls, especially in the storage tissues of seeds (fig. 14).

Gums, *mucilages*, and *pectic substances* are also mixed polysaccharides with a high pentose content. Uronic acids, oxidation products of the sugars, also occur in them and the hemicelluloses. *Glycogen*, which replaces starch in yeast and animals, is a polysaccharide of α-glucopyranose. It gives a purple colour with iodine and has a highly branched molecule like amylopectin but is soluble. *Inulin* is formed instead of starch by some members of the Compositae. It is a polysaccharide of fructofuranose. It is soluble, but precipitated from solution by alcohol, for which reason it becomes familiar as 'sphaero-crystals' in fixed sections of dahlia tubers and similar tissues. Related, but simpler, fructosans are formed in many monocotyledons.

Glycosides. Sugars will combine with many non-sugar molecules, and glucose, especially, is found linked with an immense variety of other organic substances in plants. All these compounds are now called glycosides. Some of the most important and widely spread are the water-soluble pigments: the *anthocyanins*, which give red, purple, and

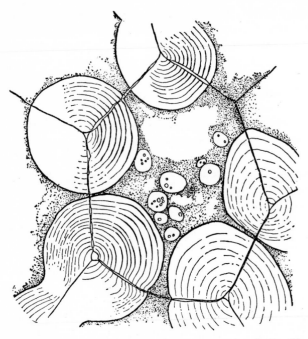

FIG. 14. CELL FROM THE COTYLEDONS (STORAGE TISSUE) OF *Lupinus pilosus*
The abundant hemicellulose is deposited in layers upon the original thin cellulose wall. Within the protoplasm are further reserves of oil and protein. Highly magnified

blue colours to flowers; and the *anthoxanthins*, which give cream flowers and yellow saps. Interesting in another way are the *digitalis glycosides* from foxglove leaves which provide an important heart stimulant. *Cyanogenetic glycosides*, which release prussic acid on hydrolysis, are found in cherry-laurel leaves and seeds of apples and bitter almonds. Many other characteristic glycosides are formed by various species.

Sugar Esters. Sugars also form compounds with the inorganic acids. The most important of these are the esters formed with phosphoric acid by glucose and fructose. The best known monophosphates are glucose 1-phosphate, glucose 6-phosphate, and fructose 6-phosphate. The number refers to the carbon atom to which the phosphoric acid is attached. Ribulose diphosphate has already been mentioned (p. 32) as the CO_2-acceptor in photosynthesis and fructofuranose 1,6-diphosphate plays a leading role in respiration (p. 96).

The Nucleotides and Phosphorylation. The nucleotides are a special class of phosphoric ester with the general structure

phosphate—pentose—nitrogen base.

They are of many kinds and are now known to play several extremely important roles in metabolism. Phosphoric esters fall into two groups: the energy-rich and the energy-poor. One group of nucleotides owes its importance to the fact that it contains members of the energy-rich type.

Adenylic acid is a nucleotide with the structure

phosphate—D ribose—adenine.

A second phosphate may be added to give adenosine diphosphate (ADP) and yet another to give adenosine triphosphate (ATP). The addition of the extra phosphates brings ATP into the energy-rich class. The accumulation of energy by ATP-formation and the 'release' of energy by the back reaction to ADP is called *phosphorylation* and is a very common reaction in metabolism. The transferable energy when ATP → ADP+phosphate is about 11 kcal per mole. The amount of energy required for the synthesis

$$phosphate + glucose \rightarrow glucose\ 6\text{-phosphate}$$

is about 3 kcal per mole. When the phosphate is linked in ATP and the appropriate enzyme, hexokinase, is present the synthesis can therefore occur spontaneously.

ATP enters into very numerous phosphorylations and appears to be the living cells' favourite vehicle for energy transfer. A similar nucleotide, uridine triphosphate, plays a similar part in building sucrose from fructose and glucose 1-phosphate.

Other groups of nucleotides are important in oxidation mechanisms (p. 103). These are dinucleotides, i.e. they have two nucleotide groups linked through their phosphate radicles. Nicotinamide-adenine dinucleotide (NAD, formerly written DPN) has the structure

phosphate—D ribose—adenine
|
phosphate—D ribose—nicotinamide

and its phosphate (NADP, formerly TPN) has a third phosphate at the point of junction. They owe their properties of easy oxidation and reduction to the nicotinamide group. The oxidized forms are commonly written as NAD and NADP and the corresponding reduced forms as $NADH_2$ and $NADPH_2$.

The flavins are also mono- or dinucleotides which have similar redox properties due to their included base, iso-alloxazine. They do not occur free; but as components of the enzymes called reductases (p. 104).

The nucleic acids are still more complex tetranucleotides with important gene functions in the nucleus.

CARBOHYDRATE METABOLISM

It is convenient to regard photosynthesis as coming to an end with the formation of a hexose sugar. There is no real break at this point, however, and the sugar, as soon as it is formed, begins to undergo further changes under the influence of the cell catalysts. Starch and probably sucrose are formed in the chloroplasts themselves, though light is not needed for their formation from hexose. Sugars are continually passing out from the chloroplasts into the surrounding tissues and may eventually be changed into other substances at a considerable distance from the chloroplasts in which they originated. The cellulose walls formed at the growing-points of the stems and roots and the starch laid down in storage organs are examples. The following diagram shows the more obvious and important changes into which the sugars enter as such.

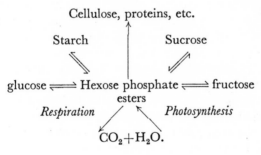

Whenever a fresh leaf is examined it is always found to contain sugars, whether photosynthesis has been going on recently or not. Sucrose, glucose, and fructose are rarely absent, if ever; but the amounts and proportions present vary considerably with time of day, season, and changes of external conditions. Much ingenuity and labour has been expended in efforts to discover which of the three is formed first and how the others are derived from it; but no conclusive answer has been obtained. Recently the attempt has been renewed with radio-active labelling of the carbon dioxide assimilated, but still with ambiguous results.

When any one of the sugars, sucrose, glucose, and fructose is fed to leaves, it is soon converted to a mixture of all three. In suitable leaves, starch may also be formed, and it seems clear that interconversion of labile carbohydrates goes on very readily in all the possible directions under the influence of the catalysts in plant cells. Oxygen is necessary for these changes but not light.

It is now generally supposed that these interconversions are catalysed by the formation of the phosphate esters of the sugars with the help of ATP. It must also be remembered that the formation of some sugar-phosphate esters in photosynthesis precedes the formation of free sugars. The unit of synthesis that can be transferred with minimal loss of energy from one partner to another is the sugar anhydride rather than the sugar molecule. Suitable enzymes (p. 177) to catalyse these changes are abundant in plant cells. Among them are phosphorylase which converts glucose 1-phosphate to amylose. This may be regarded as substituting a glucose-polysaccharide link for a glucose-phosphate one. Enzymes which similarly build up polysaccharide chains by substituting hexose-polysaccharide links for hexose-hexose (disaccharide) ones are called transferases. They may assist syntheses without phosphorylation. Isomerases are enzymes which catalyse isomeric changes such as glucose 6-phosphate to fructose 6-phosphate. Hydrolases release free hexoses from their compounds, amylases from the starch components, invertase from sucrose, and phosphatase from the phosphate esters. The result of all these activities is to form a pool of labile carbohydrates in plant tissues from which carbon may be drawn for further synthesis and for respiration.

Glycosides. Many substances with which sugars can combine are found in leaves, and it is, therefore, not surprising to learn that many sugar compounds, or glycosides, are formed during photosynthesis as well as the carbohydrates already mentioned. The behaviour in leaves of a few of the many known glycosides has been carefully examined and has been found very similar to that of sucrose—that is to say, the glycosides accumulated while photosynthesis was going on and slowly disappeared in the dark. There is thus no reason to suppose that they differ in their origin and decomposition from the more plentiful sugar derivatives. Some of the substances with which the sugars combine, such as prussic acid, are strong poisons, and it has been suggested that their combination prevents injury to the cells. This may be so, but does not, of course, explain why the glycosides are formed; this is simply due to the chemical natures of the substances involved and their powers of uniting together.

RESERVE SUBSTANCES

Metabolism is a general term for the building up of complex substances inside the organism, and their subsequent degradation during respiration and associated changes. During its course many of the substances which are formed heap up in various parts of the plant, though later they may be reconverted to simpler forms, and so disappear again. Materials which behave in this way are often called *reserves*, since it is assumed that they are only brought into active play when more available substances have been used up. It must not be supposed, however, that this storage is in any way analogous to the 'laying up against a rainy day' practised by human beings. To explain what is going on it is first necessary to describe the nature of certain chemical sequences.

Linked Reactions. In plants we rarely have to deal with single isolated reactions, but rather with chains of reactions which are linked together, the end products of one reaction being the starting-point for the next. Thus we may have the series of reactions

$$A \to B \to C \to \ldots\ldots\ldots\ldots\ldots X$$

in which A is being converted into X, through a series of intermediate substances, B, C, etc. Each reaction in the chain A→B, B→C, and so on, has its own specific rate per unit of reacting material, so that A→B may be faster than B→C, or vice versa. If A→B is the faster reaction, the substance B will be formed more rapidly than it is converted into C, and hence it will tend to accumulate. The actual rate at which B is transformed depends, however, not only on the rate per unit amount of B, called the *velocity constant* of the reaction, but also on the amount of B which is reacting. Hence, as B heaps up, the rate of its transformation to C is also increased, until finally it becomes equal to the rate of formation of B. Similar adjustments occur all along the series to X, and, when they are complete, matter is passing at the same rate through every reaction of the sequence, which is then said to have reached a dynamic equilibrium or steady state. The behaviour of X depends upon two circumstances; if, for example, the reactions are reversible, as is usual, when X has reached a certain concentration the 'back reaction' will become as fast as the formative reaction, and the concentration of X will then remain constant, instead of augmenting further. The case is altered considerably if X happens to be only slightly soluble; the solution then rapidly becomes saturated, and X is precipitated out. The solid material is chemically inactive and the effective concentration is restricted to the small amount in solution, which remains constant, and is never great enough to prevent further formation. Under these conditions, X may accumulate in the solid form indefinitely.

If the example of starch is now taken, it will be seen that we are dealing with an insoluble end product, such as X in the foregoing example. Glucose is converted through various intermediates into starch, and at medium concentrations the more glucose there is present the faster the formation of starch goes on; thus, when photosynthesis is rapid and much glucose is being formed, the synthesis of starch is correspondingly accelerated. If continuous lighting is supplied, starch continues to accumulate in the leaf practically indefinitely. The breakdown of starch to glucose is always going on simultaneously, however, and if photosynthesis stops, and glucose is steadily removed by translocation, starch synthesis is retarded, and finally becomes slower than its decomposition by hydrolysis. Under these conditions the precipitated starch slowly goes back into solution, and disappears from the leaves, being translocated as sugars.

It is thus easy to understand that insoluble substances formed during metabolism are very liable to accumulate, and so become 'reserves'. Sucrose, on the other hand, is an example of a soluble substance which readily accumulates. It is formed when fructose reacts with a product (uridinediphosphate glucose) previously formed by a series of reactions from glucose. It has no power to condense into more complex substances; but may be hydrolysed or otherwise consumed.

Metabolic Equilibria. A simple reversible reaction comes spontaneously to an equilibrium depending on the rates of the two opposite partial reactions. These rates depend in turn upon temperature and other controlling factors, so that, even in the simplest possible examples, the position of equilibrium will vary with circumstances. Inside cells, conditions are much more complex than in a test-tube containing a single set of reactants, and the equilibria that tend to be set up *in vivo* may be very different from those of the test-tube. Thus the hydrolysis of sucrose in mildly acid solutions is so much faster than the condensation of glucose and fructose that the equilibrium mixture contains practically no sucrose at all. In plant cells, the amount of sucrose present may actually exceed the amounts of glucose and fructose, and addition of glucose may lead to the formation of still more sucrose. It is clear that, if an equilibrium is attained inside the cells, it must be a very different one, depending upon different conditions from those outside. This difference cannot be due to a special action of the cellular enzymes, because it is characteristic of catalysts that they do not provide energy and, therefore, cannot alter the positions of equilibria. The difference is due, at least in large measure, to the fact that, inside cells, reactions do not occur in isolation but are linked into chains, and that the formative reactions may follow quite different paths from those of consumption. Sucrose is not formed by a direct condensation of glucose and fructose but only after a complex series of phosphorylations of the glucose. Hydrolysis may, on the other hand, be direct under the influence of the single enzyme, invertase. The phosphorylation is linked with consumption of ATP (p. 61) and needs the presence of oxygen. The energy fed into the reaction in this way is able to displace the reaction in the direction of more sucrose synthesis.

Regulation of Metabolic Rates. Many metabolic sequences, such as fermentation and respiration, are not tending to equilibria but to a steady rate of consumption of substrate and production of end products such as carbon dioxide, alcohol, and water. None of the intermediate products accumulates to a high concentration so it appears that the usual determinant of the rate is the concentration of the initial substrate–enzyme complex. Feeding with a substrate or intermediate frequently puts up the rate so it is probable that the enzymes are not normally being used to full capacity.

Two considerations complicate this simple picture. Reaction paths are not simple but may branch. For example, pyruvic acid is normally oxidized in a plant tissue to carbon dioxide and water; but if oxygen is absent it may be decarboxylated in the same tissue to acetaldehyde$+$ CO_2. In tissues that have little carboxylase activity (such as rhizomes of the big horsetail, *Equisetum limosum*) it is reduced to lactic acid and, if a high concentration of carbon dioxide builds up round the rhizomes, it is carboxylated to malic acid. Not only the rates but the actual sequence of reactions are here determined by the fact that several systems are competing for the same intermediate. Conversely, several substrates may all be competing for the same system, e.g. the oxidation of malic and other acids via NAD. The rates of consumption will depend, among other things, upon the rates of reaction of the various enzyme complexes with NAD.

The second type of built in control of metabolic rates depends on the fact that many sequences themselves form substances which tend to slow them down. When the substance is removed, or its concentration reduced, the rate picks up again. An important example of this type of control is the formation of ATP from ADP in respiration. Since ADP is not rapidly synthesized *de novo*, its locking up in ATP means that the whole reaction sequence is slowed down. Any process which consumes energy in the cell, and hence returns ATP to ADP, conversely accelerates the sequence. The syntheses involved in growth consume ATP-energy and are associated with rapid respiration rates.

While competition and 'feed-back mechanisms' of the kinds first described above are inherent in biochemical sequences and no doubt play important parts in controlling metabolic rates, it must not be assumed that they are the only controls operating in living tissues. Cells are not like homogeneous solutions and their fine structure may impose limits on competition. It is clear, for example, that respiratory and photosynthetic sequences are segregated from one another in green cells. This aspect of the matter is considered more fully in Chapter VI.

One of the best studied metabolic equilibria is that between starch and sucrose in potatoes. At normal temperatures very little sugar is present, and the labile carbohydrate in the tubers is almost wholly starch. When potatoes are cooled to temperatures just above freezing, 1 or 2 per cent. of their starch is changed to sucrose; and on rewarming, this goes back to starch again. Similar adjustments with temperature have been noted in the fat–sugar equilibrium of acorns. Clearly, these equilibria represent positions of adjustment among complex groups of reactions, not of a single reversible reaction. They have a very marked influence in determining the amount of sugar immediately available for respiration and other metabolic processes, and in determining their rates.

THE FATS

Fats or oils occur in almost all plants, but are especially abundant in the seeds of angiosperms, among which they are rare in the vegetative organs. They form, in fact, the typical reserve substances of seeds (see fig. 72), and starch replaces them only in two families, the Gramineae and Leguminosae. Nearly all plant fats are liquids at ordinary temperatures, and in common language are called oils in consequence. They are immiscible with water, but on vigorous shaking they form fine emulsions, from which they may take a long time to separate out again. Chemically they are esters formed by the union of glycerol, an alcohol with three —OH groups, and some organic acid. A large number of such acids, which are distinguished by the name of fatty acids, can enter into the formation of fats. The reaction can be written as follows, the group represented by R varying according to the nature of the fatty acid:

$$C_3H_5(OH)_3 + 3R.COOH \rightarrow C_3H_5(R.COO)_3 + 3H_2O.$$

Both the glycerol and the fatty acids are derived from sugars; but the details of the conversions are as yet uncertain. Fat is formed in ripening seeds from the sugars which are translocated into them,

$$\text{Sugars} \underset{\searrow}{\overset{\nearrow}{}} \begin{matrix} \text{Fatty acids} \searrow \\ \text{Glycerine} \nearrow \end{matrix} \searrow \text{Fats.}$$

When the seed germinates, the breakdown of the fats to sugars occurs in the reverse manner, and is so rapid that some of the sugar passes over into starch.

$$\text{Fats} \underset{\searrow}{\overset{\nearrow}{}} \begin{matrix} \text{Fatty acids} \searrow \\ \text{Glycerine} \nearrow \end{matrix} \searrow \text{Sugars} \rightarrow \text{Starch.}$$

Fats have a higher heat of combustion than the polysaccharides, and, consequently, when they are oxidized they yield an even greater amount of energy per unit weight of material consumed. The change from sugar to fat must thus involve the uptake of further energy, but this is derived from respiratory energy not from light, since fats may be formed in parts of the plant which do not photosynthesize. The conversion of sugars to fats does not, therefore, increase the total amount of energy within the plant, but merely redistributes it.

EXPERIMENTAL WORK

Exp. 15. DISAPPEARANCE OF STARCH FROM DARKENED LEAVES

a. Take a pot plant of *Pelargonium* or *Sparmannia* which has been exposed to bright light for several hours. Detach one leaf and test for starch by the iodine method (**exp. 4**); detach a second leaf and place with the petiole dipping in water. Leave in a dark room or cupboard, with the whole plant by its side. At the end of 2 days make a starch test upon the other detached leaf and upon a leaf which has been left on the plant. The detached leaves will both contain abundant starch, the leaf attached to the darkened plant will have none.

b. In another leaf of the above plant sever a large vein without otherwise damaging the tissues. When the plant has been in the dark for 2 days, detach the whole leaf and test for starch. The part beyond the cut in the vein will still contain starch, but the rest of the leaf will not.

Exp. 16. STARCH IN TUBERS, ETC.

a. Cut a potato tuber in half, and smear a few drops of iodine on the cut surface. A blue-black colour is formed.

A similar result may be obtained with crocus corms, iris rhizomes, and many bulbs.

b. Cut a section of a piece of potato tuber, mount in dilute glycerine, and examine under the microscope. The small cells are full of large shiny starch grains, with their characteristic concentric layers. Place a drop of iodine at one side of the coverslip, and draw through by touching the far side with blotting-paper. Watch the starch grains become bright blue and finally almost black.

Exp. 17. FORMATION OF GLYCOSIDES; PRULAURASIN IN LEAVES

Chop up a leaf of cherry laurel (*Prunus laurocerasus*) into small pieces and put into a flask or test-tube. Hang a moist strip of sodium picrate paper into the vessel, and fix by corking. Into a second flask or tube put an undamaged leaf and a similar strip of picrate paper.

After a short time the paper in the first tube will have changed through orange to red, but the second will show no change. The reddening is caused by prussic acid, which is liberated from the glycoside prulaurasin in the damaged leaves. In the undamaged leaves the glycoside is not split. Owing to the prussic acid formed, crushed cherry-laurel leaves will kill moths and other insects.

Exp. 18. AESCULIN IN TWIGS

Strip the bark from some young horse-chestnut twigs and boil with a little water in an evaporating dish. Filter off the liquid and then pour it into a relatively large amount of water in a large beaker. A blue fluorescent solution is formed which is characteristic of the glycoside aesculin. The fluorescence is increased by making the solution slightly alkaline.

Exp. 19. THE REACTIONS OF CELLULOSE

a. Pour some aqueous iodine solution (iodine in potassium iodide) into an evaporating basin (or clean white saucer). Immerse in the liquid a small piece of cotton-wool or a strip of good writing-paper. Pour off the iodine and add a few drops of strong sulphuric acid. On adding the acid a blue colour will be given. ,

b. Put a piece of cotton-wool or good writing-paper into a basin and add a drop or two of chlor-zinc-iodine. A blue colour will be produced as before.

Exp. 20. Cellulose in the Plant

a. Split a number of lupin seeds in half, and put in a basin. Add a drop of iodine in potassium iodide, and a few drops of strong sulphuric acid. The cell walls in this seed are particularly thick, and so the blue coloration of their cellulose is easily seen.

b. Cut a section of the seed and mount in chlor-zinc-iodine. Examine under the microscope and notice that the cell walls have become blue and much swollen.

Exp. 21. Reactions of Ligno-cellulose

a. Dip the end of a match-stick into a solution of aniline sulphate or aniline chloride. It turns a bright yellow.

b. Dip the end of a match-stick into an alcoholic solution of phloroglucin. When well soaked dip into strong hydrochloric acid. A bright red colour is produced.

It is interesting to perform these tests upon a strip of common newspaper; this is made from wood pulp, not from cotton rags like paper of better quality.

Exp. 22. Ligno-cellulose in Plants

a. Strip the bark from any woody twig, and treat the wood as in experiment 21 above. The characteristic colour of ligno-cellulose will be formed.

b. Cut sections of a young woody twig, and mount in the reagents. Notice the coloration of the woody tissues; the cellulose walls of other tissues do not react.

Exp. 23. Reactions of Fats

Pour a little olive-oil (a liquid fat) into a test-tube and add a few drops of the red dye Sudan III. Shake well and notice that the oil takes up the red colour. Pour half the coloured oil into a second test-tube. To one tube add water and to the other alcohol. Shake, and when the liquids have separated again notice that the dye has remained with the oil. Compare the density of the oil with that of water and alcohol, by the relative positions assumed.

Exp. 24. FATS IN SEEDS

Crush some linseed (seeds of flax) in a mortar, and transfer to a test-tube. One-third fill the test-tube with water and boil. Drops of oil will escape from the crushed seeds and rise to the surface of the water. When a layer of oil has been collected add Sudan III and shake. When the two layers separate again, notice that the oil is stained light red.

III

THE DECOMPOSITION OF SUGARS
AND THE LIBERATION OF ENERGY

PLANT RESPIRATION

The Nature of Plant Respiration. In the preceding chapters it has been shown how sugars are built up into the complex substances of the plant body, but a certain proportion of them is always undergoing decomposition, and may never pass through the more complicated forms of material such as starch, cellulose, or protein. The breakdown is not restricted to the cells in which sugars are manufactured, because they make their way to all parts of the plant. The presence of varying amounts of sugars is, in fact, characteristic of all living cells, and there is every reason to suppose that sugar-breakdown is always going on in them. At the same time carbon dioxide is given off and oxygen absorbed, often, though by no means invariably, in equal volumes. This exchange of gases, carried on by all actively living material, is easily observed and has been known for a long time under the name of *respiration*, and, since the gaseous exchange is the same both in plants and animals, the same name has been given to the process in both kingdoms. It may be assumed with plants that the carbon dioxide thus given off is derived from the sugars, sugar esters, or other labile carbohydrates, which they manufacture so readily.

It was believed at one time that the living protoplasm was constantly breaking down and that respiration consisted of an oxidation of its material. This is not so, since protoplasm consists largely of nitrogenous substances, and no corresponding nitrogenous waste products are formed by plants. The final external products of plant respiration are carbon dioxide and water alone, and they are produced from the oxidation of carbon and hydrogen, originally present as sugar molecules in the respiring material. Although, normally, carbohydrates alone are used up during respiration, the process only goes on in the presence of living matter, and a solution of sugar in contact with the oxygen of the air is perfectly stable and will remain unaltered for years, if it is protected from the action of living organisms such as moulds and bacteria. It follows, therefore, that we are not dealing with a simple series of chemical reactions which can proceed easily of its own accord once the initial substances have been brought together; besides the principal reactants, there must also be catalysts present to facilitate the reactions. In living cells, all the necessities are provided by the protoplasm, which regulates and controls the respiratory changes, and even the rates at which they go on.

The Rate of Respiration. By putting a plant in the dark, photosynthesis is brought to a standstill, but respiration continues. Under these conditions carbon dioxide is slowly emitted, and its formation can be shown by shutting the plant in a vessel and afterwards testing the enclosed air with lime water. If suitable arrangements are made (*see* **exp. 30,** p. 116), the rate at which the carbon dioxide is being formed can be accurately measured, and this may be called the *rate of respiration*. The respiratory rate could also be measured by the speed at which oxygen is absorbed, and much of our knowledge of respiration has been built up from observations of these two kinds. They have the great advantage that they can be made upon living tissues, both under conditions that do not depart greatly from the normal and under experimental variations of them.

There is considerable difficulty in comparing the respiration rate of different tissues, because there can be no standard unit of respiring matter. For lack of a better method, comparisons are usually made between unit amounts of dried tissue; and commonly as Q_{CO_2} or the corresponding Q_{O_2} which is cubic millimetres gas at N.T.P. exchanged per hour per milligram dry weight. On this basis, respiration rates vary enormously between different tissues: the following table will serve to give some idea of their range.

Respiration in cubic millimetres CO_2 per hour per milligram dry weight

Material	Q_{CO_2}
Yeast	60–100
Aspergillus niger, 2-day culture . .	78
4-day culture . .	11·5
Arum italicum spadix . . .	31
peduncle . . .	2·9
Tomato root tips	6–8
Barley, 7-day seedlings . . .	1·6
Peas, air-dry seeds	0·00012

One reason why the fungal values are so much greater than those of the higher plants is that the fungal cells and hyphae contain relatively little inert matter. They use external sources of respirable material, not substances stored as reserves inside as the higher plants do; and they have no inert woody cells. Since all these materials are included in the dry weight and enter the Q_{CO_2} ratio as divisor, the suggestion of a faster respiration rate in the fungi is largely illusory. This is also true of the *Arum* spadix which begins by being full of starch, which it consumes. As the starch is used up, the Q_{CO_2} rises, although the total CO_2-production per spadix slowly falls. Nevertheless, no other method of comparing the respiration rates of different tissues is, in general, more successful; and, with the

Q_{CO_2}, it is at least possible to see where the snags lie and to guard against them.

The actual rate at which respiration goes on at any particular moment depends on many things such as physical state of the respiring protoplasm, the concentration and activity of the necessary enzymes and their cofactors, and the supply of respirable materials. There are, however, two other matters which tend to stabilize the rate and damp down large fluctuations. These are the orderly arrangement of the catalysts depending on the microstructure of the cell (cf. pp. 166–74), and the cyclic nature of many stages of respiration which means that the rate is limited by that at which some product is fed back into the process (*see* p. 68).

All these internal factors are conditioned in varying degrees by external ones of which the most obvious and the easiest to control is temperature.

Effect of Temperature on Respiration Rates. The temperature relations of biological processes are usually expressed in terms of the temperature coefficient, Q_{10}. This is the ratio of the rate at a given temperature divided by the rate at 10° C lower. The coefficient varies a good deal between different types of processes: for physical effects, such as diffusion and conductivity, it usually lies between 1·2 and 1·3; but for chemical reactions it lies commonly around 2·0. Heterogeneous reactions, in which diffusion of one reactant is often an important part, may have the lower value. A reaction catalysed by an enzyme usually has a value slightly lower than the same reaction uncatalysed or assisted by an inorganic catalyst.

There are now a good many determinations of the Q_{10} of plant respiration. Irrespective of the species or part of the plant used, the Q_{10} between 5° and 15° C usually lies at 2·0 or rather higher. As the temperature rises, the Q_{10}

falls until, around 30° C, it is usually down to about 1·3. This is probably because the chemical reactions of respiration accelerate so much faster than the entry of oxygen and removal of carbon dioxide, which are largely by diffusion, that these latter come to limit the rate.

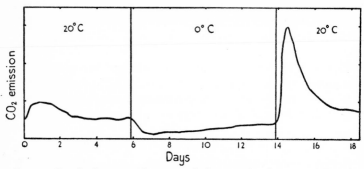

FIG. 15. Respiration rate of potatoes during transfers between 0° C and 20° C. (Data of Müller-Thurgau)

The effect of temperature on the equilibria between starch and sugar and fats and sugar mentioned on p. 70 has a striking effect on the rate of respiration. The rate may be closely related to the amount of free sugar, usually free sucrose, available at the moment. Lowering the temperature of potatoes almost to 0° C increases the sugar concentration (p. 70) with the result that the rate of CO_2-emission does not fall off as much as might be expected. When the temperature is again raised to 20° C there is a very large acceleration of respiration rate (fig. 15) which gradually falls back to a more normal level as the additional sugar is partly respired and partly converted back to starch. Similar happenings occur in germinating acorns with a fat–sugar equilibrium. When the temperature rises from about 5° to 30° C, the conversion of sugar to fat lowers the sugar concentration and so prevents a rapid rise in the rate of CO_2-output. Since oxygen is eliminated when sugar is changed to fat, there may even be a reduction in the rate of oxygen consumption as the temperature rises.

Respiration throughout the Life-cycle. The state of a living protoplast is subject to frequent changes, but during the life history of the plant to which it belongs a slow sequence of alterations goes on, and can easily be recognized. Each protoplast has its own development, so that different cells or groups of cells in different parts of a plant are not all at the same stage of their growth, and it is possible to isolate tissues from a single plant which are in different phases of protoplasmic development. Such tissues differ from one another in their rates of respiration, and five stages, depending upon the condition of their protoplasts, can be recognized:

1. Embryonic, e.g. stem and root apices; germinating embryos.
2. Juvenile, e.g. elongating zones of stems and roots; young fleshy fruits.
3. Mature, e.g. functional leaves, etc.
4. Senescent, e.g. ripe to over-ripe fruits.
5. Dormant, e.g. dry seeds; winter buds.

Tissues in the *embryonic* state are characterized by thin cell walls, and abundant protoplasm with large nuclei, giving strong reactions for protein. Carbohydrates are poorly represented, or absent even from the cell walls. In the *juvenile* state vacuoles are rapidly formed and strong sugar reactions are developed in them. There is a rapid enlargement of the tissue and the cell-walls remain thin. The *mature* state lasts much longer than either of the preceding, and is characterized by the slow differentiation of the cells into their final forms. There is little increase of size, and a rough balance is struck between gain and loss of substance. Maturity reaches its end at the *climacteric*, after which *senescence* sets in. Development ceases, cell structure begins to deteriorate, and the capacity to synthesize is lost. Irreversible hydrolyses and oxidations finally lead to *autolysis*, or self-digestion of the tissues by their own enzymes. This last post-mortem stage is usually helped by fungal and bacterial decomposition. *Dormancy* may interrupt the embryonic, juvenile, or mature stages of a tissue, but not the senescent. It is characterized by extreme inertness of the protoplasm, which nevertheless retains the capacity to resume activity. Dormancy is more fully dealt with on p. 268.

An individual cell or tissue passes through several of these stages in the course of its life. Its behaviour, depending on the condition of its protoplasm, changes as it does so, but the passage from one stage to the next is not sudden but very gradual. This slow drift of protoplasmic condition is reflected in the rate of carbon dioxide emission, or rate of respiration. If a mean value is taken for the plant as a whole, the respiratory index, i.e. the number of milligrams CO_2 produced per hour per gram of dry weight, varies in the manner shown in fig. 16. During germination, which includes the first or embryonic stage, respiration mounts rapidly to a maximum from the slow rate characteristic of the dormant seed, which may be so slow as almost to defy measurement. The highest respiratory index of the plant's life is reached as germination completes itself. As the majority of the active tissues pass into the juvenile phase, the rise is first checked, and then passes into a long-drawn-out decline lasting through maturity. A drawback of the respiratory index is that the unit of dry weight includes greater and greater amounts of inert, non-respiring matter as time goes on and the plant comes to contain an increasing proportion of wood. If the respiratory index of the stem apex, which never contains a large proportion of inert substance, is examined instead, it is found that the decline is less rapid, but it does not disappear completely (*see* fig. 16, B). From this it can be seen that even the cells of the meristem change their condition as the plant ages, and cannot maintain the high activity of their first youth.

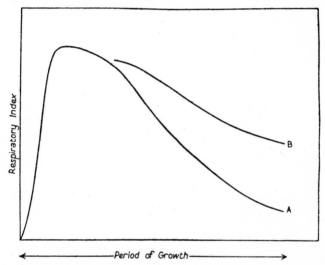

FIG. 16. Diagram of the respiratory index throughout the life-cycle of an annual plant. A. Respiratory index of the whole plant; B, of short apex

The senescent stage is best illustrated by tissues such as the flesh of ripe fruits, storage tubers, and yellowing leaves. The drift is abnormally long drawn out in fruits or tubers kept in cool storage ($\sim 2 \cdot 5°$ C) and, conversely, it can be accelerated by traces of ethylene. Fig. 17 shows the respiration drift of some keeping apples (A) and some specially long-keeping apples (B) kept at $2 \cdot 5°$ C after being taken from the tree in November. They had already reached the mature state before picking and by the following February had attained a second peak of respiration. Had it not been for the slowing-down effect of the cool temperature, this peak would have arrived much earlier. It coincided with complete ripeness and full flavour of the fruit or, in other words, was the climacteric of the apples.

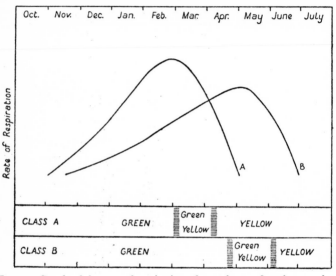

Fig. 17. Graph of the rate of respiration of two classes of apples stored at 2·5° C, with the colour of the apples indicated below. (After Blackman and Parija, modified)

There followed a rapid decline in the respiration rate accompanied by yellowing of the skin; this was the phase of senescence. The class B apples showed the same changes carried out more slowly. The art of storing fruit lies in staving off as long as possible the climacteric and senescence. Practical methods are described later on p. 92.

The Respiratory Quotient (R.Q.) is the ratio, volume CO_2 given off/volume O_2 absorbed. It has proved of service in respiration studies because its value is primarily

determined by the nature of the substance being consumed. Thus the theoretical R.Q. for the complete oxidation of any carbohydrate would be 1·0, since the molecules
of CO_2 produced are numerically equal to the molecules
of oxygen used up. The volumes exchanged are, therefore,
equal also. When fats are respired, it involves an extra
oxidation, so that the oxygen consumption exceeds the
CO_2 production and the ratio falls below 1. The equation
for triolein would be:

$$C_{57}H_{104}O_6 + 80O_2 \rightarrow 57CO_2 + 52H_2O$$

and the respiratory ratio 57/80 = 0·71. Other fats give
almost the same figure, varying a little according to the
composition of their fatty acids. Proteins, upon complete
oxidation, would give a theoretical R.Q. of about 0·99, or
so little different from 1·0 that it could not be experimentally distinguished from it. Ammonia would also be given
off, so that no confusion with a carbohydrate R.Q. would
arise. In fact, this rarely if ever happens: the usual decomposition of proteins first involves a good deal of amide
(asparagine, or glutamine) formation with an R.Q. around
0·75. If the amides are eventually oxidized further, as in
starving leaves, the R.Q. may be expected to rise to about
1·11 (glutamine) or 1·33 (asparagine). In very simple
circumstances these rules may be closely followed. The
fungus *Phycomyces*, growing and respiring vigorously on a
starchy medium, was found to have an R.Q. = 1·0. When
grown on a linseed preparation, rich in oil, its R.Q. varied
from 0·66 to 0·75.

The conditions of respiration in the higher plants are
more complex and varied, and the value of the R.Q. is
affected by many further issues. By very careful examination of the results and comparison with direct analyses,
these can sometimes be made clear. For example, fleshy
fruits have low R.Q.s when very young, because they do

not fully oxidize their sugars to CO_2, but convert much of them to malic, citric, and similar acids. As they ripen and the fruit sweetens, they cease to form these acids, and the R.Q. rises towards 1. Some succulent plants, notably the Cactaceae and Crassulaceae, go to extremes; and, at times, form only malic acid and release no CO_2 at all (R.Q. = 0).

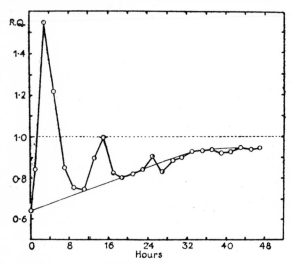

FIG. 18. Drift of the R.Q. of barley seedlings germinating in the dark

Conversely, in a phase of starvation, when the oxygen-rich malic acid is itself used up, the R.Q. rises above 1.

Figures corresponding with the oxidation of fat (R.Q. ~ 0·7) have been observed at certain stages of the germination of fatty seeds; in very advanced stages of starvation, when proteins and many other cell constituents are breaking down, the R.Q. often falls as low as 0·5.

The R.Q. varies greatly at different stages of growth and under varying conditions. Fig. 18 shows how extensively and rapidly it may vary during germination. The results were obtained with barley grains which store starch in the endosperm, but which have also a little fat in the embryo itself. The entries 1, 2, and 7 in the following table interpret the causes of the observed fluctuations. Barley may be regarded as a typical higher plant without any very outstanding peculiarities. The other entries in the table indicate how much the R.Q. may vary in its different parts and stages. The processes believed from all the available evidence to determine the R.Q. under these various conditions are given in the third column. According to taste, one may include all these reactions under the heading of respiration, or may exclude the more bizarre and then refer to the 'apparent' R.Q.s which they cause.

Respiratory Quotients of Barley at 20° C

Material	R.Q.	Determining process
1. Dormant grain	0·64	Fat → carbohydrate
2. Soaked grain	1·55	Anaerobic respiration
3. Embryos, 75 h germination	0·25	Fat → carbohydrate and cutin
4. Embryos+6 per cent. sucrose	0·80	As 3+respiration of sucrose
5. Embryos+starchy endosperms	0·74	As 3+respiration of starch
6. Embryos+pyruvic acid	0·75	As 3+respiration of pyruvic acid
7. Etiolated seedlings	0·95	Respiration of starch from endosperm
8. Seedlings starved 21 days	0·80	Decomposition of protein and protein products
9. Leaves forced in greenhouse	0·80	Mixed carbohydrate and protein respiration
10. Normal leaves from field	1·02	Respiration of sucrose
11. Leaves darkened on plant	0·88	Mixed carbohydrate and protein respiration
12. Leaves cut and starved 4 days	0·80	As 11

Respirable Materials. The evidence of starvation and R.Q. experiments suggests that carbohydrates are the normal respirable materials of healthy plant tissues. Fats are used only in special ones, such as germinating seeds; and proteins in none until starvation-breakdown sets in. The commonly respired carbohydrates are starch, sucrose, glucose, and fructose. Feeding a plant tissue with any of these under suitable conditions will put up the respiration rate. The three sugars are present in all plant cells in varying amounts, and it has been shown by direct analysis that they always diminish during a period of respiration when replenishment by photosynthesis or translocation is prevented. When starch is present it is also used up. The experiments are very difficult to carry out, but in the few that have been achieved the total loss of starch+sugars has been found approximately equivalent to the total CO_2 emitted. In other words, nothing beyond these four substances was being respired. This only applies to the short period before starvation begins to matter.

The respirable carbohydrates are all readily converted into one another in living tissues and exist side by side with numerous sugar-phosphate esters. The interconversions within this pool of carbohydrates are numerous and rapid so that if any member of the pool is consumed by respiration adjustments result affecting other members of the pool. The ultimate loss is usually borne by the starch or sucrose that has accumulated to relatively high concentrations during photosynthesis or by translocation storage. The substances directly withdrawn by respiration, that is to say those points at which sugar units are lost from the pool, are considered on p. 96.

Proteins and Respiration. Although no ammonia or carbon dioxide is liberated from plant proteins during normal respiration, it does not follow that nothing is happening to the proteins. It seems more likely that they are continually being formed and disintegrated; but the breakdown gets only so far as the formation of amino-acids and amides (p. 129). These are not further decomposed under favourable conditions, but may serve for the synthesis of new protein, perhaps after translocation to a younger part of the plant. Complete breakdown with liberation of ammonia and carbon dioxide is characteristic of extreme starvation.

It has been noticed that there is often a close connexion between the percentage of protein, or some special class of protein, in a tissue and its rate of respiration.

A possible explanation is that the enzymes that catalyse the various stages of respiration may well play a part in determining the overall respiration rate, and all enzymes are proteins. Less obvious explanations are, however, also possible.

Oxygen Effects. So far we have limited ourselves to events taking place in a normal atmosphere. We can learn a little more about respiration from its behaviour when the oxygen content of the atmosphere is varied. If oxygen is wholly withdrawn, CO_2 continues to come off; but usually at a different rate. If the tissue is not kept without oxygen for very long it will eventually settle down to a normal respiration rate again when brought back into air. Before this happens, the time-drift of CO_2-emission may have gone through a very complicated series of changes, and there is no simple relation, such as a single ratio, between the rates in pure nitrogen and in air. The course of the CO_2-emission curve when such changes are made is different for different tissues; a relatively simple example is shown in fig. 19. Since the respirable materials are unlikely to be fully oxidized to CO_2 in the absence of oxygen, it might be expected that, under nitrogen, the CO_2-emission rate would fall. Actually, in the example shown in the graph, it increases, and this is a common result. The explanation is probably that sugar is broken down faster in an atmosphere of pure nitrogen; so that oxygen can be regarded as economizing the sugar supply of the respiring cells. Strictly speaking, only direct sugar analyses can prove a change in the rate of sugar break-down, and observations on CO_2 or other end-products may lead us astray. It does, however, seem probable that,

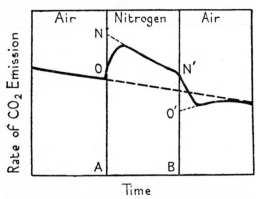

Fig. 19. The heavy line shows the rate of carbon dioxide emission of an apple transferred from air to nitrogen and back again. The ratio of anaerobic to aerobic CO_2-output can be estimated by producing the steady curves back to the moment of change (dotted lines); i.e. CO_2-output in nitrogen/CO_2-output in air = AN/AO = BN'/BO'. The broken line represents the course of CO_2 output for an apple kept continuously in air. After Blackman

besides animal tissues, yeasts and bacteria, fruits, leaves, and other plant tissues all exhibit such an effect. There is, on the other hand, some reason to suppose that it has not been developed in the young tissues of germinating seeds. The way in which the effect is brought about is still rather uncertain; indeed it seems likely that it may arise from more than one cause.

If a respiring tissue is transferred from one concentration of oxygen to another slightly higher or lower, it usually adjusts its respiration rate to the new conditions and then

the CO_2-drift runs on along a course parallel to the pre-
dictable drift in air. It is then possible to express all the
rates in all concentrations of oxygen as fixed ratios of the
rate in air. Even for zero oxygen, we may obtain such
a ratio by the method of extrapolation shown in fig. 19.

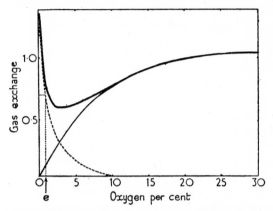

FIG. 20. The heavy line shows the rate of CO_2-output in
varying concentrations of oxygen. Rate in air $= 1$. The
oxygen consumption follows the same curve as long as
R.Q. $= 1$; but diverges, as shown by the thin line, in low
concentrations. The CO_2-output in excess of oxygen consumption, i.e. the anaerobic CO_2, is shown by the broken
line. e is the extinction coefficient. Diagrammatic

The heavy line in fig. 20 shows the CO_2-output of apples in
different oxygen concentrations. The light line shows the
simultaneous oxygen absorption, and the broken line is
the difference. This gives a measure of the 'anaerobic'
CO_2-production. So long as this is detectable, the R.Q. is
greater than 1. The point at which anaerobic respiration
becomes undetectable and the R.Q. becomes approximately equal to 1·0 is unfortunately not sharply defined.
Usually, anaerobic carbon dioxide production cannot be
detected experimentally in healthy apples above 3 to 5 per
cent. oxygen. In older apples it can be detected in higher

oxygen concentrations, apparently because the skin becomes less permeable to gases. Since the oxygen concentration for total extinction of anaerobic CO_2-production is not exactly ascertainable, the changes can best be expressed in terms of the extinction coefficient, i.e. the oxygen concentration at which anaerobic CO_2-production is reduced to one-half: this can be accurately measured as indicated in fig. 20. This value is much higher in yeast than in apples, and there may still be rapid production of anaerobic CO_2 in the 20 per cent. oxygen of air.

The observation of a minimal respiration rate at a given concentration of oxygen has been turned to practical account in the storage of fruit. It has been found that by the time a fruit has ripened it has produced an amount of CO_2 which is approximately constant for its kind. Any method of slowing down CO_2-production, such as controlling the oxygen-content of the storage chamber, will therefore delay ripening. The respiration rate can be further reduced and the storage life correspondingly prolonged by allowing CO_2 to accumulate to a moderate concentration and so induce a CO_2-narcosis. Combined control of oxygen and CO_2 in the atmosphere round stored fruits is nowadays practised on a large scale under the name of gas storage. The best gas mixture for each kind of fruit has to be determined by experience.

At concentrations of oxygen above 100 per cent., i.e. at 2 or 3 atm. pressure of pure oxygen, the rate of respiration is actually reduced below the maximum observed at about 0·5 atm. (50 per cent.). This is due to the inactivation of one or more of the respiratory enzymes by oxidation at these high concentrations.

ANAEROBIC RESPIRATION

Since carbon dioxide continues to come off in the absence of oxygen, it is evident that some sort of respiration can continue without it. This anaerobic respiration has a number of features in common with the alcoholic fermentation brought about by yeast. The resemblances are so close that the fermentation could be regarded as a particularly vigorous and persistent sort of anaerobic respiration carried on by a particular organism. It is customary, however, to limit the term anaerobic respiration to the higher types, and apply fermentation to the breakdown of sugars, proteins, and other substances by yeasts and bacteria. For example, the formation of butyric acid in butter, making it rancid, is a bacterial fermentation of the butter fats. A useful general term for the anaerobic breakdown of sugar is *glycolysis*. This may be applied whether the sugar is free or combined, whatever the products may be, and whatever plant or animal is responsible. On account of its practical importance and relative ease of investigation, more accurate knowledge has been secured about the yeast fermentation than about glycolysis in any other plant. It is known, for example, that yeast breaks down the three hexose sugars, glucose, fructose, and mannose to ethyl alcohol and carbon dioxide almost quantitatively according to the equation

$$C_6H_{12}O_6 \rightarrow 2C_2H_5OH + 2CO_2.$$

Other substances, such as succinic and lactic acids, glycerol and acetaldehyde, remain, but only in very small quantities, when the reaction ceases. The end-products of anaerobic respiration in the higher plants include carbon dioxide, alcohol, and lactic acid in varying proportions. Owing to the technical difficulties in estimating at all accurately the quantity of labile carbohydrate consumed, very few carbon balance-sheets for the anaerobic respiration of higher plants have been published. It appears probable that the fermentation equation given above represents quite closely the anaerobic respiration of peas and carrots, and, perhaps also, of some cereal seedlings.

It is a commonly observed result that the alcohol/CO_2 ratio is less, often much less, than the 1·0 predicted by the equation: what happens to the 'missing' alcohol is still uncertain, but it would not be surprising to find that it, or its precursors, enter various side reactions. Potatoes form little or no alcohol under nitrogen, unless they are chopped up or otherwise damaged. Instead, they form considerable quantities of lactic acid and release but little carbon dioxide. Apples form alcohol; but not in amounts equivalent to the carbon dioxide given off simultaneously. It has been suggested that the 'extra' CO_2 comes from malic acid, which is also known to be consumed.

Methods of Investigating Intermediary Metabolism. One of the principal tasks of metabolic studies is to discover the stages by which the vital processes, such as protein synthesis, respiration, and so forth, proceed, and the intermediate compounds formed in them. A number of methods are available but none of them is conclusive in itself; it is usually necessary to apply as many methods as can be brought to bear upon the problem; and there is need for careful judgement in assessing the results.

The principal methods used fall under seven main headings. (1) The extraction of a supposed intermediate product, and of the enzymes likely to form and decompose it, is good supporting evidence; but failure may arise from many causes and cannot usually be taken to prove a contrary. (2) Some important metabolic substances are visible by colour, or by means of a characteristic absorption spectrum, and their participation may be proved by optical means. This is particularly convenient, because little or no interference with the tissue is called for. For example, the correlation between the absorption spectrum of the chlorophylls and the action spectrum of photosynthesis proves the chlorophylls to be an essential part of the process.

A further illustration is provided by **exp. 31**, p. 118. (3) The application of a fixative, that is to say a substance with which a suspected intermediate may be expected to react, is useful in reactions where the rate of decomposition of the intermediate may be faster than its rate of formation. Without the fixative, the substance does not accumulate, and so cannot be extracted. The danger of the method is that it may cause the accumulation of the product of an unimportant side reaction, which may then be mistaken for a member of the main reaction sequence. (4) An inhibitor, more or less specific for a particular enzyme, may be used to break the sequence at its point of action. The intermediate normally decomposed by the enzyme should then accumulate and become identifiable. This is a much used and very useful method, its main short-comings being the lack of absolute specificity of known inhibitors, and possible failure of the inhibitor to enter the tissues. (5) Feeding experiments have been used, but are very uncertain in action. Failure of the supplied substance to reach the appropriate enzymes, and saturation of the enzyme by the substances already in the cell complicate the experiment. Further, it does not follow that, because a cell can metabolize an applied substance, it normally forms the substance itself. (6) Conversely, the tissue may be deprived of an essential reactant such as oxygen. (7) Comparatively recently, the use of radioactive and other isotopes has been introduced into metabolic studies. With suitable precautions, this has great advantages, notably its high degree of sensitivity. It is also subject to serious difficulties. Generally, the labelled material must be fed to the tissue concerned with the resulting difficulties mentioned under heading (5); there may also be exchanges of isotopes from one compound to another that have nothing to do with normal metabolism.

In working out a metabolic reaction-sequence it is therefore necessary to have regard to all available evidence. As an example, we may consider the evidence for pyruvic acid as an intermediate substance in respiration. Pyruvic acid does not accumulate in sufficient quantities to be extracted from healthy tissues; but enzymes catalysing its decarboxylation have been extracted from yeast and many plants; enzymes for its formation are also present (Method 1). Pyruvic acid has been fixed and caused to accumulate as calcium pyruvate by addition of lime to fermenting yeast preparations (Method 3). It has also been caused to accumulate in barley saps and in undamaged barley leaves by blocking the destructive enzyme, carboxylase, with 1-naphthol-2-sulphonic acid (Method 4). When it is fed to barley seedlings, the rate of CO_2-production increases and the R.Q. rises towards the value of 1·2 which would be observed if pyruvic acid only were being oxidized (Method 5.) When pyruvic acid, $\overset{1}{C}H_3\overset{2}{C}O\overset{3}{C}OOH$, is labelled with a radio-active carbon atom at position 1 the carbon dioxide given off by the roots to which it is fed rapidly becomes radio-active also. If the labelling is on carbon atom 3 it is soon found in acids such as citric and malic which are intermediary products of pyruvic acid oxidation (p. 102). Methods 2 and 6 are not applicable.

Intermediate Reactions of Anaerobic Respiration. Although we cannot say that any particular sugar is the starting-point of respiration, yet we may remember that all the normally respirable substances consist of glucose or fructose units either free or condensed. Mannose is not usually present, but is respired if given artificially. All these respirable substances yield a phosphate ester which is found to be the same whether the initial reactant was starch (replaced by glycogen in yeast) or one of the hexoses. This very interesting substance is called hexosediphosphate, or more precisely fructofuranose 1:6-diphosphate, and has the following formula:

$$H_2PO_3.OCH_2 \qquad O \qquad CH_2O.PO_3H_2$$

The addition of the two phosphate radicals forces the hexose molecule into a five-membered fructofuranose ring, its active form (cf. the sugar formulae on p. 53). Hexose-diphosphate is the first molecule actually split during anaerobic respiration. Its decomposition is a complicated series of reactions; but is of great interest as showing how a fundamental cell process retains the same general character, subject only to minor changes, in both plant and animal kingdoms. The chain of reactions which results in the formation of pyruvic acid from the hexosediphosphate may be written

$$\frac{1}{2} \text{ Hexosediphosphate}$$
$$\downarrow \qquad \qquad \cdot \quad \cdot \quad \cdot \quad \cdot \quad \cdot \quad 1$$
$$\text{Triosephosphate}$$
$$\downarrow \quad +H_3PO_4 \; \cdot \quad \cdot \quad \cdot \quad \cdot \quad 2$$
$$\text{Diphosphoglyceric acid}$$
$$\downarrow \quad -H_3PO_4 \; \cdot \quad \cdot \quad \cdot \quad \cdot \quad 3$$
$$\text{Phosphoglyceric acid}$$
$$\downarrow \qquad \qquad \cdot \quad \cdot \quad \cdot \quad \cdot \quad \cdot \quad 4$$
$$\text{Phosphoenolpyruvic acid}$$
$$\downarrow \quad -H_3PO_4 \; \cdot \quad \cdot \quad \cdot \quad \cdot \quad 5$$
$$\text{Pyruvic acid}$$

Two things should be specially noted about it. (1) The second step needs the addition of an equivalent of phosphate, and (2) it also involves the oxidation of the aldehydic triose to a carboxylic acid. Since these changes are anaerobic, the oxidant cannot be atmospheric oxygen; and is, in fact, the nucleotide NAD (*see* p. 62). Both phosphate radicles, the one acquired in reaction 2 and the one originally present, are shed—in reactions 3 and 5 respectively. Although the acquired radicle may be taken up from the cell's supply of inorganic phosphate the two which are given up are given to ADP to form two equivalents of ATP. There is thus a storage of energy in labile phosphate bonds and it is important to note that without the initial addition of phosphate no oxidation at all occurs. Oxidation and phosphorylation are linked into one process by their common reactant, diphosphoglyceric acid.

Anaerobic respiration or fermentation is not complete with the formation of pyruvic acid which is much too active a substance to accumulate inside cells in quantity. The CO_2 of anaerobic respiration is formed by breaking out the carboxyl (—COOH) group from pyruvic acid leaving acetaldehyde as a residue.

Both pyruvic acid and acetaldehyde are active oxidizers and both are capable of re-oxidizing $NADH_2$ such as the NAD which has accepted 2H in oxidizing triosephosphate to diphosphoglyceric acid (reaction 2 above). As the concentration of NAD in plant cells is low it is only this re-oxidation that keeps the system going. Acetaldehyde thus becomes reduced to ethanol or, if no CO_2 is released, pyruvic acid itself is reduced to lactic acid:

$$CH_3COCOOH \rightarrow CO_2 + CH_3CHO$$
$$CH_3CHO + [2H] \rightarrow C_2H_5OH$$
or
$$CH_3COCOOH + [2H] \rightarrow CH_3CHOHCOOH.$$

The first reaction is characteristic of yeast, carrots, and

other plants with a strong decarboxylating enzyme (carboxylase), and the second of animal muscle and intact potatoes, which either do not possess a carboxylase or suppress its activity.

Enzymes of Glycolysis. The enzymes of yeast responsible for fermentation are collectively called zymase. They have been very intensively studied on account of their great practical importance in brewing, baking, and medicine. The original discovery of zymase was made during an attempt to preserve a yeast extract. It had been obtained for medical purposes by grinding a mass of yeast until the majority of the cells were broken, and then pressing out the juice. Ordinary antiseptics were found to be unsuitable, and when sugar was added as a preservative (as in making jam) a quite unexpected result was obtained: the sugar was fermented by the non-living extract. Up to that time it had been supposed that fermentation was a property of the living cell alone.

Without zymase, fermentation does not occur; but it is not necessary for the cells which have produced it to be still alive at the time of fermentation. It is not easy to separate an active zymase from yeast cells; but if they are killed, washed with acetone, and dried, the non-living mass contains active zymase among the cell residues. Such a preparation is called *zymin* and when added to sugar solutions is able to cause fermentation much more vigorously than pressed juice. Unlike living yeast, it soon loses its activity and, of course, has no powers of multiplication or regeneration. It will keep almost indefinitely in the dry state, and similar preparations are used for a variety of practical purposes, though in brewing or baking living yeasts are more useful.

The enzymes concerned in breaking down sugar to carbon dioxide and alcohol or to lactic acid have now been found in many plants. They include *zymohexase*, which splits hexosediphosphate; *triosephosphate dehydrogenase* which oxidizes the triosephosphate; *carboxylase*, which splits pyruvic acid; *lactic dehydrogenase*, which reduces it; and *alcohol dehydrogenase*, which reduces acetaldehyde to alcohol. They also include the two *kinases* which catalyse the transfer of phosphate to ADP in reactions 3 and 5 (p. 97).

Natural Anaerobiosis. For the great majority of plants respiration without oxygen is an unnatural condition which they manage to survive. The withholding of oxygen must not last too long, since the plant's sugar supplies are used up very rapidly (cf. p. 89) and the internal accumulation of alcohol soon becomes poisonous. In fact, in the absence of oxygen protoplasm breaks down irretrievably even before starvation becomes acute. The majority of plants do, therefore, require oxygen for their normal respiration, though some *facultative anaerobes*, such as *Bacterium mycoides* which brings about rotting in the soil, may survive relatively long periods without it. *Obligate anaerobes*, like the tetanus bacillus, are actually killed by oxygen and are very rare. At the other extreme, some few plants cannot survive even short periods without oxygen; they include some bacteria and, it is said, the Canadian water-weed, *Elodea*.

Some higher plants succeed in colonizing habitats that have little or no oxygen, notably swamps. It appears, for example, that rice grains can sprout in the total absence of oxygen; but they may, in this, be unique, and their seedlings soon come to need oxygen at least in low concentrations. The roots of rice and other swamp plants may live in soils completely devoid of oxygen; but this they succeed in doing because oxygen diffuses down the continuous intercellular spaces in the leaves and roots themselves. It has even been shown that rice roots oxidize the layers of anaerobic blue clay in contact with them, forming a red deposit on the root surface. It is unlikely that anaerobic respiration has any great adaptational value, or that the higher plants can survive indefinitely in oxygen-starved sites by means of it.

AEROBIC RESPIRATION

Plant tissues in air do not accumulate either ethanol or lactic acid. They have been shown to be unable to oxidize alcohol and its formation must therefore be prevented in air. Pyruvic acid does continue to be formed in air, which suggests that the initial stages of aerobic and anaerobic respiration must be similar. Other evidence supporting this assumption may be briefly summarized as follows: (1) The anaerobic production of carbon dioxide, like the aerobic production, is universal among plants. (2) After short periods without oxygen, many plant tissues show a temporary increase of CO_2-production on return to air. This suggests the oxidation of anaerobic products, though the substance oxidized is not necessarily alcohol. (3) Variations of conditions that affect anaerobic respiration affect aerobic respiration equally. The temperature coefficients, for example, of the two forms of respiration have been found identical under a variety of circumstances. (4) Selective inhibitors like sodium iodoacetate that restrict the rate of anaerobic respiration restrict aerobic respiration similarly. (5) Enzymes of fermentation are found in plant tissues and are not inactivated by the presence of oxygen. (6) Phosphorylation occurs both under anaerobic and aerobic conditions.

In the presence of oxygen pyruvic acid is oxidized instead of being reduced to lactic acid or anaerobically decarboxylated to acetaldehyde. The first step in its oxidation is still a decarboxylation, but is now an oxidative one in the presence of a complex nucleotide, coenzyme A, and the products are CO_2+acetyl-Co A.

During recent years evidence has slowly accumulated which makes it virtually certain that the oxidation of pyruvic acid in plant tissues is by means of the citric acid cycle first discovered in the wing muscles of birds, which have an exceptionally active respiration to provide the energy required for flight. The final acid formed in the cycle is oxaloacetic acid which reacts with a fresh acetyl-Co A molecule to give citric acid and so starts another turn of the cycle.

The successive stages of the cycle may be outlined as follows:

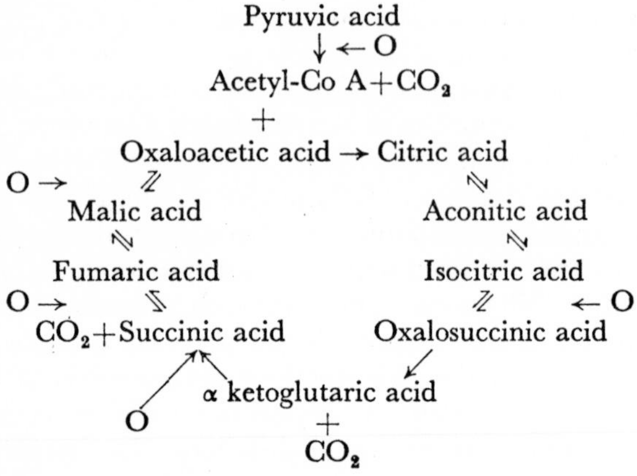

It will be seen that in each revolution of the cycle one molecule of $CH_3COCOOH$ is completely oxidized with the release of $3CO_3$. There is a simultaneous consumption of 5 equivalents ($2\frac{1}{2}$ molecules) of oxygen at the points marked $\leftarrow$ O.

Evidence indicating the occurrence of this cycle has now been obtained from numerous plant tissues. It consists of the following points which are numbered to correspond with the general scheme on p. 94. The acids have been widely identified in plant cells and also enzymes capable of catalysing each of its stages (1). Malonic acid competes with succinic acid for succinic dehydrogenase, the enzyme which oxidizes it. Malonic acid is not oxidized and so 'jams' the enzyme. Its application to root tips, etc., strongly inhibits their respiration. The inhibition both of the enzyme and of respiration can be reversed by an excess of succinic acid. When respiration is inhibited by malonic acid succinic acid accumulates in the tissue much above its normal concentration which is quite low. Similarly, citric acid can be caused to accumulate and respiration can be reduced by substances which inhibit the enzyme aconitase which converts citric to aconitic acid (4). Under favourable conditions feeding pyruvic or a cycle acid will somewhat increase the rate of respiration (5). Feeding ^{14}C labelled pyruvic acid rapidly causes both the cycle acids and the CO_2 emitted to become labelled (7).

Respiratory Oxidations. The substances oxidized are pyruvic acid, isocitric acid, α-ketoglutaric acid, succinic acid, and malic acid. The sixth equivalent of oxygen (which brings the oxygen consumption to 3 molecules, equal to the simultaneous CO_2-production) is consumed in the oxidation of the triosephosphate which continues just as in the absence of oxygen to produce the pyruvic acid. None of the substances reacts directly with oxygen. The oxidation is still carried out by means of NAD (or NADP) like the anaerobic oxidation of triosephosphate through a dehydrogenase enzyme. The difference is that the reduced $NADH_2$ (or $NADPH_2$) is now re-oxidized at the expense of atmospheric oxygen instead of by pyruvic acid or acetaldehyde.

It is usual to think of oxygen as a very active element able to combine with a large number of other substances.

Molecular oxygen as it exists in the atmosphere, however, will react spontaneously with very few of the substances found in living cells and will not, for example, oxidize NAD and NADP directly.

The oxidations characteristic of respiration are catalysed by systems built up by the cells. Many oxidizing systems exist in cells and between them they are able to oxidize a wide variety of substances. Biological oxidations involve the transfer of electrons (with or without H⁺) from the substance oxidized along chains of electron carriers which may include a variety of catalysts. Those that have protein molecules are called enzymes and are distinguished by the termination -ase. Non-proteins closely associated with enzymes in a redox chain are called co-enzymes (e.g. NAD and NADP) or carriers (e.g. some polyphenols).

A typical example is afforded by the chain in which NAD oxidizes malic acid and is re-oxidized by oxygen. The steps may be summarized as follows:

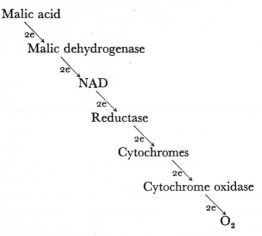

Reductases are flavoproteins (p. 62). They, the cytochromes and their oxidase, are the most important system oxidizing NAD and NADP in plant cells. The cyto-chromes owe their ability to transfer electrons to the presence of iron, which in its association with the cyto-chrome structure fluctuates readily from the ferrous (Fe^{2+}) to the ferric (Fe^{3+}) state. This system is most readily demonstrated in yeast (*see* **exp. 31,** p. 118); but probably occurs with some modifications in all tissues capable of aerobic respiration.

Other Oxidation Cycles. In addition to the citric acid cycle two others appear to catalyse respiratory oxidations at least in some plant tissues.

The pentose phosphate cycle results from the oxidation of glucose 6-phosphate (cf. p. 61) by oxidized NADP with the formation of pentose phosphates and the release of carbon dioxide. Owing to complex interactions some glucose 6-phosphate is reformed. Each turn of the cycle results in the following overall change:

6 Glucose 6-phosphate + 12NADP

$\rightarrow$ 4 Glucose 6-phosphate + 2 triosephosphate + 12NADPH$_2$

The NADPH$_2$ is re-oxidized only in the presence of oxygen and the cycle does not occur anaerobically. Only one carbon atom of the hexose is oxidized in each turn of the cycle and the fate of the triosephosphate is uncertain. The pentose phosphate cycle may occur simultaneously with pyruvic acid formation and oxidation in plant tissues and it is difficult to decide what proportion of the oxygen consumption each is responsible for.

The glyoxylic acid cycle may be regarded as a modification of the citric acid cycle due to the presence of the enzyme isocitritase. This causes the splitting of isocitric acid into succinic + glyoxylic acids. The succinic acid is then converted to oxaloacetic acid by the same reactions as in the citric acid cycle; but the glyoxylic acid reacts with a second molecule of acetyl-Co A to give malic acid+free Co A.

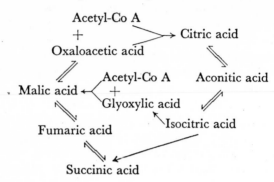

As compared with the citric acid cycle the glyoxylic acid cycle consumes a second acetyl group and accumulates one malic acid molecule instead of breaking off 2 carbon dioxide molecules. It appears to be limited to tissues in which fats are being rapidly consumed such as the endosperms of germinating fatty seeds. It is said that in pumpkin seeds isocitritase is an adaptive enzyme, i.e. is present only so long as fats are being oxidized. The fatty acid chains are broken down step by step until eventually they give acetyl groups combined with Coenzyme A.

The Common Plant Acids. Most plant tissues contain appreciable quantities of organic acids, in the order of 0·1 per cent. of the total dry matter; and some, like lemons, a hundred times as much. Most plant saps are, as a result, slightly acid at about pH 6; but those of acid fruits may fall between pH 2 and pH 3.[1] The presence of free acids and acid salts can be shown quite simply by titrating the extracted juice with any strong base. Some of the acids

---

[1] The pH value is the negative logarithm of the free hydrion concentration. pH 3 is therefore a thousand times more acid than pH 6.

will be neutralized by bases, such as calcium and potassium and, occasionally, ammonium already in the plant sap. These bases must be determined and allowed for if the total acidity is to be ascertained. Since the amount of base in a tissue usually changes only very slowly, acid formation or loss can usually be measured by changes in the titratable acidity alone. This will include all the organic acids present; but also phosphoric which, like the bases, is not likely to change its concentration rapidly.

The acids which commonly accumulate in relatively large amounts in plant cells are malic, citric, and oxalic. Particular tissues may accumulate special acids, like tartaric acid in grapes. It has repeatedly been found that the total acidity of a tissue is not all accounted for when the known constituents are added up, and still unknown acids must occur in important amounts.

Young fruits commonly accumulate relatively high concentrations of acids, 1 or 2 per cent. of their fresh weight. In apples this is practically all malic acid, while in lemons and other citrus fruits it is practically all citric acid. The sweetening typical of their growth and ripening is partly due to a reduction of the acid concentration (though not necessarily in the total amount per fruit) and to accumulation of sugar, mostly fructose.

The metabolism of malic acid has been most closely studied in succulent leaves of the family Crassulaceae. It seems established that the principal requirements for rapid malic acid formation are breakdown of sugars, a fairly high concentration of carbon dioxide, and a relatively low temperature. Respiration assists malic acid production by forming carbon dioxide and intermediates of sugar breakdown, especially pyruvic acid. Photosynthesis on the other hand hinders malic acid formation by removing carbon dioxide. The formation of malic acid in succulent leaves appears to be an example of the dark fixation

of carbon dioxide by means of a carboxylation (cf. p. 39).
The substance accepting the carbon dioxide is either
pyruvic acid or phosphoenolpyruvic acid formed in glycolysis (p. 97). Enzymes catalysing both reactions have
been extracted from plant tissues. The citric acid cycle also
forms malic acid; but cannot cause it to accumulate.

Energy Changes accompanying Respiration. Both
aerobic and anaerobic respirations are accompanied by
decreases of free energy, which seem to be a necessary
condition for the continuance of life. Animals devote a
good deal of this energy to the performance of mechanical
(muscular) work, but only the minutest amounts of work
are done by plants. Moreover, the most obvious work they
do, lifting water from the soil into their leaves, depends
directly upon sun energy and not upon respiration. In a
plant that has stopped growing, the total energy released
from the sugar molecule (i.e. its heat of combustion) is
eventually all converted to heat and dissipated into the
atmosphere. With very trifling exceptions, this heat is
useless to the plant. In this it resembles the carbon dioxide
escaping at the same time. Before the carbon atoms of the
sugar molecule escape as CO_2, they have been through
a number of important changes inside the plant, and the
same is also true of the escaping energy.

The decrease of free energy during the conversion of
sugar to carbon dioxide and water is large. Under biological conditions the complete change can be represented:

$$C_6H_{12}O_6 + 6O_2 \rightarrow 6CO_2 + 6H_2O + 710 \text{ kcal.}[1]$$

During the course of its degradation, part of this energy
brings about changes inside the living tissues. Some that
are most important and that involve the greatest amounts
of energy are chemical. A spontaneous reaction proceeding

[1] Free energy; heat of combustion under standard conditions = 674 kcal.

with a decrease of free energy 'releases energy'; but a reaction which involves an increase of free energy 'needs energy', and can only occur if it is supplied. Many of the reactions taking place inside living cells are of this latter kind; the syntheses of proteins, polysaccharides, and other complex substances and, indeed, growth in general being notable examples. Even some of the reactions of respiration itself require energy, e.g. the attachment of phosphate to the phosphate carrier, ADP (*see also* p. 61), needs about 12 kcal per mole. The various stages of respiration thus have very different energy relations; some need energy; some release a little energy, and some—particularly the oxidations—release rather more. Provided that the complete series shows a net decrease of free energy, which respiration does, the reactions allowing free energy to decrease can drive those that involve an increase. Precisely the same is true of all plant syntheses, which, taken by themselves, would imply an increase of free energy. They must be linked with those stages of respiration that occur with a sufficient decrease; and this means that some chemical mechanism for the connexion must exist also. Connexion between two chemical reactions is made by molecules able to take part in both of them; but the particular molecules linking the most important respiratory and synthetic reactions are not yet known. Nevertheless, the reasons are clear why syntheses which lock up energy but not oxygen will not take place in its absence.

It will have been noted that biological oxidations occur by many stages and give rise to many intermediate compounds. There are, for example, nine different acids formed in the citric acid cycle alone. This multiplicity is important because each of the intermediates may become the starting-point of one of the syntheses by which the carbon, derived from photosynthesis via the sugars, is converted into all the complex materials of the growing plant (cf. p. 128).

Also important is the long chain of electron transfers when any respiratory intermediate is oxidized. The oxidation of malic acid, for example, includes at least seven, of which three involve a potential drop great enough to promote the formation of a molecule of ATP. If the electron transfer occurred in one catastrophic drop, direct from malic acid to oxygen, not more than one ATP molecule could be synthesized.

Although the aerobic stages of respiration release the most energy, the amount released in anaerobic respiration is still far from negligible. Under biological conditions

$$C_6H_{12}O_6 \rightarrow 2C_2H_5OH + 2CO_2 + 72 \text{ kcal}$$

free energy (the heat of reaction under standard conditions = 21 kcal). The free energy available from the anaerobic breakdown of a hexose molecule is thus about one-tenth of the free energy available from the aerobic breakdown. Nevertheless, it seems that most plants are unable to use this energy for most of their normal needs. In the absence of oxygen, not only syntheses but cell division, circulation of the protoplasm, response to stimulus, translocation, germination, absorption of salts, maintenance of semi-permeability, and probably many other activities all come to a stop. The amount of energy available from anaerobic respiration is far in excess of the amount needed; but there are apparently no suitable reactions linking them with the reactions of anaerobic respiration, and so the energy cannot become effective.

Respiration in Plants and Animals. It is very hard to define respiration exactly, and the word gets used in different ways. If we take it in its widest sense, the spontaneous breakdown of organic substances in living cells with release of free energy, it is clear that it is capable of many variations. Different substances may be consumed, different end-products formed, and different chemical methods employed. Nevertheless, from one end of the living world to the other, there is enough similarity to show that we are dealing with variations of a theme rather than with a range of different subjects. Hexose units in one form or another are always the principal substance consumed, fats and proteins never being more than auxiliaries. Phosphates have a very wide distribution as respiration catalysts, causing the conversion of sugar units to hexosediphosphate in practically all cells and tissues examined. The decomposition of hexosediphosphate appears to take place according to the scheme outlined on p. 97 in many organisms, at least as far as pyruvic acid. There are species which can tolerate complete absence of oxygen among both plants and animals. The extent to which an oxygen shortage can be tolerated may differ more among the tissues of a single organism than between widely separated species. After 3 or 4 minutes of complete deprivation, human nerve tissue fails to function and the result is death. Human muscle, on the other hand, can accumulate lactic acid and incur an 'oxygen debt' for a long time without being destroyed.

We shall probably be nearest the truth if we think of respiration as a fundamental process into which various organisms have introduced minor variations of their own. Among the relatively unimportant differences between the higher plants and the higher animals are the more normal breakdown of a proportion of nitrogenous substances by animals, their weaker carboxylase leading to lactic acid formation instead of to alcohol formation in the absence of oxygen, and their possession of specialized breathing organs assisting gaseous exchange. The following normal variations occur among plants and may be mentioned: the consumption of fats in some seeds and algae, and the aerobic formation of malic and other acids instead of CO_2 by succulents and fungi.

EXPERIMENTAL WORK

Exp. 25. LIBERATION OF CARBON DIOXIDE IN AIR AND NITROGEN

Fit two small flasks (about 200 ml capacity) with new rubber corks and exit tubes as shown in fig. 21. The tubes should rise at least 6 inches above the corks. The exit tubes are to dip into small test-tubes as shown. Fill each test-tube with a solution of brom cresol purple, adding

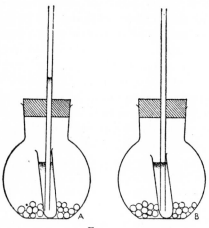

FIG. 21

1 drop of indicator per millilitre of freshly boiled distilled water. The indicator must give a purple colour. If necessary draw CO_2-free air through until it does so. Place the tubes in position and add enough germinating peas to each flask to cover the bottom. Leaving one flask (B) filled with air, blow a brisk stream of nitrogen through the other (A) until all air has been expelled. A cylinder of compressed nitrogen is convenient for the purpose. Cork up the flasks with the vertical tubes dipping into the test-tubes as shown. Note the level of the liquid in each tube, and allow to

stand in a position sheltered from draughts; considerable changes of temperature must also be guarded against; if possible, in a constant-temperature bath or incubator.

In a short time the indicator solution will be seen to rise in the exit tube of A, and in time it may overflow. The colour of the indicator will also change from violet to yellow showing the formation of an acid (dissolved carbon dioxide). In the flask B there will be a similar colour change but no alteration of level, since a volume of oxygen has been absorbed equal to the volume of carbon dioxide produced. If a little lime-water is now added to each flask and shaken round, it will turn milky, showing the presence of carbon dioxide in each.

If the flask B is left long enough, the indicator will begin to rise in its tube. This happens when the peas have absorbed all the oxygen in the flask and begin to respire anaerobically as in the flask A. A lighted splint put into the flask at this stage will be extinguished.

Exp. 26. CONSUMPTION OF OXYGEN

If the carbon dioxide formed during respiration is removed, the simultaneous consumption of oxygen becomes apparent in a closed system by the reduction of gas pressure. This is conveniently shown as follows. Fit a water manometer between two boiling tubes as shown in fig. 22. Fill the bottom inch of the left-hand tube loosely with pieces of pumice or with glass beads. Pipette about 2 ml of 10 per cent. KOH into each tube taking care not to wet the top of the beads or pumice. Put ten peas that have been germinating for about 50 hours into the left-hand tube and insert the manometer stoppers with the taps open to allow the excess air to escape. Close the taps and note the level of the manometric liquid on both sides of the manometer. Observe again after about half an hour. The compensation tube on the right side will prevent changes of temperature and atmospheric pressure from affecting the reading.

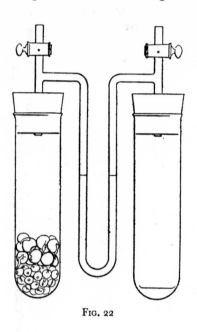

Fig. 22

Exp. 27. FORMATION OF CARBON DIOXIDE FROM SUGAR BY YEAST

Add about 5 g of baker's yeast to 25 ml of 10 per cent. glucose solution in a boiling tube. Fit the tube with a cork and delivery tube bent into a right angle. Lead this tube into a test-tube containing lime-water. Place the tube with the yeast and sugar in a water-bath containing water at about 35° C. Bubbles of carbon dioxide will be given off, producing a milkiness in the lime-water.

After an hour uncork the boiling tube; the smell of alcohol will be noticeable.

Exp. 28. LIBERATION OF HEAT DURING RESPIRATION

Fill a thermos flask to about two-thirds of its capacity with germinating seeds (peas or wheat) and put in a long-stemmed thermometer, burying the bulb among the seeds. Close the neck of the flask with a tight wad of cotton-wool. Fit up a second flask with seed that has been killed by boiling. Read the temperatures indicated by the two thermometers and continue to take readings at intervals of about 1 hour. What is the greatest difference recorded?

Large or compound flower buds such as chrysanthemum and dandelion when opening are also suitable for this experiment.

Exp. 29. LOSS OF WEIGHT DURING RESPIRATION

Count out two lots of 100 wheat grains, avoiding noticeably shrunk or damaged specimens. Weigh each lot to the nearest milligram; the two samples should not differ by more than 5 per cent.; transfer one lot to an evaporating basin, and place in an oven to dry, and after 24 hours' drying remove to a desiccator. When cool, weigh again. This gives the dry weight of 100 ungerminated seeds. Germinate the second sample on damp sawdust on a petri dish or saucer, which must be kept in the dark, and not allowed to dry up. After 7 days, etiolated seedlings will have formed. Remove these to an evaporating basin, after carefully washing away the sawdust adhering to the roots. This is much easier if the plants are allowed to soak in water for a while. Dry in an oven *for the same length of time as before*, allow to cool in a desiccator, and weigh. Compare the dry weight of the seedlings with that of the seeds. What percentage of the solid material has been lost? It represents the amount that has been oxidized to carbon dioxide and water, and given off during the 7 days of germination; compare **exp. 25,** the liberation of carbon dioxide by peas.

Dried plant material is very hydroscopic and great care is necessary in cooling and weighing the samples. The time allowed in the desiccator should be the same in both cases, and weighing should be done in stoppered weighing bottles.

Exp. 30. The Rate of Respiration. Effect of Starvation

Assemble the apparatus shown in fig. 23 and connect the tube E to a filter-pump. The exact form of the vessels A→E is not important, but those shown in the diagram reduce the number of joints, and hence the possibilities of leaks, as far as possible. If all the necessary corks and pressure tubing are of new and springy rubber, there will be no difficulty in making the apparatus air-tight; no waxing is necessary. Support each vessel individually by means of clamps and retort stands, or trouble is sure to ensue. The small gas cylinder C is to serve as the plant chamber, and must be darkened by tying it up in a black bag, or better by pasting dull black paper over its sides and base. Fill the vessels as follows:

A. Soda lime, which should be slightly moist.
B. About 1 inch of lime-water, which must be perfectly clear when first put into the filter-flask.
C. Three or four freshly cut leaves of cherry laurel, about 4 inches long, the petioles dipping into water in the bottom of the cylinder.
D. 100 ml of N/10 baryta water.
E. Ditto.

Having filled the apparatus, turn on the filter-pump and air will be drawn through. Regulate the stream to a slow steady rate of bubbling (about 60 to the minute) in B, D, and E. Test the apparatus for leaks by corking up the open end of A for a few minutes. If the apparatus is air-tight bubbling will soon cease. Remove the cork and allow air to be drawn through the apparatus for 4 hours. Note the temperature. At the end of this time there will be a marked precipitate in the absorption tube D. If there is any precipitate in E the two lots should be run together in a larger tube or cylinder, taking care to wash in the last traces of precipitate. Cork carefully and put aside for comparison

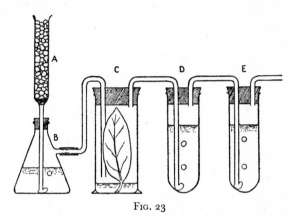

FIG. 23

with the sample to be obtained later. A gentle stream of air must now be kept passing through the plant chamber for a week. If the tubes D and E are replaced they should be filled with pure water only. When the week has passed, refit the apparatus as before, and put 100 ml of N/10 baryta water into D and E again. Draw air through for 4 hours and put the final solution from D and E into a vessel similar to that containing the first sample. Compare the two. Which contains the heavier precipitate, the first or the last? If there is any doubt, shake up and notice which solution appears the cloudier. The heavier precipitate indicates the greater production of carbon dioxide.

The above experiment can be made more precise by titrating the residual baryta in the absorption tubes with N/10 HCl. It will be better in this case to put 25 ml of baryta into each tube and make up to 100 ml with water free from carbon dioxide (freshly boiled distilled water, cooled under soda lime). At the end of each 4-hour period pour the baryta water from the tubes D and E into a large beaker. Rinse the tubes with carbon dioxide free water, and pour the rinsings also into the beaker. Add one or two drops of phenol phthalein and titrate with N/10 HCl until the colour disappears.

100 ml original solution $\equiv$ 25 ml N/10 HCl
Run in x ml N/10 HCl

Baryta neutralized by respiratory CO_2

$$\equiv 25 - x \text{ ml N/10 HCl}$$
$$\equiv (25 - x) \times 1 \cdot 12 \text{ ml } CO_2 \text{ at N.T.P.}$$
$$\equiv \frac{(25 - x) \times 1 \cdot 12}{4} \text{ ml } CO_2 \text{ per h}$$

Exp. 31. CYTOCHROME IN YEAST

Boil and rapidly cool about 100 ml of water to remove its oxygen. Use some of it to moisten (with as little stirring as possible) some baker's yeast. Place a layer about 2 mm thick and a centimetre diameter on a microscope slide, and lay a second slide on top. View the sandwich through a small hand spectroscope, or other instrument with low dispersion, using as strong a light as possible. Two faint absorption bands will be seen in the green zone due to cytochromes b and c. A still fainter band in the red due to cytochrome a may also be detected. If a similar preparation is made with well-aerated water, the bands will not be visible, but will become visible as the oxygen is used up and the cytochrome becomes reduced.

Exp. 32. TITRATABLE ACIDITY

The most favourable material is afforded by leaves of *Bryophyllum* or similar succulent plants; but smaller quantities of titratable acids can be found in almost any tissue used.

Weigh out about 50 g of leaves from a plant that has been kept 12 hours in the dark after strong illumination. Chop up finely and plunge into 100 ml of boiling distilled water. Continue to boil for about 10 minutes to expel all carbon dioxide. Then cool, filter off the water which will now contain the plant acids, and titrate with N/10 NaOH using phenolphthalein as indicator. Express the result as ml N/10 acid in 50 g fresh leaf.

NITROGENOUS COMPOUNDS

THE CHEMISTRY OF THE PROTEINS

THE substances dealt with in the previous chapter possess only carbon, hydrogen, and oxygen in their molecules, but many important compounds are found which contain nitrogen in addition. The most important of these are the *proteins* and *amino acids*, which are related to one another in somewhat the same way as polysaccharides and sugars, though there are several important differences. There are numerous amino acids, but they resemble one another in possessing both acidic and basic groups in their molecules, so that they behave as weak acids towards strong bases, and as weak bases towards strong acids. Substances of this kind are called *amphoteric*, and amino acids and proteins are the most important examples of the class. The simplest amino acid is called *glycine*, or *aminoacetic acid*, and has the formula

$$NH_2CH_2COOH.$$

The hydrogen of the carboxyl, —COOH, group is easily replaceable, or in other words is acidic, and reacts with an alkali as follows:

$$NH_2CH_2COOH + NaOH \rightarrow NH_2CH_2COONa + H_2O.$$

The product of the reaction in this case is sodium amino-acetate. With hydrochloric acid, the basic amino, NH_2, group forms a salt called glycine hydrochloride:

$$HCl + NH_2CH_2COOH \rightarrow NH_3Cl \cdot CH_2COOH.$$

The basic group of one amino-acid molecule can react

with the acidic group of a second molecule to form a *dipeptide*, thus:

$$NH_2CH_2COOH + NH_2CH_2COOH \rightarrow$$
$$NH_2CH_2CO.NH.CH_2COOH + H_2O.$$
diglycine

This process is a condensation and the elements of water are removed from the amino acid molecules; but, like the linking of sugars, it probably does not happen directly, but through a phosphorylated intermediate with the assistance of ATP. The dipeptide thus formed is still amphoteric, possessing a free amino and a free carboxyl grouping, and is able to condense again with further amino acids. Such condensations are called peptide linkages and may result in the formation of long unbranched chains of which the peptide linkages form the backbone on to which the remainder of the amino acid molecules (R_1, R_2, R_3, . . .) are set as side chains, thus

Proteins are formed by the union of numerous amino-acid molecules joined in such primary valency chains and each protein molecule may contain two or more chains lying more or less parallel to one another. There are about a score of different amino acids which occur in appreciable amounts in almost all plant proteins. They occur in definite sequences along the primary valency chains and in the relatively simple protein, insulin, which has two valency chains, the details of their arrangement are now known.

Protein molecules vary greatly in size. Insulin is the smallest known with a molecular weight of 6000. The enzymatic protein, peroxidase, has MW = 44,000 and edestin, the reserve protein of hemp seeds, 309,000. Urease, a purified enzyme from jack beans, has an even higher MW = 480,000.

There are two rather sharply contrasting types of protein molecule. The first is fibrous, i.e. long and narrow,

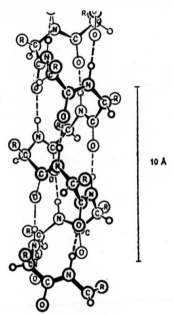

10 Å

FIG. 24. THE HELIX OF A PROTEIN PRIMARY VALENCY
CHAIN AS FIGURED BY PAULING AND COREY
R represents a side chain

and insoluble, and includes such substances as silk fibroin and muscle proteins. The secondary bonds of primary valency chains probably cause them to contract into a helix such as that shown in fig. 24. The second type is globular and much more soluble, and it is supposed that the primary valency chains or the helices are folded to and fro into a ball as indicated in fig. 25. Enzymatic and soluble reserve proteins belong to this type. If the constituent amino acids have suitable side chains, the protein molecules may be able to lie together in regular patterns and so form crystals. Some seed proteins can be crystallized,

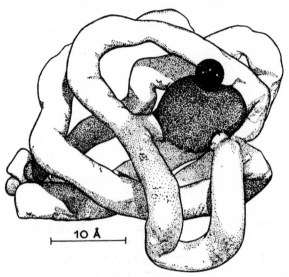

FIG. 25. MODEL OF A MYOGLOBIN MOLECULE SHOWING THE FOLDING OF THE PEPTIDE CHAIN
The shaded portion represents a haem group. (After Perutz)

and those of castor-oil seeds form well-known crystals in the living cells of the endosperm (fig. 26). The amino acid side chains of most natural proteins are many and various, and there is no tendency to crystallize.

The solubility of seed proteins varies a good deal and the following solubility classes are recognized.

ALBUMINS.   Soluble in water and neutral salt solutions.
GLOBULINS.   Insoluble in water, but soluble in neutral salt solutions.

PROLAMINS. Insoluble in water and salt solutions, but soluble in dilute alcohol.

GLUTELINS. Insoluble in water and salts, but soluble in dilute acids and alkalis.

The last two classes are probably to be regarded as reserve proteins limited to storage tissues; and the prolamins are known only from cereal grains. The first two classes, which

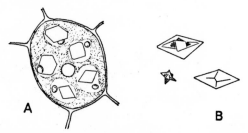

FIG. 26. A. Endosperm cell of castor-oil seed showing angular protein crystals (aleurone grains). B. Crystals of an enzymatic protein

are more soluble, are also more widely distributed and may include actual protoplasmic proteins.

The chemical properties of proteins depend on the side chains. The structures of a few amino acids are shown below

NH
CH.CH$_2$.COOH
CO

aspartic acid (acidic)

NH
CH.CH$_2$.CH
CH$_3$
CO
CH$_3$

leucine (fat soluble)

NH
CH.CH$_2$.CH$_2$.CH$_2$.CH$_2$.NH$_2$
CO

lysine (basic)

NH
CH.CH$_2$OH
CO

serine (water soluble)

with their peptide-linking amino and carboxyl groups on the left and their side chains on the right.

The acidic properties of proteins depends on amino acids like aspartic acid with two carboxyl groups, one of which is in the side chain; and the basic properties on diamino acids like lysine. The free acid groups of aspartic (and glutamic) acids can form amide groups with ammonia,

$$\begin{array}{c} NH \diagup \\ \qquad \diagdown CH.CH_2.C \diagup O \\ CO \diagup \qquad\qquad \diagdown NH \end{array}$$

and proteins always contain a certain number of asparagine and glutamine residues in consequence.

One of the most important amino acids is cysteine which has a thiol (—SH) group on its side chain:

$$\begin{array}{c} HN \diagup \\ \qquad \diagdown CH.CH_2.SH. \\ CO \diagup \end{array}$$

This is readily oxidized, and, where two cysteine residues lie opposite one another on primary valency chains, a sulphur bridge may be formed which makes a firm link between the two chains:

$$\begin{array}{c} NH \diagup \qquad\qquad\qquad\qquad \diagdown HN \\ \qquad \diagdown CH.CH_2S\text{—}SH_2CHC \diagup \\ CO \diagup \qquad\qquad\qquad\qquad \diagdown OC \end{array}$$

Where free thiol groups remain their reversible oxidation and reduction may be important in proteins which are oxidizing enzymes.

CONJUGATED PROTEINS

Owing to the great variety of side chains provided by their score of amino acids proteins react with a very wide range of other substances from simple salts to other complex organic compounds.

Lipoproteins are complexes of proteins and lipids. The protein moiety renders the whole soluble in water even though the lipid content of the complex may be high. Lipoproteins are not soluble in fat solvents such as ether or petrol ether; but the bond between lipid and protein is not usually very strong and is broken by treatment with ethanol. When the lipid fraction is a phospholipid it seems likely that the union is between the acid groups of the phospholipid and the basic residues such as lysine (and argenine) in the proteins. Lipoproteins occur in seeds and are important in the lamellae of chloroplasts (p. 27) and probably also in protoplasmic surfaces.

Enzymatic Complexes. Many proteins with catalytic properties (enzymes) are conjugated with a variety of 'prosthetic groups'. *Haems* (iron-porphyrins) conjugate with proteins to form peroxidase, catalase, and all the cytochromes. In another series of oxidizing enzymes proteins are linked with riboflavin phosphate or flavin-adenine dinucleotide to form flavoproteins. It is also likely that the chlorophylls are linked to proteins in the chloroplasts.

Nucleoproteins. Unstable associations of proteins with nucleic acids can be extracted from green leaves; but there is a suspicion that the union takes place during extraction and that the nucleic acids exist separately in intact cells.

NITROGEN METABOLISM

The nitrogen metabolism of plants results in the synthesis of the proteins, alkaloids, chlorophyll, and other complex substances. Only its most important branch, the formation of proteins, will be mentioned further here. The bulk of the material that is worked up into the protein form is originally introduced into the plant by photosynthesis, but these carbohydrates contain no nitrogen, which is gained exclusively from the soil. The roots absorb nitrogen mostly as nitrates, but sometimes as other simple salts as well (*see* p. 133). Nitrogen from the soil and carbon, hydrogen, and oxygen derived from photosyntheses come together with the eventual formation of proteins.

The Acquisition of Ammonia. Nitrates are usually very scarce in leaves, but comparatively plentiful in roots, and it has been said that the amount diminishes in regular order from the fine rootlets upwards. It appears that protein synthesis can occur in any active plant cell. It is not certain that the method by which the synthesis is achieved is the same in all types of cell; but, if nitrogen has been absorbed as nitrate, the first stage is always its stepwise reduction to the level of ammonia. This is only avoided if the nitrogen has been absorbed as ammonium ions from the soil.

The reductant appears always to be $NADH_2$ (or $NADPH_2$). The first step of the reduction, i.e. nitrate to nitrite is known to involve a transfer of electrons from the reduced nucleotide by way of a flavoprotein (nitrate reductase) and the metal molybdenum to the nitrate:

$$NADH_2 \xrightarrow{e} \underset{\text{reductase}}{\text{nitrate}} \xrightarrow{e} \text{molybdenum} \xrightarrow{e} NO_3^-$$

The products of the sequence are oxidized NAD, nitrite and water. The nitrite is reduced by further stages, possibly with similar mechanisms, to ammonia.

The NAD can be reduced again to $NADH_2$ either by respiration or by photosynthesis. The uptake of most salts is favoured by an adequate supply of oxygen in the surrounding atmosphere; but the curious exception has been noted that nitrate is often best absorbed and reduced at low oxygen concentrations. This, of course, suggests that nitrate can act as at least a partial replacement for oxygen in respiration and gets reduced in doing so. In illuminated green cells the reduced nucleotides produced by photosynthesis also reduce nitrates and are possibly more efficient than those of respiration.

The Synthesis of Amino Acids. The ammonia derived from nitrate or ammonium ions unites with carbon compounds to form amino acids. It now seems clear that the substance with which it unites in the first place is α-ketoglutaric acid. This is a member of the citric acid cycle (p. 102) and is produced from sugars during respiration. When ^{14}C-labelled pyruvic acid is fed to roots, the acids of the citric acid cycle rapidly become labelled showing that they are derived from it. At the same time glutamic acid is rapidly labelled also. Glutamic acid is the α-amino-acid corresponding to α-ketoglutaric acid. Glutamic dehydrogenase has long been known as the most active amino acid dehydrogenase in plants; but the significance of the observation has only become clear comparatively recently. It catalyses the reversible reaction

$$
\begin{array}{c}
\text{COOH} \\
| \\
\text{CH}_2 \\
| \\
\text{CH}_2 \\
| \\
\text{CO} \\
| \\
\text{COOH}
\end{array}
+ \text{NH}_3 + \text{DPNH} + \text{H}^+ \rightleftharpoons
\begin{array}{c}
\text{COOH} \\
| \\
\text{CH}_2 \\
| \\
\text{CH}_2 \\
| \\
\text{CHNH}_2 \\
| \\
\text{COOH}
\end{array}
+ \text{DPN}^+ + \text{H}_2\text{O}
$$

α-ketoglutaric acid   glutamic acid

Although other α-keto acids (pyruvic and oxaloacetic) are simultaneously produced in respiration it is likely that there are no corresponding dehydrogenases to catalyse their amination to alanine and aspartic acid by similar reactions. Nevertheless, ^{14}C-labelled alanine and aspartic acid rapidly appear when labelled pyruvic acid is fed. The ammonia which brings about these two aminations; pyruvic acid to alanine, and oxaloacetic acid to aspartic acid is transferred from glutamic acid which is thereby oxidized back to α-ketoglutaric acid. Enzymes which catalyse such transaminations are called transaminases and two separate enzymes have been found in plants which catalyse the two transaminations. Others are also found; but are usually of lesser activity. It appears that many, perhaps most, amino-acids are formed from their α-keto analogues by transaminations directly or indirectly from glutamic acid.

Formation of Acid Amides. Glutamic acid can react further with ammonia to form glutamine by amidation of its distal carboxyl group:

$$HOOCCH_2CH_2CHNH_2COOH + NH_3$$

glutamic acid

$$\underset{ADP}{\overset{ATP}{\rightleftharpoons}} NH_2OCCH_2CH_2CHNH_2COOH + H_2O$$

glutamine

The reaction requires the assistance of ATP and the enzyme responsible, glutamine synthetase, has been isolated and considerably purified from peas. A similar system forming asparagine from aspartic acid has been isolated from lupin seeds and wheat grains.

Protein Metabolism. The protein content of a plant cell or tissue is subject to continual change. This is well illustrated by leaves since in them protein synthesis and hydrolysis are both specially apparent. Synthesis is favoured by light or the presence of pre-formed carbohydrates, and by a youthful condition of the leaves. The converse conditions always favour hydrolysis, which results in loss of protein and the formation of both amino-acids and amides. The amides formed in this way have been regarded as waste products comparable with the urea of animals. They are not excreted from the plant, however, and together with the amino acids they seem to be freely translocated into other parts of the plant and specially towards the meristems. Here the amino acids are resynthesized into proteins (see farther on, p. 131), but various views have been held concerning the fate of the amides. Either directly or indirectly, however, they provide material for further protein formation, and their nitrogen is not entirely lost to the plant as the nitrogen of urea is lost from an animal. The chemical mechanism by which the resynthesis takes place may, it is true, involve a complete chemical breakdown of the amide rather than a direct fitting of its molecule into the protein pattern.

Translocation is particularly evident at night or from leaves that have been starved by prolonged darkening. Old leaves whose power of synthesis has been much diminished are often exhausted of their nitrogenous materials in this way, the compounds being consumed in further growth at the meristems.

In healthy tissues synthesis of protein continues even though breakdown is occurring also. Cut leaves fed with amino acids labelled with the non-radio-active isotope ^{15}N build the label into their proteins, even though there is an overall loss. The evidence available does not necessarily show that entirely new protein is being built up; conversions and the building of new peptide blocks into the old are probable reactions.

It is not surprising to find that rates of protein synthesis and rates of respiration tend to run parallel. The fundamental reaction of protein synthesis is almost certainly a peptide linkage (p. 120) coupled to the consumption of

ATP to provide the necessary increment of energy. The regeneration of the ATP depends as usual upon respiration.

The exact part played by light in leaf synthesis of proteins is rather difficult to assess. It is generally believed that, if a supply of sugar is provided, leaves continue to form proteins, at least for a time; but evidence is meagre. It is certain that protein formation is much more vigorous when leaves are illuminated and that if ^{14}C-labelled CO_2 is supplied the label appears very rapidly in the leaf proteins. This may perhaps be explained by saying that some of the products of photosynthesis react more readily than the sugars themselves with the leaf's ammonia sources to give glutamic acid or other compounds capable of being polymerized into a protein structure.

Protein Formation in Meristems. The distribution of proteins in a young plant is shown in fig. 27, and it will be seen that they are most abundant in the various meristems, or actively dividing tissues, where the cells have no vacuoles, and all their volume is occupied by protoplasm, containing a large proportion of protein material. These cells are continually increasing their number, and at the same time new material, including proteins, is formed in them. Conditions in meristematic cells seem to be particularly favourable to condensations in general, since many complex substances are built up in them in this way. Their walls are said to be very impermeable to water while they are young, and there are no large central vacuoles, such as occur in fully developed cells. It is probable that the proteins found so plentifully in meristems are synthesized in the usual way by the phosphate-catalysed condensation of amino acids. The amino acids themselves are most probably formed in other parts of the plant, such as the leaves and roots, and together with amides are

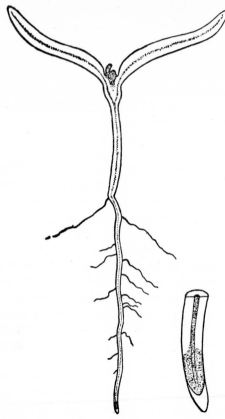

FIG. 27. THE DISTRIBUTION OF PROTEINS IN A SUGAR-BEET SEEDLING
Regions rich in protein are shaded; the root tip is shown enlarged.
(After de Vries, modified)

translocated to the meristems, where conditions are most favourable for the further changes to occur.

NITROGEN ASSIMILATION

The formation of proteins involves a supply of carbohydrate and nitrogenous materials, and the origin of the former in plants has already been explained in speaking of carbon assimilation. Something may now be said of the assimilation of nitrogen, which differs in many respects from that of carbon, and so presents its own series of problems. In one respect, however, the two processes show a striking similarity. It has been mentioned that carbon dioxide is probably the only carbon compound taken up by autotrophic plants, and while the restriction is not quite so narrow with nitrogen compounds, there are large quantities of such materials in the neighbourhood of plants which are not affected by them at all.

Soil Nitrogen. In all ordinary soils, nitrates, nitrites, and ammonium salts seem to be the only forms which are directly available, and these are taken in by the roots, ramifying through the soil. As far as is known at present, the penetration of these ions into the roots does not differ from the action of other inorganic ions, except as noted below, and it will be more convenient to deal with this stage of the process in a general way, taking all these substances into consideration. This is done in Chapter VII.

When the nitrates have entered the root cells, reactions begin to take place, with the result that the nitrates are reduced to nitrites and eventually to amino compounds. It is often stated that nitrates are more readily assimilated than the other forms, though it might seem curious since more energy is required for their reduction. Ammonium salts are used for fertilizing soils with very satisfactory results, but there are always bacteria present in the soil which slowly convert the ammonia into nitrate form, so that the nitrogen may enter the plant as nitrate even if provided as ammonium. Experiments have been done with sterile cultures, and, in these, nitrates were usually, though not always, found to give the best results, but even here a difficulty arises. Ammonia is basic, and when it is taken up rapidly from a culture the solution becomes acid, whereas if a nitrate is used both its ions are taken up more equally and there is usually little change of acidity. It is probable that differences of growth produced by ammonium and nitrate ions are due to secondary causes of this and other kinds rather than to direct effects of the NH_4^+ and NO_3^- ions themselves. It is probable, therefore, that any of these simple inorganic compounds of nitrogen can enter the plant and eventually give rise to amino acids, and since nitrates are more abundant than nitrites and ammonium compounds in most soils, they are probably the most important under natural conditions.

In addition to these simple substances there is a great deal of organic nitrogen in fertile soils, very much more, in fact, than there is of the inorganic. This is contained in the dark-coloured residues formed by the decay of plant remains, and contains nitrogenous and other organic compounds of all stages of complexity. The more elaborate of these substances are usually indiffusible, and may release their nitrogen only with great difficulty so that it is not available to the roots of most plants.

Roots do not, however, live alone in the soil. There is an abundant population of micro-organisms of many kinds in any fertile soil, and it has been shown that the interface between roots and the soil, the rhizoplane, and the layers of soil close to it, named the rhizosphere, contain larger numbers of soil bacteria and other micro-organisms than the bulk of the soil as a whole. There seems little doubt that these organisms are able to extract and convert into forms available to the plant substances which the roots themselves could not absorb. Conversely, the roots secrete substances, including amino acids and the growth factors aneurin and biotin, which are valuable to the bacteria. There are also numerous fungi in the rhizosphere which may attack the root or may live in varying degrees of symbiosis with it. The composition of the rhizosphere flora may be to a large extent fortuitous, but not wholly so, and it may vary with the species of the plant and with its stage of growth and other factors. Flax roots contain the cyanogenetic glycoside linamarin, and it is said that its decomposition leads to the excretion of small amounts of HCN which eliminate some pathogenic fungi from their rhizosphere flora. Definite and more or less stable associations occur between roots and some fungi and bacteria. As examples of the first we may consider the mycorrhizas, and as examples of the second the root nodules of the Leguminosae; they both greatly affect the nitrogen nutrition of green plants.

Mycorrhizas. Mycorrhizas are formed by many species of the higher plants. They are morphologically of two kinds. In ectotrophic mycorrhizas, the mycelium of the fungus forms a closely woven mantle over the surface of the root and enters the intercellular spaces, but rarely the cells, of its cortical tissues. Endotrophic mycorrhizas, on the other hand, form little or no mantle on the surface but penetrate more frequently into living root cells, though again, rarely deeper than the root cortex.

Ectotrophic mycorrhizas are formed by forest trees, notably pines and beeches, with toadstool fungi of the genera *Boletus, Lactarius, Scleroderma,* and others. Forest soils frequently hold very little inorganic nitrogen, because of the immense drain upon it and the comparatively slow rate of restitution from their raw acid humus and leaf litter. Under these conditions, the growth of the trees is very poor unless mycorrhizal fungi are also present. The fungi themselves make only slow growth on raw humus; but do better if free sugars with aneurin and biotin are added. If tree seedlings are infected by the fungus at an early stage, both grow more satisfactorily. The nature of the association seems to be that the provision of sugar and growth factors by the tree roots enables the symbiotic fungus to compete satisfactorily with the other soil organisms in obtaining nitrogenous and other necessary nutrients from the humus, some of which find their way into the host. The planting of suitably infected seedlings has made it possible to raise soft-wood plantations on wide areas of waste land where previous attempts at afforestation had failed. If for any reason the soil relationships are reversed, and inorganic nitrogen becomes the more abundant substance, the tree roots absorb this and the fungal threads disappear, being dissolved by the enzymes of the root cells.

Endotrophic mycorrhizas are formed by *Calluna* growing on wide areas of acid heathy soils which also have a very low content of available nitrogen. One fungus concerned is *Phoma*, and its hyphae penetrate to all parts of the heather plants, even into the ovary and seed, but are most abundant in the cortex of the root. In other hosts, the penetration of the fungus is often controlled by the production of substances capable of arresting the fungal growth; but *Calluna* does not seem to do this. The mycorrhizas produced by the *Calluna–Phoma* association are able to break down and utilize the nitrogen compounds of the raw humus; but some strains of the fungus may possess the mysterious ability to fix atmospheric nitrogen, and so have this additional advantage over the mycorrhizas of forest trees.

Insectivorous Plants. A few unrelated species of plants obtain nitrogen from animal sources. They trap insects by specialized leaves and digest them and absorb the products. *Sarracenia* and *Nepenthes* have leaves modified to the form of deep pitchers containing fluid in their lower parts: *Drosera* leaves are beset with sticky tentacles, while others, such as those of *Dionaea* and *Utricularia*, form mechanical traps. When insects are caught in any of these devices, they are bathed in fluids containing enzymes secreted from glandular cells on the leaf surfaces. Proteinases are abundant in these secretions, and the insect's proteins are slowly hydrolysed to peptones and other soluble products. Putrefaction does not occur, and breakdown does not proceed to the point of releasing ammonia; the soluble organic compounds of nitrogen are absorbed into the leaf. The fluids of pitcher plants often contain bacteria, which may also benefit, but which seem to have very restricted proteolytic activity themselves and probably do not assist much in the actual protein hydrolysis. These pitchers also often contain insects, larvae, and other organisms which are immune to the digestive fluids and which flourish in them like tape-worms in the digestive tracts of animals.

Attention has been focused mainly on the proteolytic enzymes and the nitrogen nutrition of insectivorous plants; but it has been shown that other enzymes, including amylase, invertase, and lipase, are secreted, and that sucrose and starch are digested. It also appears that nutrient salts may be obtained from the decomposed insect bodies.

It is difficult to assess how much this special type of feeding contributes to the growth of the plants that practise it; but *Drosera* has been experimentally shown to benefit to a considerable extent. Plants grown on ordinary nutrient solutions showed greatly increased dry weight, and formed more numerous flowers and seeds when protein was fed to the tentacles. Such feeding is, nevertheless, accessory rather than essential, since the plants do survive and grow healthily without it.

Atmospheric Nitrogen. About four-fifths of the atmosphere which surrounds the aerial parts of plants consists of free nitrogen, a large amount of which is also dissolved in natural water. The question at once arises, therefore, whether the uncombined element is taken up and converted to proteins in plants, or whether it is inactive in plant processes. The problem is of considerable importance in agriculture and for this reason it was investigated in the early days of agricultural science. The method employed was to grow plants such as wheat seedlings in pots of soil deficient in nitrogen, or in sand which was moistened with solutions containing only mineral nutrients. Air was allowed free access, and usually it was found that seedlings thus grown contained no more nitrogen than a sample of the seeds from which they were derived. The only accessible nitrogen was that present in the air, and the seedlings were not able to elaborate any of this into organic material. Leguminous seedlings such as peas and clover when grown in soil exhibited a marked difference from the usual rule, and appeared able to assimilate atmospheric nitrogen in considerable quantities. Experiments were also performed with crop plants growing in farm fields, parts of which had become depleted of their soil nitrogen, and from these similar results were obtained. As an outcome of these experiments most people were convinced that the majority of plants do not assimilate nitrogen from the air as a free element, though the contrary idea has been revived from time to time. More elaborate and critical experiments have been done of recent years and their result has been to confirm the early work.

The Root Nodules of Leguminosae. The peculiar behaviour of leguminous plants remained for some years a mystery; but was eventually discovered to depend upon the close association of these plants with bacteria living in their roots. If the roots of a young bean plant (fig. 28) are carefully washed and examined they will be found to be swollen in various places into small excrescences or nodules, which have been formed in the following manner. The

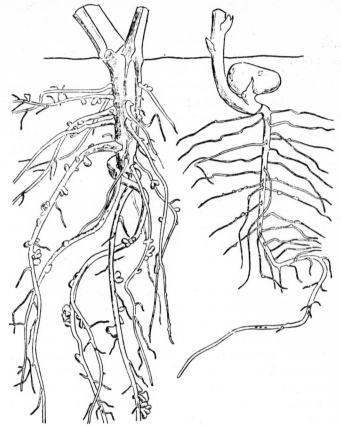

FIG. 28. ROOT SYSTEM OF *Vicia faba* SHOWING NODULES

Right, young plant with nodules just beginning to form; left, mature plant with nodules well developed. Reduced

group of bacteria called collectively *Rhizobium leguminosarum* is generally found in fertile soils, and almost invariably where peas and beans have recently been grown. Other species of *Rhizobium* are associated with other legumes. *Rhizobium leguminosarum* can exist in a number of different forms, but is usually to be found as small spheres, or cocci, which may develop cilia and move about to a limited extent. If a coccus comes into contact with a root-hair of one of the Leguminosae, it becomes attached and multiplies upon the surface of the hair, the wall of which is softened, so that the bacteria find their way into the cell. Inside the plant, the bacteria change their shape to a short rod, and penetrate as far as the inner cortex of the root, but beyond this they never seem to go. Round the infected region the cortical cells divide repeatedly, while the cells which contain the bacteria considerably increase their size, so that a mass of new tissue is formed, which becomes visible externally as the nodule. In their final position the bacterial rods take on yet another shape, many of them branching into the form of a Y or a T, thus completing the cycle of changes shown in the accompanying diagram (fig. 29 A).

The bacteria which become immured in this way in the roots of suitable host plants convert uncombined nitrogen into simple nitrogenous compounds and finally into proteins. It is unlikely that they do this while they exist independently in the soil, but there are bacteria which do. When the root-nodule is being formed, the vascular tissues of the root form new branches, which envelop the infected region (fig. 29 C), and through this channel an exchange of soluble substances goes on between the host and the bacteria. Sugars, which the bacteria do not form themselves, pass from the autotrophic plant into the nodule, while soluble nitrogenous substances pass in the reverse direction. If insufficient sugar reaches the bacteria through a failure of the special vascular tissues to develop, or for any other reason, the bacteria become parasitic on the host. Conversely, when there is abundant nitrate in a soil, the number and size of nodules formed is greatly reduced and the legume grows more independently.

Very little is known of the means by which the nitrogen is brought into organic combination. It requires the consumption of sugar and oxygen, and the respiration rate

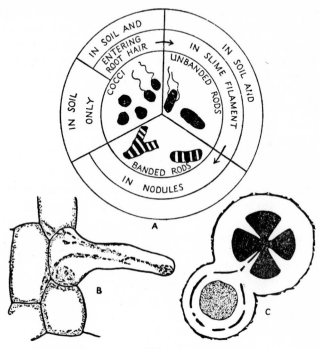

FIG. 29

A. Diagram of the life-cycle of *Rhizobium leguminosarum*
B. Bacteria of the same species infecting a root hair of *Phyllocladus*. × 500
C. Transverse section of a root of *Vicia faba* passing through a nodule.
   Bacterial region shaded with dots; vascular tissue cross hatched
                (B redrawn after Spratt. M.S.)

of nodulated roots is exceptionally high. The fixation also depends on the presence of molybdenum, not needed for the leguminous plant itself, or even for the development of nodules which in its absence fail to fix nitrogen.

The most notable result of this combination of organisms is the fixation of quite large quantities of atmospheric nitrogen amounting to as much as 100 lb nitrogen per acre in a season. The effectiveness of the fixation depends upon the species of legume, perennial forage plants like lucerne and clover with their continuously enlarging root systems being usually more effective than peas and beans. There are many strains of *Rhizobium*, and rapid nitrogen fixation only results when a given legume is infected by a suitable strain. Ineffective strains may cause the formation of nodules, but such nodules have little power of nitrogen fixation. When fixation is rapid, secretion of soluble nitrogen, especially aspartic acid, into the soil may occur. This may be taken up by non-leguminous plants growing near by, but conditions in a soil are so complex that it does not necessarily follow that improved growth will result. Nitrogen may also be added to a soil by the sloughing-off of root nodules which are shorter-lived than the roots that form them. If the plants rot upon the ground, or are ploughed into it, there is an appreciable increase in the combined nitrogen store of the soil, with a corresponding increase in fertility. The advantage of growing vetches or clover, which are both members of the Leguminosae, upon impoverished soil has been known to farmers of all ages, and was recorded by Theophrastus, the earliest botanical writer. The explanation of the gain is, on the other hand, not much older than the present century.

Nitrogen Fixation by Free-living Organisms. Some free-living micro-organisms of the soil are able to fix nitrogen and are much more widely spread than *Rhizobium leguminosarum* which is abundant only in the neighbourhood of leguminous roots. They normally occur only in relatively small numbers and belong to three groups: (1) aerobic bacteria of the genus *Azotobacter*, (2) facultative anaerobic bacteria of the *Clostridia* group, and (3) blue-green algae of the Nostocaceae.

Azotobacter is commonly present in soils in numbers varying from about 2000 to 20,000 per g. It brings about appreciable nitrogen fixation only if soluble sugars, or other simple organic substances, are available to provide respiratory materials and energy. It cannot utilize starch or other polysaccharides. It grows well in the presence of numerous sources of nitrogen such as nitrates, ammonium salts, or urea; but if they are abundant it does not fix atmospheric nitrogen. If they are at low concentrations, it may fix free nitrogen at the rate of about 1 g nitrogen for each 20 g carbon used.

Clostridium in pure culture will only fix nitrogen when oxygen is rigidly excluded; but in the soil and in the presence of certain protecting bacteria, oxygen has no inhibiting effect. It is usually present in higher numbers than *Azotobacter*.

Nostoc differs sharply from the nitrogen-fixing bacteria in one important respect. Being a green plant, it photosynthesizes and, therefore, does not need a supply of preformed sugars. Like the bacteria it only fixes nitrogen if more available forms, nitrates, ammonia, and asparagine, are scarce. Under the appropriate conditions, *Nostoc* can live and grow with simpler materials, CO_2 and N_2, than any other organism. The nitrogen-fixing bacteria are rarely, if ever, present in sufficient numbers to have much effect upon the nitrogen balance of the soil; but the film of blue-green algae on the surface of rice fields in India has been shown to keep their soils replenished with available nitrogen almost indefinitely. The mechanism of nitrogen fixation is still quite obscure; but there is a hint that it may be the same, or at least similar, in all these microorganisms, from the fact that they all show a special requirement for molybdenum.

It will be clear from the preceding pages that the higher plant is only one out of many nitrogen transformers which exist in nature. The cycle of changes through which the element is continually passing is indeed very complex, but its main outlines can be fairly easily stated, and will become clear from an inspection of fig. 30, p. 147.

Nitrogen Fixation in Air and Soil. Many of the changes represented have been described already, and others, such as the transformation of plant to animal proteins, need no further comment. During thunderstorms, small quantities of nitrogen may combine with oxygen, or with the traces of hydrogen present in the upper air, under the influence of the high-tension electric discharges. In this way, traces of nitric oxide and ammonia are formed, which, being very soluble, are easily washed down by rain to form nitrates and ammonium compounds in the soil. The amount of nitrogen turnover due to this cause is comparatively small, however, and by far the most important 'fixations' are those going on in the soil, the air spaces of which contain free nitrogen, so that blue-green algae, *Azotobacter*, and *Clostridium*, as well as *Rhizobium*, exist in an atmosphere containing a large proportion of nitrogen just as an aerial plant does.

Nitrification. The action of the nitrifying bacteria, *Nitrosomonas* and *Nitrobacter*, which also exist in all common soils, has already been described to some extent (p. 38). The nitrogen transformations which they bring about make them independent of light, since the reaction in each species releases free energy. In this respect they differ very markedly from the nitrogen-fixing bacteria, which depend upon preformed organic matter for their energy supplies, and which without such supplies no longer assimilate nitrogen, or continue any other vital activity.

Nitrosomonas oxidizes ammonium ions in the soil. Its action is specific and it will not oxidize other nitrogen compounds such as urea or nitrites. *Nitrobacter* is similar in this respect, its action being limited to the oxidation of nitrites alone. A curious property of these two organisms is that neither tolerates the presence of gelatine, and since this used to be used as a medium for the cultivation of pure strains of bacteria, it was a long time before they could be isolated and their mode of life studied. Finally, cultures were successfully obtained with silica jellies free from organic matter, and their absorption of carbon dioxide to form carbohydrates, with the energy derived from ammonia or nitrite oxidation, was then made clear. Light was found to be not only unnecessary but actually fatal to these organisms.

The Formation of Ammonia. The proteins of plant and animal remains, which become added to the soil after the death of the organism, pass through the processes of decay. These are brought about in the main by a group of bacteria, though other members of the soil population also play a part, and some of the later stages go on even under sterile conditions. The principal agents are those known as *Bacillus mycoides*, though this name includes not a single species, but rather a group of species, all rather similar.

In their energy relationships, these bacteria differ from the nitrogen-fixing bacteria in an interesting way. If proteins are scarce and sugars abundant, it has been noticed that they cease to produce ammonia, and absorb nitrogen compounds like the others, energy being derived from the oxidation of the sugars. If proteins are present, on the other hand, they are decomposed by the bacteria, which become independent of sugars and simpler nitrogen compounds, deriving both their energy and materials from the single source. During this process, more ammonia is formed than is absorbed by the bacteria, and the surplus is therefore released into the soil, when it forms compounds, principally the carbonate. Unlike most organisms, these bacteria are able to use combined oxygen, and will bring about oxidation of proteins or sugars in the absence of the free element, if compounds such as nitrates are present.

The three processes leading to the formation of ammonium carbonate, nitrites, and nitrates in soils are closely connected, since the final product of each is the starting-point for a further reaction. They form, in fact, a linked series of reactions, so that the amount of each of these substances to be found in the soil depends upon the relative rates of the three reactions in the chain. Direct analysis shows that, even when proteins are abundant, ammonium carbonate and nitrites are only to be found in traces, though nitrates are somewhat more plentiful. From this it can be deduced that the formation of nitrates from nitrites is a comparatively rapid process, nitrite formation rather less rapid, and the formation of ammonium carbonate slower than either of the other reactions.

Oxidizing Bacteria. The same conditions favour the action of bacteria which oxidize decaying organic matter with the liberation of a certain amount of free nitrogen. Their activity in ordinary soils is very slight; but in sewage or manure heaps they may cause the loss of appreciable quantities of the element by liberating it into the air. Since losses of this kind are a drawback in agriculture, the process has been extensively examined, but up to the present the nature of the chemical reactions has not been explained.

The Nitrogen Balance of the Soil. Since the amount of nitrogen in simple inorganic combination to be found in the soil is one of the most important factors in plant growth, it will be well briefly to summarize the processes which control it. The most important of those tending to increase

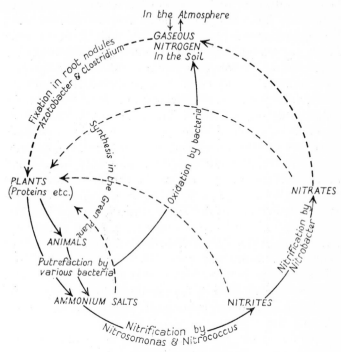

FIG. 30. THE NITROGEN CYCLE

Diagram to show the principal natural transformations of nitrogen. The broken lines indicate reactions for which energy is required (endergonic reactions), and the continuous lines indicate exergonic reactions proceeding with decrease of free energy

the amount are the putrefactions of plant and animal remains, so it might easily be supposed that the addition of such substances to soils would lead to the formation of nitrites and nitrates in due course. This depends very largely, however, upon the relative amount of carbonaceous and nitrogenous substances present in the residues. If the material added has much nitrogen in protein and other complex forms, the putrefying bacteria will produce large quantities of ammonia, which is afterwards converted to nitrate. This happens when farmyard manure or a leguminous crop is ploughed into the soil. If, on the other hand, the material is poor in nitrogen, but supplies a good deal of carbohydrate, many soil bacteria increase their numbers owing to the energy they derive from the latter, and consequently draw upon nitrates already in the soil, and so impoverish it. The incorporation of a non-leguminous 'green manure' into a soil is apt to produce this effect. On the other hand, the nitrogen-fixing bacteria are favoured by these conditions and may, to a small extent, increase the nitrates at the expense of the carbo-hydrates. As a consequence of these and many other re-actions going on at the same time, the ratio between carbon and nitrogen is not easily altered, and usually has a numerical value of about 10 in damp soils such as are found in the temperate zone. The stability of this ratio is illustrated by the observation that addition of inorganic nitrates does not lead to a permanent enrichment of the soil unless carbonaceous material, such as wheat stubble, is added also.

Nitrates do not accumulate to any high concentration in a soil and, failing rapid utilization by plant roots or soil micro-organisms, are likely to be leached out either into the subsoil or away in drainage water. In a bare English soil, leaching may account for the total nitrogen loss. It has, however, been observed that soils under crops lose more nitrogen than is recovered in the crop itself and the drainage, and the nature of this dissipation is still un-certain.

The following list is a summary of the principal known transformations of nitrogen going on in fertile soils.

Process	Agent	Chemical change involved
Nitrogen fixation	*Rhizobium leguminosarum* *Phoma* *Azotobacter* spp. *Clostridium* spp.	N_2 gas $\rightarrow$ proteins
Nitrification	*Nitrosomonas* *Nitrobacter*	$(NH_4)_2CO_3 + 3O_2 \rightarrow$ $\quad\quad 2HNO_2 + CO_2 + 3H_2O$ $Ca(NO_2)_2 + O_2 \rightarrow Ca(NO_3)_2$
Putrefaction	'*Bacillus mycoides*', etc.	Proteins $\rightarrow$ Ammonia, etc.
Denitrification	'*Bacillus mycoides*', etc.	Nitrates $\rightarrow$ Nitrites $\rightarrow$ $\quad\quad$ Ammonia or N_2 gas
Oxidation	Various oxidizing bacteria	Oxidation of organic compounds with liberation of free nitrogen

EXPERIMENTAL WORK

Exp. 33. NITROGEN IN PLANT MATERIALS

The presence of nitrogen in plants can be shown by dry distillation as follows. A short length of iron tube (such as inch-diameter gas-pipe) closed at one end is fitted at the

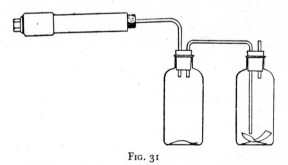

FIG. 31

open end with a glass delivery tube. The glass tube can be wound with asbestos tape to form a stopper to plug it into the iron (fig. 31). About half fill the iron retort-tube with dry barley grains, clamp it horizontally, and connect it with a wash-bottle containing Nessler's reagent (p. 318). Heat the iron tube with a bunsen, at first cautiously and then more strongly. Organic nitrogenous compounds will be broken down to ammonia which gives a yellow precipitate of $Hg_2O.NH_2I$ in Nessler's solution.

Exp. 34. INORGANIC NITROGEN IN PLANTS

a. Free nitrate ions occur in some tissues and can be detected by the blue colour given with diphenylamine sulphate (0·5 g diphenylamine in 100 ml concentrated sulphuric acid). Immerse thick sections in the reagent. Hypocotyls of cress seedlings and leaves of nettles and elder are usually rich in unreduced nitrate.

b. Free ammonium ions are released as ammonia on addition of a little 10 per cent. KOH to some plant saps. Mince a sugar-beet and strain off some of the sap through muslin. To about 5 ml in a test-tube, add a few drops of 10 per cent. KOH and warm gently. Test for ammonia by smell and by holding the stopper of a concentrated HCl bottle at the mouth of the test-tube.

Exp. 35. REACTIONS OF PROTEINS

Break an egg and collect the white in a cup. About half fill the cup with water, and stir briskly until an even solution of the egg albumin (a protein) is obtained.

a. Xanthoproteic test. One-third fill a test-tube with the protein solution and add about one-third as much strong nitric acid. A cloudy white precipitate will be formed. Boil; the precipitate will turn canary yellow; cool by holding the end of the test-tube under the tap, and then make alkaline by adding ammonia. The yellow colour will turn to orange.

b. Biuret reaction. Put some protein solution into a second test-tube; add about 2 ml of 40 per cent. sodium hydroxide, and one drop of 1 per cent. copper sulphate. A pale purple colour is produced.

c. Add a few drops of Millon's reagent to 2 or 3 ml of the solution of protein; on boiling, a brick-red precipitate or solution will be obtained.

Exp. 36. Presence of Proteins in Plants

a. By means of the above tests, examine the following plant materials for proteins: peas, potato peelings and centres, and flour.

b. Take a very young cress seedling and lay it upon a microscope slide. With a dropping rod cover the root and hypocotyl with Millon's reagent. Warm gently for several minutes over a flame or beaker of boiling water, adding water if necessary to prevent the reagent from drying up. Examine under a microscope. A reddish colour showing the presence of protein (and related substances) will be seen, especially at the root tip. If necessary the root may be crushed by pressing gently on the coverslip with a pencil.

Exp. 37. Root Nodules

Sterilize enough good potting soil to fill a 5-inch pot, by heating with an excess of water in a large metal dish or open saucepan. Keep at the boil for about 10 minutes, and finally evaporate the water by more cautious heating. When dry enough, cool and put into a well-cleaned pot. Prepare a second pot with untreated soil and sow several broad or runner beans in each. When the young plants are about 10 inches high knock them out of the pots, and wash the soil away from the roots. Those grown in unsterilized soil will show numerous small nodules, whereas the others will have none.

V

SOME PHYSICAL CHARACTERS OF ORGANIC SUBSTANCES

THE physical behaviour of protoplasm, of many of its constituent materials, and of many of its more complex derivatives, such as starch and cellulose, indicates that they exist in a colloidal state. Colloidal matter exhibits important properties not depending on its chemical nature and causing behaviour different from that of the same material existing as a crystalloid. Some important attributes of biological substances can be accounted for by their colloidal state, which therefore repays study.

CRYSTALLOIDS AND COLLOIDS

Substances brought into contact with water, provided they do not react chemically with it like sodium, may disperse in it in a number of different ways. They may dissolve in the water to form true solutions; that is to say they may separate into free molecules, as in a sugar solution, and the molecules may dissociate to a greater or lesser extent into their constituent ions, as in a salt solution. At the other extreme, the substances may remain more or less unaltered, like grains of sand or drops of chloroform, and simply drop to the bottom on account of their high specific gravity. If, however, the grains or drops are reduced to smaller sizes, a degree of fineness is eventually reached at which they stay suspended in the water for a considerable time. Such suspensions or emulsions slowly separate or 'break'; but, if the disintegration can be carried far enough in a colloid mill, a dispersion is eventually achieved which is stable more or less indefinitely and is called a colloidal sol. Particles distributed throughout the whole of this size range are normally present in a soil. If a handful of dried soil is stirred in a beaker of water, the coarser sand particles sink immediately to the bottom; others, the silt, sink more slowly; but the very fine colloidal particles of the clay form a sol; and the salts also present go into true solution.

Colloidal systems can therefore be described as those whose dispersed particles are larger than isolated molecules, but smaller than those of a suspension or emulsion. The extremes of this range may be taken to lie from rather above 1 mμ diameter up to nearly 1 μ.[1] Some substances with exceptionally long chain molecules, e.g. the proteins, form sols with water but no true solutions. Many, with smaller molecules, can, by different methods of preparation, be induced to form either true solutions or colloidal sols containing molecular aggregates, though usually they show a decided preference for one or the other state. Those that readily form solutions are loosely termed crystalloids, because many of them also readily form crystals, and those which most readily form sols are called colloids. Sugar and salt are typical crystalloids; clay and glue, in Greek *kolla*, are typical colloids.

Colloidal 'Phases'. Every colloidal system must have at least two components, one of which is continuous and is sometimes called the dispersion medium. The second component may be discontinuous as in the examples quoted above; but when it is formed of long-chain molecules, as in protein sols, these may be in more or less continuous, though perhaps sliding, contact throughout the system. The two components of a colloidal system are not phases

[1] μ = micron, the thousandth of a millimetre, is the normal unit of microscopic measurement. mμ = millimicron, i.e. $\mu/1000$, and is the unit of ultramicroscopic measurement. Molecules are commonly measured in Ångström units, Å = m$\mu/10$.

according to the definition used in physical chemistry, because they are not homogeneous. They may be themselves solutions, and they show surface properties in a high degree, because of their vast interface surface with one another. The two components may be in any physical state; a fog, for example, is a colloidal system of liquid dispersed in gas; but biological colloids are almost always systems of immiscible liquids or of liquids with solids.

Lyophobic Sols. More important in determining the properties of the sol than the physical states of the two components are the relations between them. Some colloids can be separated by simple physical means, such as centrifuging, or addition of small amounts of electrically charged ions, into their two components. These are called lyophobic, and typical examples are the purple sols obtained from a submerged arc with gold electrodes. They owe their moderate degree of stability to two causes. The first is the continual erratic movement of their particles, resulting from the unequal impacts of molecules of the dispersion medium upon them. This movement is called Brownian movement after Robert Brown, the botanist who first observed it in 1826 when studying *Lycopodium* spores. As the size of particles becomes smaller, gravitational pull becomes less and Brownian movement more rapid. Within the colloidal size range the two balance, and sedimentation is prolonged indefinitely. The second cause of stability is provided by electric charges on the surface of the particles causing mutual repulsion. It is not possible to prepare a stable electro-neutral gold sol; but, if a small amount of electrolyte is added, ions become attached to the gold particles and render the sol stable. Sols of this type, prepared by Faraday (1791–1867), are still in existence. Addition of a slight excess of ions of opposite charge causes immediate precipitation.

Lyophilic Sols. These have much greater stability than lyophobic sols, because of interaction between their two components. If water provides the continuous medium of a lyophilic sol, it hydrates the dispersed particles; that is to say a more or less diffuse shell of water molecules is strongly attracted to the particle as well as to other water molecules. Separation of the particles will only be achieved if the water shell is reduced or removed by strong de-hydrating agents, such as alcohol, or saturated salt solutions.

The biologically important colloids as illustrated by the proteins (**exp. 40,** p. 162) are nearly all lyophilic. Clays exhibit some lyophobic qualities and are comparatively easily flocculated and dispersed by adjustments of their electrolyte content. Proteins, the most important of all biological colloids, form stable sols with water, but are fairly easily dehydrated. They carry both positive and negative charges which are easily influenced by external conditions, and when they are reduced to a minimum the protein may coagulate without further treatment. Protein sols are, therefore, in some ways intermediate between the lyophobic and lyophilic.

Particle Sizes. The upper limit of the colloidal size-range corresponds roughly with the lower limit of microscopic vision. The largest colloidal particles of indian ink can just be seen under the high power of a microscope; and when freely suspended, and not attached to the slide or coverslip, are detectably in Brownian movement. The disperse particles of finer sols are too small to be seen; but their presence can be revealed by viewing with lateral illumination against a dark background. Seen by the naked eye, such a sol shows the Tyndall effect, i.e. a milkiness in the path of the lateral beam. Under a microscope with a 'dark ground' condenser this is resolved into separate splashes of bright light that show the presence, but not the shape, of the colloidal particles. The dots are in Brownian movement, which is more rapid than that seen under direct illumination because the particles concerned are smaller. A cell under dark ground illumination shows a dark vacuole, because its solutes are true solutions; but the colloidal wall and protoplasm are brilliantly lit. Used in this way, the instrument is usually referred to as an ultramicroscope, and will detect particles down to a diameter of about 5 mμ. The shapes of ultramicroscopic particles cannot be seen in this way; but it may be possible to deduce them by other means, such as studies of their molecular morphology. Particles down to about 10 Å diameter can now be resolved by the electron microscope.

Table of Magnitudes

MICROSCOPIC PARTICLES

Volvox aureus	200–500 μ
Limit of direct vision	100 μ
Parenchyma cell	50–100 μ
Protococcus, yeast	10 μ
Clay suspension particles	3 μ
Coccus (spherical bacterium)	1 μ
Limit of microscopic vision	0·15–0·2 μ

ULTRAMICROSCOPIC PARTICLES

Viruses	20–200 mμ
Gold sol particles	2–15 mμ
Limit of ultramicroscopic detection	5 mμ

SUBMICROSCOPIC PARTICLES

Large molecule (soluble starch)	50 Å
Limit of electron-microscopic resolution	10 Å
Medium molecule (glucose)	6 Å
Smallest molecule (H_2)	1 Å

1 mm = 1000 μ = 1,000,000 mμ = 10,000,000 Å

Gels. Both lyophobic and lyophilic gels flow more or less freely, though the latter may become viscous. Gels, which are also colloidal, have a large degree of rigidity and resist forces tending to make them flow. The 'disperse phases' of the commonest biological gels have long thread-like molecules, sometimes with side branches, and may not really be discontinuous, especially when they contain relatively

FIG. 32

little water. Owing to the tangling of the molecules, the sols are viscous, and, with loss of water or lowering of temperature, may finally set into a more or less rigid and elastic gel. If the molecular chains interact as well as tangle, a still more rigid and less elastic gel results. Gelatine, a protein extract of hide and bones, dissolves in warm water to form a viscous sol, which sets on cooling into a gel akin to a table jelly. This may be turned back to a sol by gentle heating or, gradually, by adding an excess of water. The sudden change of rigidity at the time of gelation may be due to the formation of adhesions at various points along the chain molecules to form particles or micelles. These remain connected by the more freely solvated parts of the gelatine molecules which are not attached to one another laterally (fig. 32). Much water is still present in the parts between the micelles; but is not easily withdrawn, because a good deal of it is the water of hydration of the gelatine particles. If it is withdrawn by adding alcohol, the gel structure is destroyed and the gelatine precipitated out. Less drastic removal of water causes the gel to shrink, and to become more solid. It then becomes a powerful absorbent, swelling again as it imbibes water and finally passing back to the sol condition. The forces of imbibition (hydration) in a dry gel are very powerful, especially in the presence of a little electrolyte. Dry seeds and grains consist largely of gels and the first stages of water uptake are imbibitional. If confined, the grain by its swelling is liable to burst open its container: ships carrying grain in bulk have been split open and sunk after springing a leak in the hold.

In the normal condition of plant cells, the protoplasm does not gel; but the walls, whether of pure cellulose or any of its modifications, are always in this state. Starch grains are also gels.

Diffusion and Dialysis. Compared with those in true solutions, the particles in colloidal sols are large, and generally much less numerous, and as a consequence diffusion is much slower. By dividing two solutions by a thin membrane, the passage of large particles can be prevented without stopping that of finer ones. Saturated parchment paper, for example, has pores of such a size that it will allow most molecules to pass through it, but the very large molecules, or aggregates of molecules, found in colloidal solutions cannot penetrate. It was, in fact, this property of parchment paper which provided the first rough distinction between crystalloid and colloid solutions, and substances which could not penetrate such a membrane were said to be colloidal. There is, of course, no sharp division of the sizes in which dissolved particles can exist, but rather a fine gradation from the comparatively large, right down to the very small. Thin membranes of collodion can be prepared, having pores of various sizes according to the concentration of alcohol in which they are washed. Typical crystalloids, such as common salt, will pass through the finest pores; larger molecules, such as those of Congo Red, which give a borderline solution between crystalloid and colloid, will only pass through coarser membranes, and typical colloids, such as starch, will not pass at all.

This property can be utilized to separate crystalloid and colloidal substances; the mixed solution is placed in an open vessel, one end of which is closed by a parchment paper, or other suitable membrane. This is immersed in an outer jacket containing pure water. The small molecules and ions of the crystalloid diffuse slowly through the membrane into the solvent outside, but the larger colloidal particles are retained. If the outside water is repeatedly changed, or a continuous flow passed through the vessel, practically the whole of the crystalloid is eventually removed. This process is called *dialysis* (**exp. 42**), and is frequently employed in purifying colloidal substances.

Surface Action and Adsorption. The surface layers of substances possess physical properties which are not shared by the substances as a whole. One of the most important of these is the presence of *surface tension*, which causes them to behave as though they were stretched. This is most easily seen in liquids in contact with air, since they very easily run into round droplets, presenting the minimum surface possible. In order to increase the amount of surface, work must be done, as in the familiar example of blowing a bubble by forcing air inside a soap film. One may picture the surface molecules of the film as being dragged apart from one another against their tendency to cohere. The condition thus set up is very unstable, and the film easily returns to the form of a small droplet in which surface area, and in consequence surface energy, are at a minimum. The more the surface is expanded, the greater is the amount of energy which will have to be present to maintain it in this condition.

When a solid block of material is broken into fragments,

the pieces present much more surface than the original block. For example, a cube with 1 cm sides has a surface area of 6 sq. cm.; if broken into pieces having sides 10 mμ long, approximating to the size of an average colloidal particle, the area would be multiplied a million times. The amount of surface of a solid body is thus enormously increased when it goes into colloidal solution, and since it still consists of groups of molecules its total surface energy is very great.

The actual amount of energy present per unit of surface depends upon the nature of the material. For example, mercury in contact with air has a very high surface tension, whereas oil in contact with water has a very low one, with the result that the oil easily spreads over a large area of water, instead of running into round droplets like mercury in air. The presence of substances in solution in the water may affect the surface tension to a very marked extent, in many cases lowering it considerably. The most familiar example is the action of soap in lowering the surface tension of water against air. It is a matter of universal experience that any change which causes a reduction of free energy may be expected to occur, and when a substance such as soap is added to water it tends to collect at the surface because by this means free surface energy is diminished. If there are two immiscible liquids, such as oil and water, in contact, it is immaterial which of them originally contained the dissolved substance, as it will always accumulate at the dividing surface. This local concentration is called *adsorption*, and since colloidal solutions possess an enormous amount of internal surface between the two components, adsorption of foreign matter very readily occurs, and may lead to the concentration of considerable amounts of material.

Adsorption is not limited to the surface between two liquids, although such cases are probably of the greatest importance in the living cell. Any finely divided solid, such as powdered charcoal or platinum black, very readily adsorbs substances from solution in a neighbouring liquid, or gases from a free atmosphere.

EXPERIMENTAL WORK

Exp. 38. CRYSTALLOIDS AND COLLOIDS

a. Crystalloid. Put about ¼ inch of granulated sugar (sucrose) into the bottom of a test-tube, add 1 or 2 inches of distilled water, and shake vigorously. The sugar gradually disappears, leaving a clear colourless solution, which cannot be distinguished by the naked eye from water. The process is hastened by heating the tube gently over a flame. No change occurs on cooling.

b. Colloid. Into a second tube put a similar quantity of powdered glue and add water as before. On heating, the glue dissolves, but the resulting sol is turbid. Allow the sol to cool and notice that it sets into a firm jelly (gel). Add the same amount of water again, and warm in a water bath. The gel will return to the sol condition.

Glue is of animal origin; agar-agar, which is obtained from oriental seaweeds, is also convenient for this experiment.

Exp. 39. FLOCCULATION OF A LYOPHOBIC SOL

Prepare a colloidal sol of ferric hydroxide by pouring 1 ml of a 33 per cent. solution of ferric chloride into 100 ml of boiling distilled water. When it is cool, put 1 ml of the sol into each of two test-tubes. To the first add 1 ml N sodium sulphate solution, to the second 1 ml N sodium chloride solution. If necessary add a second ml to each tube. Note that the positively charged iron sol is more readily precipitated by the divalent sulphate ions than by the monovalent chloride ions.

Exp. 40. Flocculation of a Lyophilic Sol

Allow about 10 g wheat flour to stand for 2 to 3 hours with 100 ml distilled water and then filter. The filtrate will contain soluble wheat proteins. To 20 or 30 ml add saturated ammonium sulphate solution until the protein sol is precipitated. Note the very large quantity of sulphate ions necessary for this 'salting out'. Filter off the protein, and again shake up with water. A new sol will be formed.

Exp. 41. Diffusion of a Crystalloid into a Colloid

Dissolve 6–7 g of sheet gelatine in water by warming in a beaker. Add 3 or 4 drops of phenolphthalein and pour into a *warm* test-tube until the tube is full. Put on one side to cool, and when the gelatine has set invert the tube with the open end dipping into 10 per cent. caustic soda or potash solution. Clamp firmly. As the alkali diffuses into the gel, the colour of the indicator will show its progress.

Exp. 42. Diffusion through a Parchment Paper Membrane. Dialysis

Make 50 ml of starch solution (*see* p. 318) and dissolve in it about half a gram of common salt. Pour the mixture into a parchment paper thimble having a glass rod passed through its upper edges (fig. 33). Hang the thimble into a beaker of distilled water, which has previously been found to give no precipitate with silver nitrate. After 1 hour test the distilled water (*a*) for chloride

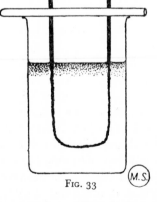

Fig. 33

(salt) with silver nitrate, (*b*) for starch by adding iodine.

Exp. 43. Swelling of Gelatine in Water

Cut a piece of sheet gelatine into a rectangle about 4 cm by 2 cm. Place this on a piece of glass at least three or four times as large, and having a sheet of squared paper beneath it. Measure accurately the area of the gelatine rectangle, and then run on to it 2 or 3 ml of water from a pipette. The gelatine will at once begin to swell; when the process is complete, measure the final area. Remove the gelatine to a piece of gauze, allow it to dry and again measure its area. It will be found to have decreased.

Exp. 44. Swelling of Plant Tissues in Water

a. Cut 2 cm or so of the narrow lamina of the seaweed *Chondrus crispus*, sold dried as carragheen, and treat it like the gelatine in experiment 43.

b. Take ten dried peas, and measure their displacement in a measuring cylinder partly filled with water. Allow them to soak in a dish for at least 24 hours, and again determine their displacement in the measuring cylinder. By what percentage has their volume increased?

Exp. 45. Development of Pressure during Swelling

Take a small tin with a tightly fitting lid, and punch several small holes in the bottom. Pack the tin tightly with dry rice and stand in a dish of water. As the water enters, the rice will expand and push up the lid.

Exp. 46. Brownian Movement

Keep a thin-leaved plant, such as *Elodea* or a moss, in the dark until the green colour is lost. This usually takes about a week. Then mount a single leaf and examine under the microscope. The smaller cell inclusions will be in Brownian movement, owing to the increased fluidity of the starved protoplasm.

VI

CATALYTIC PROTOPLASM

THE PROTOPLAST

THE previous chapters have given an account of the chemical transformations which make up plant metabolism. It has been shown how energy and material are absorbed from external sources, and together build up the fabric of the complete plant. While this is going on a large number of changes have taken place, simple enough in their general outline, but very complex in their details. All of them occur in living cells, and it is important to realize that without the intervention of such cells few of the common metabolic reactions will go on. It may be mentioned, for example, that a mixed solution of carbon dioxide and chlorophyll will not form sugars, however long it is exposed to sunlight, and sugars once formed are stable substances in solutions outside the plant. They do not condense spontaneously to polysaccharides, nor do they break down to carbon dioxide and alcohol. There are many reactions which are known to occur inside plant cells, but which up to the present have not been brought about outside them. Some reactions which are known to the chemist occur under biological conditions in modified forms, and it becomes clear that the protoplasm, in which they are going on, exercises a controlling influence upon them. This it does mainly in two ways: first by accelerating reactions by means of cell catalysts, the enzymes; and secondly by organizing the reactions into specific sequences. Organization depends very largely on the fine structure of protoplasm, which must be briefly considered.

The Visible Protoplast. It is possible to see protoplasm by examining living tissues under a high power of the compound microscope, and something of its nature can be learnt from such an inspection. The young cells that are found just behind the growing points (fig. 34 A) consist of a tiny body of protoplasm, surrounded by a very thin wall. At the centre lies a comparatively large *nucleus*, which is spherical and appears rather denser than the general mass of the protoplasm, which for distinction is called *cytoplasm*. The latter is translucent and colourless, but contains numerous minute particles which give it a granular appearance. Cells such as this are formed by the repeated divisions of the cells of the growing point (meristem). They do not remain in this condition permanently, but slowly increase their volume, while the wall around them gradually thickens. The growth of the protoplasm does not keep pace with the enlargement of the cell volume, and droplets of clear liquid appear in it at various places. On account of their empty appearance, these droplets were originally called *vacuoles*, and the name has been kept, although it is known that they consist of water containing many substances in solution. As enlargement continues, the vacuoles increase their size and their numbers, and finally begin to run together, and form one large drop of liquid in the middle of the cell. At this stage the protoplasm forms a sac round the single vacuole separating it from the cell wall. In many cells there are also *plastids*, firm-looking bodies defined from the general cytoplasm. These are particularly conspicuous when they carry pigments, such as chloroplasts with their chlorophyll. Just upon the limits of visibility with the light microscope, i.e. about 1 μ in diameter, there are also numerous (several hundred per cell) minute organelles, the *mitochondria*. Their structure has been elucidated with the help of the electron microscope and, although it appears to differ somewhat in different cells,

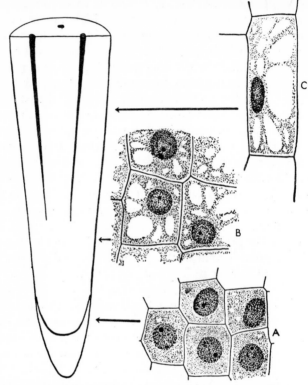

FIG. 34. YOUNG CELLS FROM THE TIP OF A BEAN ROOT

The arrows indicate the distance from the root tip of the cells in successive stages of development A, B, and C. The final stage of vacuolation,
in which all the vacuoles have coalesced, is not shown, but occurs
higher up the root. A, B, and C highly magnified. (M.S.)

its main features are illustrated in fig. 36. Each mitochondrion is a small sphere with a complex wall, the inner layer
of which is infolded into the central cavity. In many plant
mitochondria the infoldings are tubular as shown in the
figure. The centre is occupied by an osmotically active
solution and the walls are semipermeable, with the result

that mitochondria burst when put into a liquid of low osmotic pressure.

The fine structure of chloroplasts as revealed by the electron microscope has already been described on p. 26. Colourless plastids, such as amyloplasts, do not possess internal lamellae and appear more or less uniformly

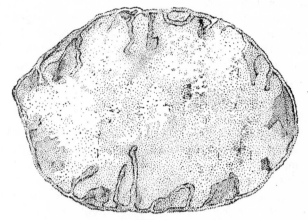

FIG. 35. A MITOCHONDRION FROM *Spirogyra* SHOWING THE OUTER WALL AND NUMEROUS INFOLDINGS FROM THE INNER LAYER (MICROVILLI)
The centre of the mitochondrion is occupied by an osmotically active solution. × 50,000

granular under the electron microscope. The general cytoplasm in which all the organelles, nucleus, plastids and mitochondria, are embedded has further structural features which are in process of elucidation. It is separated from the vacuole by a definite membrane, the tonoplast, and its surface towards the cell wall probably has a special structure also. The long cellulose fibrils of which the wall consists must be built up by cytoplasmic enzymes and the nature of the interface is a difficult problem at present under investigation. At least in young protoplasts there is also a system of membranes, the endoplasmic reticulum, connected with the surface membrane of the nucleus and carrying some of the microsomes, particles even smaller than the mitochondria, but just big enough to be revealed as minute spheres by the electron microscope. They are rich in ribonucleic acid and probably consist very largely of ribonucleoprotein; the name ribosome has been given them on this account.

The various organelles are not built up from the general cytoplasm in each new cell. Like the nucleus, the chloroplasts derive from identical bodies in the parent cell. Microsomes are believed to ·be synthesized in the nucleus and to pass out from it into their position in the cytoplasm.

Localization of Function. It has been realized for quite a long time that the orderly way in which different reaction sequences go on inside cells must depend upon their fine structure. The cells in a tissue that is ground up or dosed with chloroform autolyse, i.e. run down to more or less complete oxidation and hydrolysis. Polyphenols which are stable in the intact cell are oxidized, for example, to brown melanins. Some plant cells contain enough malonic acid to inhibit their succinic dehydrogenase; but the enzyme is protected until the cell structure is broken down. The polyphenols are isolated in the cell vacuole and normally traverse the tonoplast only slowly if at all.

It is reasonable to suppose that the different cellular organelles are the sites of particular functions, and it was easy to show that some parts of photosynthesis are sited in the chloroplasts. Fuller knowledge of the special activities of all the cell structures has only been made possible by extracting the individual organelles in relatively large amounts and freeing them from all others. The method that has brought success depends on their different densities. In principal the cells are broken by grinding in a bland

PLATE III

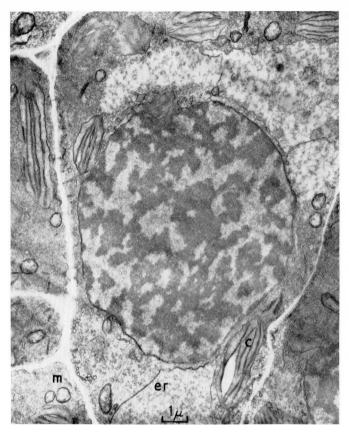

A young plant cell showing a large central nucleus with dark zones of nucleoprotein; young chloroplasts (c), mitochondria (m), and membranes of the endoplasmic reticulum (e r). × 6,700. (See also Plate IV)

PLATE IV

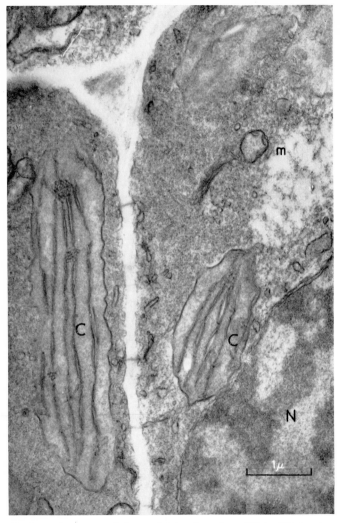

Further enlargement of the top left-hand portion of Plate III showing a nucleus (N) with double membrane; young chloroplasts (C) with developing lamellae and starch vacuole (white), and mitochondria (m). The dividing wall between two cells is penetrated by plasmodesmata which are related to membranes in the cytoplasm. × 18,000

PLATE V

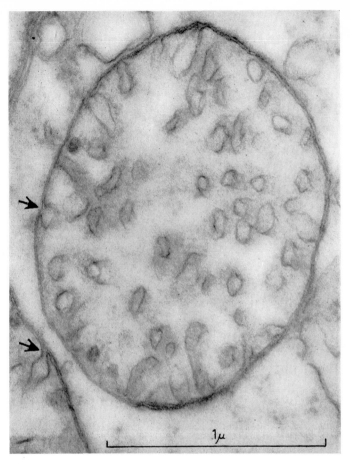

Mitochondrion from the alga *Botrydium* showing double wall and numerous microvilli (compare Plate II and fig. 36). The arrows indicate the points of origin of microvilli from the walls. Others arise from upper and lower walls out of the plane of section. ×60,000

suspending fluid and the suspension then centrifugated in the cold under known forces to separate the various particles. From a solution of half molar sucrose, the plastids are sedimented by about 10 minutes at $500 \times g$; the mitochondria by about 20 minutes at $20,000 \times g$ and the microsomes by about an hour at $100,000 \times g$. The nuclei present special difficulties on account of their relative scarcity (only one per cell) and the fragility of their bounding membranes. They have, however, been isolated from specially suitable tissues such as wheat embryos.

Careful examination of purified suspensions suggests that all stages of photosynthesis occur in the *chloroplasts* (*see* p. 33); but none of the stages of glycolysis or the respiratory oxidations. In chloroplasts 3-phosphoglyceraldehyde is formed by the reduction of 3-phosphoglyceric acid, due to a transfer of hydrogen from $NADPH_2$. In glycolysis the aldehyde is oxidized to the acid by transfer of hydrogen to NAD. There is evidence that the triosephosphate dehydrogenase that catalyses the first reaction is restricted to the chloroplasts whereas a second triosephosphate dehydrogenase responsible for the glycolytic reaction is found in the general cytoplasm outside.

All the enzymes of glycolysis that have been examined are 'soluble', i.e. they are not attached to any of the well-defined organelles and it appears that glycolysis goes on in the general cytoplasm.

The Mitochondria have been shown to be the sites of the respiratory oxidations. Cytochrome oxidase and the carrier cytochromes (p. 104) are firmly attached to the mitochondrial walls and remain active even when the mitochondria are broken into small fragments. Succinic dehydrogenase is similarly placed and disintegrated mitochondria continue to oxidize succinic acid through the cytochrome system. Fumarase and the other dehydrogenases required by the citric acid cycle are also located in the mitochondria; but are lost when the mitochondria are disintegrated or even when they collapse so that their internal fluid escapes. It may therefore be supposed that they are in solution in the mitochondrial sap or perhaps very loosely attached to the walls. It seems reasonable to suppose that pyruvic acid is fed to the mitochondria as a result of glycolysis going on in the external cytoplasm and that the successive oxidation stages then occur within the mitochondria from which carbon dioxide escapes.

The enzymes responsible for oxidative phosphorylation are also localized in the mitochondria and the mitochondria are continually regenerating the cells' supplies of ATP. They are therefore the site at which energy readily available for syntheses and other cellular requirements is generated. They have been called the 'power house' of the cell. Some of the ATP may be used (i.e. dephosphorylated to ADP) in the mitochondria themselves; but they also export ATP to other parts of the cell. Isolated nuclei have been caused to synthesize insoluble nitrogen compounds when supplied with glutamic acid and mitochondria generating ATP.

The Ribosomes appear to be the principal site at which the building of amino acids into proteins goes on, and by their possession of nucleotides in the form of ribonucleic acid they are probably able to determine the sequences in which the amino acids are built into the protein.

Membranes. Many different parts of the cell, the nucleus, plastids, and mitochondria seem to be surrounded by membranes. There is also a membrane separating the cytoplasm from the vacuole and possibly one at the outer surface of the cytoplasm where it is in contact with the cell wall. While, no doubt, each of these membranes has some characteristic properties of its own, they also seem to have a fundamental structure in common. The basic fluid of protoplasm is aqueous, and slightly soluble substances, such as lipids, might therefore be expected to accumulate at interfaces with gas or immiscible lipid solvents. Lipids, such as lecithins, carrying polar groups might be expected to orientate themselves at the interface with the polar groups towards the water and their non-polar groups towards the non-aqueous phase. Actually, such interfaces are rare in cells and both the phases on the two sides of the boundary are predominantly aqueous. It is therefore probable that the stable membranes separating them will be double with a region rich in polar groups facing outwards on both sides. Observations with the electron microscope have now confirmed that the tonoplast and the membranes of chloroplasts, nuclei, and mitochondria are indeed all double.

The low conductivity and low permeability to ions of cell membranes and, conversely, their relatively high permeability to many fat-soluble substances suggest that lipids enter largely into their composition. On the other hand, at least some cell membranes have a low surface tension against water and behave as ampholytes with an isoelectric point at pH 3–4. These latter properties suggest that a layer of protein lies on each side between the lipoid and the aqueous phases. Calculation suggests that the thickness of such a double lipo-protein membrane would lie between 70 and 150 Å according to the thickness of the outer protein layers. Measurements on electron micrographs accord well with this estimate.

Although the resistance to the passage of electrolytes is often high, yet ions do penetrate cell membranes and water penetrates them much faster. This may be accounted for by supposing that very fine 'aqueous pores' pass through the lipid layers in places. If these pores are very fine it

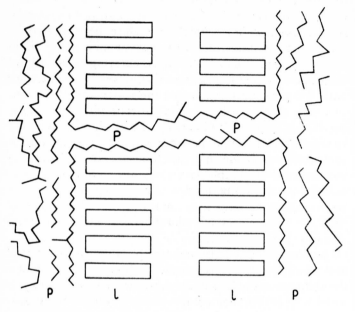

FIG. 36. DIAGRAM OF MEMBRANE STRUCTURE

The columns **of** closed rectangles (*l*, *l*) represent the lipid layers and the outer zones (*p*, *p*) the outer protein layers. At P, P is indicated an 'aqueous pore' would account for the much greater permeability to water than to dissolved electrolytes.

The general membrane structure that appears most probable may therefore be represented as in fig. 36. It is not possible to say which way round the ionizing lipids are arranged as they may be associated with the protein layers either by their polar or non-polar ends, and a large part of the layer must consist of non-ionizing neutral fats. The strength of the membrane is largely due to the van der Waals forces of their long aliphatic chains lying side by side. It should, however, be remembered that the molecules of an actual membrane are not static as in a diagram; but are in thermal agitation allowing the brief formation of 'holes'. This may explain why the permeability to large water-soluble molecules increases rapidly with temperature.

Organization of Reaction Sequences. Each of the processes that can now be assigned to a particular position in the cell involves numerous reactions with a corresponding number of enzymes to catalyse them. It is highly probable that the enzymes are fixed in definite positions in relation to one another and that the distance between successive members of the series is kept to a minimum. It has often been noticed that, when an enzyme is extracted and purified, the most difficult impurity to remove is the enzyme adjacent to it in the reaction sequence. The soluble metabolite passing along a series of catalytic proteins in the cell has been likened to an industrial product on a conveyer belt undergoing changes at each operative stage. As yet we know very few details of the actual placing of the enzymes in any given structure.

The 'soluble' enzymes of the general cytoplasm and in the mitochondrial sap may be free. Organization of the reaction sequence would then depend on the specificity of the enzymes which is usually very high; that is to say, each enzyme is capable of reacting only with the right substance and only catalyses its alteration in a single way. This arrangement would be less efficient than the spatial organization described above, since far more movement of the metabolite molecules would be required. It may yet be that arrangements of the 'soluble' enzymes may come to light, when our methods of examination become more delicate. In particular it is likely that the soluble cytoplasm is far from homogeneous. Fine particles do not travel through it at a uniform rate, but in an irregular and jerky manner like small shot dropping through a heap of brushwood. It appears that it must contain threads or membranes of higher density and that these may perhaps carry the enzymes. We know, for example, that the endoplasmic reticulum breaks up very easily during centrifugation and that the microsomes attached to it are released.

The Living Unit. The whole cell as described above is a living unit and, although it is usual to recognize the protoplasm as living matter *par excellence*, it cannot ordinarily be separated from the other portions of the cell and retain its properties uninjured. Meristematic cells do not have vacuoles as such but even in their youngest stages they have minute gel structures which are recognizable on account of their high affinity for the dye, neutral red. When a meristematic cell divides each of these bodies divides also, one member of each pair going to each daughter cell. When the cell ceases to be meristematic and begins to enlarge, these gel structures take up water, liquify, and become vacuoles. In short, the vacuole appears to be an integral part of the plants' living unit.

When cells have been divided into two halves, one of which has contained the nucleus uninjured, while the other is enucleate, the part containing the nucleus has continued

to exist and form new cells. The other half has remained
alive for some time but without being able to grow, divide,
or even to reform the missing cell wall. For these reasons
it seems probable that the unit of living matter is the portion of protoplasm dominated, in some way at present
obscure, by a single nucleus, and this is sometimes called
the *energid* or *protoplast* (fig. 37).

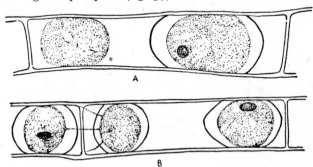

FIG. 37. CELLS FROM HAIRS OF *Cucurbita Pepo*

A shows the protoplasm separated into two parts by plasmolysis. The
nucleated part has formed new walls, but not the other part.

B shows protoplasm without a nucleus linked to a nucleated fragment
by protoplasmic fibrils passing through the cell wall. Both fragments
have formed new walls. Highly magnified. (Redrawn after Townsend)

The Association of Protoplasts. The simplest plants
such as bacteria, and the unicellular algae, consist of a
single protoplast living independently, but in more advanced types large numbers of protoplasts are associated
together into *tissues*. The cells of a tissue are all very similar,
and are usually specialized in their metabolism, so that
they perform one or more processes with special efficiency.
The result is that the tissue as a whole becomes a plant
organ carrying on the process in question on behalf of the
entire plant. Protoplasts which are grouped together into
a tissue are no longer independent in their actions, and it
has been shown that they are often continuous with one

another. Thin fibrils of protoplasm pass through pits in the inert cell walls, as shown in fig. 38, so that the living matter of one cell is not entirely isolated from that of the next, but is on the contrary organically connected with it.

It is sometimes found that the protoplasm contained within a single cell wall possesses numerous nuclei instead

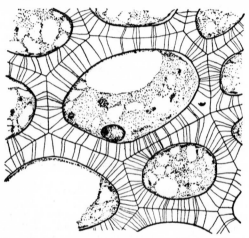

FIG. 38. CELLS FROM THE RIPE SEED OF *Diospyros ahernii* showing protoplasmic fibrils penetrating the thick cellulose walls. × about 600. (Redrawn after Quisumbing)

of only one. Such a structure is called a *coenocyte* and is probably to be regarded as a collection of energids within a common wall, each nucleus dominating the cytoplasm in its immediate neighbourhood. Coenocytes are not so common as tissues composed of numerous uninucleate cells in the higher plants, but are often found among the algae and fungi. The latter have no chlorophyll, and so lack the power to synthesize carbohydrates, including cellulose, from inorganic sources. The comparative scarcity of their cell walls may be due to this inability, which they share with animals.

ENZYMES

Enzyme Catalysis. It has already been mentioned on several occasions that plant cells contain substances called enzymes, which enable them to carry out reactions that do not occur without assistance. These substances are distributed throughout the protoplasm and, now that we have described the nature of the matrix in which enzymes work, we can go on to consider their own outstanding characteristics.

The simplest kind of catalyst, technically called an 'ideal catalyst', is characterized by three properties: (1) it accelerates the velocity of one or more chemical reactions; (2) it remains itself unchanged in nature and quantity at the end of the reaction; (3) it does not alter the final result of the reaction, but only the speed at which it is attained. If the reaction is reversible, each of its components is affected equally by the catalyst, so that the final equilibrium point is not altered, although it is reached sooner. The most important of the simple catalysts is the hydrogen ion which is set free by all acids in solution.

Many catalysts, including enzymes, form temporary compounds with the primary reacting substances. Their effect is thus to provide an alternative path of reaction, so that the reactants arrive at the same end by easier means. The catalyst does not provide any additional energy, as is shown by the fact that it leaves the reaction in the identical state that would be reached if no catalyst were present.

Enzymes differ from ideal catalysts in several ways. They are very sensitive to the influence of *temperature*: from 0° C to about 40° C enzyme activity increases, but at higher temperatures falls off again owing to destruction of the enzyme by coagulation. This becomes very much faster as the temperature rises, but at moderate temperatures it takes some considerable time to become apparent. The temperature at which activity appears to be greatest, the optimum temperature, thus depends on the time taken to measure it—the quicker the measurement the higher the optimum.

Enzymes are also highly sensitive to *acidity*. All enzymes are destroyed by strongly acid or alkaline media, and show reversible changes of activity within a restricted range of acidities. Most of them exhibit their greatest effect at some optimal acidity; but this may vary within limits according to other conditions. The enzyme *pepsin*, that hydrolyses proteins and polypeptides in the pitchers of pitcher plants, works best in a slightly acid medium; but the similar enzyme in leaves, *papain*, works best in a neutral solution. *Trypsin*, which is formed chiefly by animals, but probably also by the fungi and bacteria, hydrolyses proteins best in slightly alkaline solutions. Enzymes are also highly sensitive to a wide range of activators and poisons which may even be produced while they are at work. As a result, reactions catalysed by enzymes rarely go to completion, and the simple rules which apply to ideal catalysts are not fulfilled.

Many biological reactions are reversible and, theoretically, one would expect enzymes to accelerate them equally in both directions. It is readily shown outside the plant that enzymes will perform the hydrolysis of carbohydrates, fats, proteins, etc. (**exp. 49**); but it is more difficult to show that they accelerate the corresponding condensations. This is sometimes due to the fact that, under laboratory conditions, the reactions can only be performed in the presence of an excess of water, i.e. in solution. When a dehydrating agent, such as a large excess of glycerine, is added to the solution, it may be possible to effect condensation. The enzyme lipase has thus been enabled to synthesize fats *in vitro*. Proteins, starch, and glycosides have also been produced enzymically outside living cells. It is, therefore, usual to suppose that enzymes catalyse up-grade as well as down-grade reactions inside the plant. It must not, however, be assumed that this is always done by means of reversible reactions; the up-grade process may proceed by an entirely different reaction-path from the down-grade one; e.g. down-grade processes frequently proceed by direct hydrolysis, but corresponding syntheses only indirectly through phosphorylation. Starch is hydrolysed by the amylases; but is synthesized by phosphorylase which eliminates phosphate, not water, from glucose 1-phosphate. Similarly, peptide linkages are hydrolysed by proteinases, but are formed only in the presence of phosphate donors.

Extraction and Purification. Most enzymes are soluble in water, and it is, therefore, an easy matter to extract them from disintegrated tissues. The solvent used may be pure water or a dilute solution of glycerine, phosphate, etc., suitable for the particular enzyme to be extracted. Some, like cytochrome oxidase which is present in mitochondria, cannot be so simply obtained and up to the present have not been brought into solution. It is interesting to note that a kind of natural extraction goes on inside the plant, since many enzymes have been found in the transpiration stream, described in the next chapter. Extracted enzymes can usually be precipitated by adding a dehydrating agent such as cold alcohol to their solutions; the precipitate can then be filtered off and, if dried at a moderate temperature, can be kept indefinitely without losing activity. Commercial preparations of invertase, diastase (amylase), and other enzymes prepared by such means are·on the market. These powders are not, of course, pure enzymes; further purification is usually a difficult and elaborate process. It may involve many precipitations by graded strengths of alcohol, etc., or 'salting out' with ammonium sulphate at various concentrations. Some impurities may be dialysed away, but the most selective method of all has proved to be adsorption upon specially prepared surfaces of alumina, kaolin, or other suspensions. The enzyme may have to be adsorbed and released many times before purification is complete.

Enzyme Proteins and Prosthetic Groups. As a result of work with the above methods, some enzymes have been obtained as pure crystals of protein without any other component. Urease was the first to be thus obtained and hydrolases and dehydrogenases appear generally to belong to this type.

The proteins of the oxidases and reductases are always conjugated with some non-protein *prosthetic group* which is essential to their catalytic activity. The simplest prosthetic 'group' is the copper ion belonging to ascorbic and polyphenol oxidases; cytochrome oxidase has an iron porphyrin, and the reductases all have nucleotides of the flavin type (p. 62). Many reductases also have firmly bound metals (iron, copper, molybdenum, or manganese); but it is the flavin and not the metal which varies its valency during oxidation and reduction. Prosthetic groups also occur in the desmolases.

Beside the firmly attached prosthetic groups the activity of enzymes is often affected by more loosely associated substances. The enzyme aconitase, for example, only works efficiently in the presence of free ferrous ions. All such substances are called *cofactors*.

The nucleotides NAD and NADP often make firm compounds with the dehydrogenases which catalyse their reduction and they were originally called coenzymes I and II respectively. As it is supposed that enzymes combine with their substrate molecules in general, it no longer seems necessary to put NAD and NADP into a special category.

Specificity. Individual enzymes are more restricted in their action than inorganic catalysts such as the H^+ ion. Invertase hydrolyses sucrose much more rapidly than acids do, but its action is limited to one or two sugars, whereas the acids catalyse the hydrolysis of innumerable compounds. A few enzymes can catalyse only one reaction, e.g. catalase decomposes hydrogen peroxide to O_2 and water, and urease hydrolyses urea to carbon dioxide and ammonia. Neither of these two enzymes can catalyse any other reaction. Such a high degree of specificity is rather exceptional, and it is more usual to find that an enzyme will catalyse a series of reactions, all very similar; e.g. lipase will catalyse the hydrolysis of any fat:

$$C_3H_5 \begin{cases} OOC.R_1 \\ OOC.R_2 \\ OOC.R_3 \end{cases} + 3H_2O \rightarrow C_3H_5(OH)_3 + \begin{cases} HOOC.R_1 \\ HOOC.R_2 \\ HOOC.R_3 \end{cases}$$

The nature of the fat depends upon the radicals $R_1 \ldots$ of the fatty acid; but the enzyme operates upon groupings which are common to all fats, splitting them at the position of the broken line. The one enzyme is thus able to catalyse the hydrolysis or condensation of any fat. Specificity may thus relate to some particular part of the substrate molecule and not necessarily to the molecule as a whole, just how much is involved varying with different enzymes. The adjustment of enzyme and substrate molecules is often so close that it has been likened to the fit of a key to its lock. All enzymes are asymmetric and will only operate with one stereoisomer of a pair (p. 54). Maltase will hydrolyse compounds of α-glucose including maltase (= glucose α-glucoside), but will not hydrolyse β-glucosides. Conversely, the enzyme, prunase, will hydrolyse only β-glucosides.

The high degree of specificity depends on the protein nature of enzymes. For example all haems (iron porphyrins) catalyse oxidations; the haem of cytochrome oxidase attached to the appropriate protein will only oxidize one cytochrome.

Specific Inhibitions. Enzymes are inhibited by many substances acting in many different ways. Some inhibitors are more or less specific, i.e. will poison a few enzymes very strongly and others only weakly or not at all. Carbon monoxide forms an iron carbonyl with the ferrous ions in cytochrome oxidase and thereby inhibits it. Blue light decomposes the carbonyl and restores the activity of the enzyme. Dilute cyanide and other strong chelating agents will react with metals such as iron and copper in prosthetic groups and so inactivate enzymes like cytochrome oxidase and ascorbic oxidase. Enzymes which have no prosthetic groups nevertheless have thiol (—SH) groups on their proteins which are necessary to their catalytic activity. They can be inactivated by thiol reagents such as iodoacetate. The triosephosphate dehydrogenases are particularly susceptible to this sort of poisoning. Substances which are akin to an enzyme's substrate may combine with it but fail to react further. Malonic acid, which has a molecule akin to succinic acid, will compete with it for the enzyme succinic dehydrogenase and so reduce the enzyme's activity. Inhibitions due to substrate and inhibitor similarities are naturally fairly specific. It is doubtful whether enzyme activity is controlled in plant cells by the production of natural inhibitors; but their application artificially has been a useful tool in the elucidation of reaction sequences (p. 94).

Classification. Knowledge of the constitution of enzymes is not yet sufficiently advanced to allow of a complete classification by its means. Enzymes are, therefore, arranged according to the reactions they catalyse, and from a biologist's standpoint the plan has considerable advantages. There are fifty to a hundred well-known enzymes, of which some of the best characterized are listed below:

1. HYDROLASES, *hydrolysing and condensing enzymes*

Lipase	catalyses Fats $\rightleftharpoons$ fatty acids+glycerine
Cellulase	,, Cellulose $\rightleftharpoons$ cellobiose
Amylase	,, Starch $\rightarrow$ maltose
Maltase	,, α-glucosides $\rightleftharpoons$ α-glucose, etc.
Prunase	,, β-glucosides $\rightleftharpoons$ β-glucose, etc.
Invertase	,, Sucrose $\rightleftharpoons$ glucose+fructose

Proteinases $\begin{cases} \text{Pepsin} \\ \text{Papain} \\ \text{Trypsin} \end{cases}$ catalyse Proteins $\rightleftharpoons$ polypeptides

| Polypeptides | ,, Polypeptides $\rightleftharpoons$ amino-acids |
| Urease | catalyses Urea $\rightarrow$ $2NH_3 + CO_2$ |

2. PHOSPHORYLASES

| (Starch) phos-phorylase | ,, Starch+H_3PO_4 $\rightleftharpoons$ glucose 1-phosphate |
| Kinases | catalyse Transfer of phosphate from ATP |

3. DESMOLASES, *enzymes splitting or forming the C–C link without hydrolysis*

| Aldolase (Zymohexase) | catalyses Hexosediphosphate $\rightleftharpoons$ 2 triosephosphate |
| Carboxylase | ,, Pyruvic acid $\rightarrow$ acetalde-hyde+CO_2 |

4. HYDRASES, *enzymes adding or removing H_2O without hydrolysis*

| Aconitase | catalyses Citric acid $\rightleftharpoons$ aconitic acid $\rightleftharpoons$ isocitric acid |
| Fumarase | ,, Fumaric acid $\rightleftharpoons$ malic acid |

5. OXIDOREDUCTASES, *oxidizing and reducing enzymes*

Dehydrogenases	catalyse Transfer of H_2 (not to O_2)
Oxidases	,, Transfer of H_2 to O_2
Reductases	,, Transfer of H_2 from nucleo-tides to cytochromes, etc.
Peroxidase	catalyses Oxidation by H_2O_2

Further details of the behaviour of individual enzymes are given in the appropriate sections: hydrolases mainly in Chapters II and IV; desmolases and oxidoreductases in Chapter III. Where no enzyme is specifically named in the text, it may be assumed that the appropriate enzyme in the list above is responsible.

Enzymes and Genes. Enzymes form a large part of the protein in an active cell, possibly even the whole of it. They increase in amount as the cell grows. Some enzymes may be there only at certain stages of the cell's development, or only when appropriate substrates are present. These are the facultative enzymes most abundant in micro-organisms, but also found to a less extent in higher plants. α-amylase is found in germinating barley grains only when long-chain dextrins are also present.

A particular enzyme, as defined by its catalytic activity, may differ according to the source from which it is derived. The triosephosphate dehydrogenase from yeast differs somewhat in its proprties from the corresponding enzyme from higher plants. Indeed, it is probable that there are small differences in the composition of an enzyme protein from species to species, but that it remains constant within a species.

The enzymes are not, however, self-propagating bodies, that is to say genes. Enzymes are proteins and it is now known that the essential constituent of a gene is the complex nucleotide DNA (desoxyribonucleic acid). The power of self duplication and of passing on genetic information is apparently limited to the DNA characteristic of the species.

Some strains of white clover contain an enzyme, lina-marase, which hydrolyses the glycoside linamarin with release of HCN. Other strains which contain the glycoside do not release any HCN because the enzyme is missing from their cells. The formation of the enzyme has been shown to be due to a single dominant gene in the strains which possess it.

The fungus *Neurospora crassa* has yielded much information of this kind because of the relative ease with which mutations lacking a particular enzyme are obtained. The wild type is able, for example, to convert ornithine, through citrulline, to arginine. Mutants are, however, known which will only form arginine from citrulline and others which will only grow if supplied with arginine ready made. These mutants lack the enzymes to convert ornithine to citrulline and citrulline to arginine respectively. The genetic block operates at one position only because the intermediate immediately in front of it in the series accumulates as would be expected.

These and similar results have led to the supposition that genes give rise more or less directly to enzymes and it has even been suggested that each gene forms its single enzyme. The arrangement of amino-acid radicles in the primary valency chain, which is what determines the chemical identity of a protein molecule is, in general, believed to be coded by the appropriate nucleic acid. How this comes about is not yet known for any enzymatic or other protein.

EXPERIMENTAL WORK

Exp. 47. ACTION OF CHLOROFORM

Peel a piece of potato, dry the cut surfaces with blotting paper, and suspend by a piece of thread in a corked bottle. No sap will come out. Add a drop or two of chloroform and cork the bottle again. After a short time the surface of the potato will become moist, and finally sap will drip off it on to the bottom of the bottle. Chloroform makes the cell membranes more permeable, so that they no longer retain the sap as in the natural condition.

Exp. 48. Action of Heat and Water

Count out ten dry peas, and ten which have been soaked. Heat both lots to 50° C in a beaker suspended in a water bath; then soak the dry peas and sow both lots in separate pans. Most of the peas which were heated when dry will germinate, but few or none of the others.

Exp. 49. Hydrolysis by Amylase

Half fill a test-tube with a 0·5 per cent. starch solution. (For method of preparation see p. 318.) Set out a row of six watch-glasses on a strip of white paper and in each put a drop of dilute iodine solution. Dip a rod into the starch sol and transfer a drop to the first watch-glass. The characteristic colour of the starch-iodine compound will be formed. Dissolve 0·2 g of taka-diastase, a commercial preparation of amylase, in 100 ml of water and add a few drops to the starch. Shake the tube vigorously at intervals. Remove drops of the solution to successive watch-glasses after 30 seconds, 1, 2, and 5 minutes. They will then show a gradation of colour from the pure blue of the starch compound via purple to brown. The middle colour is caused by the presence of dextrin, a hydrolysis product of starch. After half an hour test again; there will be no reaction. Add some of the contents of the tube to Fehling's solution, and boil. A red precipitate will be formed, since the dextrin will have been further hydrolysed to reducing sugars (maltose and, since taka-diastase contains some maltase, glucose).

Exp. 50. Presence of Amylase in Plants

Soak about fifty barley grains and allow them to germinate on moist filter paper for 4 or 5 days at room temperature. Then remove the sprouted grains to a mortar, just cover them with distilled water, and grind to a fine mush. Filter off the liquid, which will then contain diastase and other enzymes, since they are soluble in water. Take two test-tubes and put some starch solution and some of the filtrate into each. Boil one tube immediately and allow both to stand for about 10 minutes. Then remove a drop of the mixture from each tube to a watch-glass containing iodine solution. If necessary repeat at intervals. The unboiled mixture will gradually show the dextrin colour, while the boiled mixture will continue to show the starch unchanged. The hydrolysis in the second tube is due to the amylase originally present in the barley grains. A high temperature destroys the enzyme, and so no hydrolysis was caused in the boiled mixture.

Leaves of pea (*Pisum sativum*) or clover (*Trifolium pratense*) may also be used.

Exp. 51. DIGESTION OF STARCH GRAINS

Tease out starch grains from the endosperms of barley grains that have been germinating for 1, 2, 3, . . . days up to a week. Mount in water and examine under the microscope. Irrigate with a little very dilute iodine in potassium iodide solution and note the progressive corrosion of the starch grains as they are attacked by the amylases inside a resistant pellicle which is only penetrated here and there.

Exp. 52. HYDROLYSIS OF UREA BY UREASE

Urea is converted by the enzyme to ammonium carbonate which can be titrated with sulphuric acid to obtain a quantitative estimate of the activity of the enzyme preparation.

Put 10 ml of 1 per cent. urea in water into a test-tube. Crush up one standard tablet of urea (B.D.H.) in 3 ml of water and decant into a second test-tube. Raise with test-tubes to 25° C in a water bath. Pour the urea solution into the urease; note the time and allow to incubate at 25° C for 45 minutes. Decant the fluid off rapidly through a small cotton wool plug or coarse filter paper and pipette off 10 ml of the clear solution. Titrate with 0·1 N sulphuric acid:

1 ml 0·1 N sulphuric acid $\equiv$ 6 mg urea.

If the experiment is carried out at a series of temperatures a curve relating enzyme activity to temperature may be obtained.

VII

WATER

WATER is one of the most abundant and widely distributed substances in nature. Besides the great bulk of it which makes up rivers, lakes, and oceans, practically all rocks and soils are impregnated with it; and it is present as vapour in the atmosphere. The water in each of these phases is not rigidly bound up in it, but under the influence of natural forces passes from one to another. In dry weather, when there is little water vapour in the air, liquid water evaporates from any free surfaces, such as rivers, seas, and lakes, and from damp soils. If the atmosphere becomes well charged with moisture, and is then suddenly cooled, the vapour it contains is liquified again and falls as rain. An adjustment is thus set up between soil water and atmospheric water vapour, and water passes spontaneously from one to the other to maintain the balance. The higher the temperature the more water vapour it takes to saturate the air, and hence any rise of temperature tends to cause the movement of a further quantity from the soil. Similarly the displacement of damp air by a wind bringing drier air from a distance will cause further evaporation and loss of soil moisture.

Water is not lost so easily by soil as by a free water surface because there are in the soil various forces tending to keep it back. The most important of these is the imbibing power of the soil colloids, which, when water is scarce, opposes great resistance to further losses. When water is abundant the resistance thus set up is only very small, so that evaporation occurs quite easily. Clay and humus are both largely colloidal, and, as a result, their power of retaining water against its tendency to evaporate is very high. Sand, on the contrary, consists of large particles, which do not imbibe water, although they hold a certain amount as a film on their surfaces. The surface tensions holding these films in position are nothing like so powerful as imbibition forces, and sandy soils lose water comparatively easily.

There is, in fact, no sharp division between imbibitional and capillary water, since all the spaces in a soil may be regarded as capillaries of continuously varying size from the relatively large spaces in sand to the infinitesimal in clay. In addition to capillary and imbibitional water, a soil may hold gravitational water, i.e. water soaking through it under the pull of gravity, and water vapour in its interstices.

In describing the relations of plants to soil water the important consideration is the strength of its retention, whatever cause it may be due to. It can be expressed as free energy of the soil water. The zero is taken as the free energy of a flat surface of pure water outside the influence of gravity. The free energy of the soil water is raised above this zero by hydrostatic pressure, dissolved substances, gravity and adsorption on surrounding particles. In wet soil gravity is important because the other factors are saturated. In dry soils adsorption becomes important and in highly saline soils the osmotic potential of the dissolved substances. All these things tend to resist any lifting of water out of the soil.

The free energy of the moisture in an oven-dry soil is 10 million times greater than that of free water. It is therefore usually expressed on a logarithmic scale and designated pF. The scale varies from 0 for free water to 7 for an oven-dry soil.

Five cardinal points with their pF values are shown in

fig. 39. Particularly important are the field capacity and the wilting point. At field capacity, a soil contains the maximum amount of water it can retain against gravity. If the top layer of a soil is wetted to field capacity and further rain falls upon it, a corresponding amount will

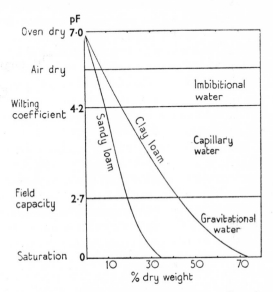

FIG. 39. Diagram to illustrate the relations between soils and water.
(After Kramer, modified)

pass into lower layers. There is usually a fairly sharp boundary between the wetted and dry soil below. The wilting coefficient indicates the amount of water in a soil when plants growing in it droop permanently. Provided that transpiration is not too rapid this is reasonably definite, and does not vary with different plants so much as might be expected. At air dryness, the soil water is in equilibrium with dry air at room temperature, and, at oven dryness, it contains no removable moisture. The amount of water in the soil, expressed as a percentage of the weight of oven-dry soil, varies for different soil types at each level. It is always greater in clayey than in sandy soils (fig. 39). The available water for plant growth is given by the difference between wilting coefficient and the field capacity. The amount of water between the wilting coefficient and air dryness may be available for survival, but does not allow active growth.

The amount of water in the plant at any moment will clearly depend upon two factors, the amount it is gaining from the soil (*water absorption*) and the amount it is losing to the air (*transpiration*). The net gain or loss will be the difference between the two, and the total amount in the plant will be the amount by which gain has exceeded loss since the plant began to germinate. Without such an accumulation, aerial plants could not exist, since water is an integral part of all their substance. The amount of water which passes through a plant from soil to air is much greater than the amount which becomes imbibed in protoplasmic colloids, or is otherwise retained in the plant. There is thus a continuous flow from the roots embedded in the ground towards the leaves spreading in the air; this is called the *transpiration stream*.

TRANSPIRATION

The forces tending to draw water from the leaves are exactly the same as those which draw it from a damp soil, but important differences between the two processes are introduced depending upon the leaf's nature. The forces opposing the loss of water from leaves are not identical with those present in soils, although they have certain similarities. For example, the colloidal protoplasm, cellulose, etc., hold water by imbibition just as do the colloids of the soil. When water is plentiful, the resistance to loss thus set up is very slight, as in soils, but as water becomes scarce it increases very rapidly.

The Site of Transpiration. The structure of the leaf introduces further differences, since the cuticle is impermeable to water, and direct evaporation into the atmosphere does not occur by this path. This applies to nearly all land plants, but delicate mosses and shade plants are without such an impermeable covering. In submerged plants, also, there is a free passage of water across the leaf surface. By reference to fig. 2 it will be seen that the thin-walled cells of the spongy mesophyll (*b*) have a large area of contact with the intercellular spaces between them. This surface consists of thin cellulose walls, themselves saturated with water from the living cells which they contain. Evaporation goes on very readily over this area, and is often assisted by the fact that heat is being released from absorbed sunlight. The air in the intercellular spaces thus tends to become saturated with water vapour, but, if the air outside is drier, the vapour diffuses slowly through the stomata, and so leaves the plant.

The surprisingly large amount of gas or vapour that can diffuse through a large number of small pores, such as the stomata, has already been mentioned in connexion with the entry of carbon dioxide. The diffusion of water vapour out of the leaf is similar to the latter movement except in its direction, depending upon the fact that its higher concentration is inside the leaf instead of in the external atmosphere.

In many circumstances, the rate of water loss from a leaf is roughly equal to the loss from a free surface of water of equal shape and area. This may seem surprising since the stomata form only about 1 per cent. of the area; but it must be remembered that the actual evaporating surface, the walls of the mesophyll cells, is many times the external surface of the leaf, and that the diffusion through the stomata is not proportional to their small area.

Changes of Stomatal Opening. The stomata of most plants open by day and close at night, the period of opening and closing differing among species and to some extent according to external conditions (*see* fig. 4). When the stomata close, transpiration comes practically to a standstill, although when the air is very dry a small amount of water will penetrate the cuticle. Small changes in the size of the stomatal pores have very little effect on the rate at which water vapour passes, and it is not until closure is almost complete that the blocking effect becomes at all noticeable.

Wilting. If a leaf is transpiring water away more rapidly than it is receiving it from the stem, the bulk of water it contains naturally diminishes, and in 'soft' leaves, which depend upon turgor (*see* p. 200) for extending their laminae, such a water deficit leads to temporary drooping, which is called *wilting*. In some English mesophytes, a drop of no more than 1 per cent. of the total water-content of the leaf causes wilting, but in other plants much greater losses are necessary.

When a leaf has wilted, the guard cells lose water and so close the stomata. Photosynthesis is brought to a standstill in consequence, and frequent wilting is thus likely to hinder the development of the plant. The drying up of the internal tissues may also cause a certain amount of injury if it is sufficiently severe, and at one time it was believed that stomata behaved in such a way as to minimize the risk of wilting, closing when water was scarce in the leaf, and opening when it was comparatively plentiful. This is not so; there is actually little connexion between the opening and closing of the stomata, and the amount of water in the leaf. The guard cells respond readily to influences, principally light, which have comparatively little effect upon the rate of water loss, and are less directly affected by temperature and atmospheric dryness. Once the leaf has wilted, however, still further losses of water are prevented, so that wilting may itself retard severe drying up.

THE UPTAKE OF WATER

The uptake of water by plants has been described as of two kinds: passive (under tension), and active (causing positive pressures in conducting tissues).

Passive absorption results from the pull of transpiration transmitted down to the roots by the cohesion of the transpiration stream (p. 205). The roots perform the functions of a conduit and of an extensive surface of contact with the soil. When transpiration rates are high passive absorption accounts for practically the whole of the absorption. Simultaneous measurements of transpiration and absorption throughout the day have shown that absorption approximately follows transpiration until the evening and lags slightly behind it. At the same time an increasing tension proportionate to the rate of transpiration develops in the water in the plant's conducting strands.

Active absorption depends on the osmotic properties of the root cells, and probably accounts for only a negligible fraction of the total uptake of water. Transpiring plants can absorb water against much higher resistances than can root systems deprived of their tops. Active absorption may have its importance in replacing during the night the water lost by a wilted or nearly wilted plant in the day.

Root Systems. Plants exploit the water in the soil beneath them. Lateral movement of water in soils is very slight, as can readily be seen by examining the dry mud at the margin of a stream or pond. Continuous uptake of water into the plant is secured because the root system is always rapidly growing a thick network of roots and root hairs into new soil layers. It has been estimated that a rapidly growing rye plant develops more than 3 miles of new roots with 55 miles of root hairs per day. The root system of a plant spreads much more widely than its aerial parts, and only its coarsest branches are recovered when it is uprooted. Most plants produce a good excess of roots, and can lose a quarter to a half of them without seriously wilting.

Rapid root growth is thus an essential to rapid absorption of water. This in turn is dependent upon favourable soil conditions, the most important of which are good tilth, ensuring adequate ventilation; enough water, but not so much as to cause waterlogging; adequate nutrients; and a suitable temperature. Water enters the plant by the root hairs, which grow into the fine openings between the soil particles (fig. 40). They present a large area of surface, which is constantly being renewed as the lengthening roots penetrate new regions. Their thin walls and protoplasmic linings are very easily penetrated, whenever any force arises which tends to drive water through them.

OSMOTIC RELATIONS OF CELLS

All hygroscopic bodies, including cells, may be said to possess a suction pressure, which varies according to their nature and the conditions in which they are placed. A substance which is already half saturated will not have so high a suction pressure as when it was quite dry. If two absorbing substances are in contact, water will pass from that with the lower suction pressure to that with the higher until a balance is established. Cells are, in the main, liquid systems and the origins of their suction pressures may be considered in the following terms.

Liquids possess a diffusion pressure, which will cause a diffusion of water molecules from one region to an adjacent one having a lower diffusion pressure. Solutes depress the diffusion pressure of water in proportion to the activity (in dilute solutions equal to the concentration) of the solute, and water will tend to diffuse from a volume of pure water into an adjacent solution, or from a weak solution into a stronger one. The difference of diffusion pressure between

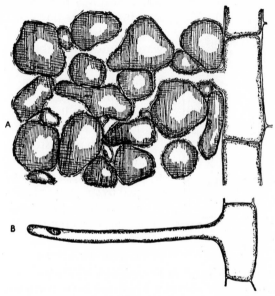

FIG. 40

A shows the relation between a root hair and soil particles, which may be saturated with water and have water films over their surfaces. Diagrammatic. B. a root hair grown in water, showing the nucleus, protoplasmic lining, and single continuous vacuole

pure water and the solution can be opposed by an equivalent hydrostatic pressure which is called the osmotic pressure of the solution. Put slightly differently, the osmotic pressure is the extra hydrostatic pressure which must be applied to the solution to make the diffusion pressure, or activity, of its water equal to that of pure water.

These pressures and pressure deficits are properties of

the solutions concerned quite independent of any containing membranes. If, however, it is desired to apply a hydrostatic pressure to a solution without affecting any adjacent

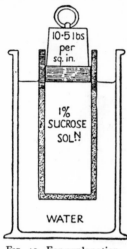

pure water, the solution and the
water must be separated by a rigid
membrane. It is possible to prepare membranes that will allow
water, but not substances dissolved in it, to diffuse through.
Such a membrane is said to be
semi-permeable and water will
diffuse through it into a solution
on the other side.

In the system illustrated by fig.
41 the diffusion of water into the
1 per cent. sucrose solution can be
stopped by subjecting the solution
to an extra pressure of about 10·5
lb per sq. in. (about 0·66 atm.).
That is to say the osmotic pressure
of the solution is about 0·66 atm.;

FIG. 41. For explanation,
see text

but the suction pressure of the system, the diffusion pressure deficit of the solution, is nil and there is no tendency
for more water to pass into the solution.

Since molecular activities depend on temperature,
osmotic pressures and equilibria in which they are involved
will vary with temperature also.

Wall Pressure. If the sugar solution were enclosed in a
semi-permeable and elastic bladder, and the bladder were
then immersed in water, the entrance of the latter would
first fill it, and then begin to distend it. When elastic
bodies are stretched, the cohesion of their particles opposes
a resistance to further stretching, and the more they are
stretched the greater this resistance becomes. In the

expanding bladder, diffusion pressure forces water through its interstices; but the accumulating liquid sets up a hydrostatic pressure which tends to stretch the membrane. The more liquid there is inside, the greater is the stretching, and, consequently, the greater is the elastic tension, which opposes any further entry of water. Finally, the pressure thus set up becomes equal to the osmotic pressure, and there is no further movement of water, even though the concentration of sugar inside the bladder is still greater than that outside.

The suction pressure (S.P.) of the bladder at any moment thus depends upon two things, the osmotic pressure (O.P.) of its contents and the *wall pressure* (W.P.) due to the elasticity of its membrane, and the magnitude of the suction pressure is the difference between these two:

$$S.P. = O.P. - W.P.$$

If the outside solution is not pure water, but has an osmotic value of its own, this will act against the suction pressure of the cell, and reduce the absorption of water. If the two pressures are equal no water will be exchanged. The behaviour of the bladder is a little more complex than that of the rigid cylinder, because the stretching of its walls allows the internal solution to change its osmotic pressure due to dilution. The suction pressure (= diffusion pressure deficit) changes much more, and falls rapidly, as osmotic pressure is reduced by the dilution and, at the same time, the wall pressure rises owing to the increased stretching.

The Suction Pressure of Cells. In their relations to water, root hairs and other living cells (fig. 42) behave rather similarly to a bladder of the kind described above. The vacuole contains a mixed solution of many osmotically active substances, among which sugars are usually prominent. The protoplasmic lining is semi-permeable towards many of these substances, so that an osmotic pressure is developed whenever the cells come into contact with water or other solutions. The protoplasm itself has little elastic strength, but the thin cellulose wall surrounding it provides this, though it is easily penetrated by most substances in solution (fig. 42).

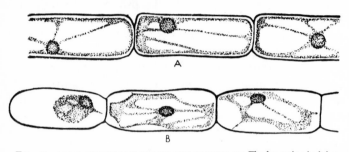

FIG. 42. CELLS FROM THE HAIRS ON THE STAMENS OF *Tradescantia virginica* showing walls, vacuoles, and protoplasm, which lines the walls and also has fine threads passing through the vacuole. A. natural condition, B. plasmolysed with strong sucrose solution. Owing to the withdrawal of water from the vacuole the surrounding protoplasm has shrunk away from the walls. Highly magnified. (M.S.)

Turgor. When cells are fully distended by taking up water, their contents press outwards upon the cell wall and they become tight and rigid like a blown-up football: they are then said to be in a state of turgor. The cells of internal tissues, such as the medulla of young stems, increase their size considerably as they become turgid: they consequently press outwards against one another and against the external tissues which usually have smaller and less extensible cells and which are firmly cemented together. The balancing of the resultant thrusts makes the whole organ firm; many young stems and most leaves owe their rigidity to this mechanism.

Changes of turgor are frequently the cause of changes of shape, and hence of movements, by plant members. The

turgor of the guard cells leads to the opening of stomata
and loss of turgor to their closure. Swollen pulvini at the
base of leaflets (fig. 86) and petioles (fig. 78) cause leaf
movements by their changes of shape following changes
of turgor on their two sides. Sudden and even explosive
movements sometimes result from the slow building up of
turgor in a tissue until some point of predetermined weak-
ness all at once gives way. The discharge of seeds from the
fruits of *Impatiens* is an example. Here, the outermost
layers of the fruit wall consist of large cells which swell and
tend to curve the wall inwards; but their inner layer is
harder and resists the curvature. The fruit consists of five
carpels which are joined to one another vertically only by
rounded, thin-walled cells. Finally, these give way at the
slightest shock or touch: the separate carpels roll up like
springs, and flick the seeds inside to distances of 5 feet or
more.

The Passage of Water from Soil to Plant. The forces
holding water in the soil have been expressed in the early
part of this chapter in terms of the free energy of the soil
water, which is the method usually adopted by soil physi-
cists. They can, however, also be expressed as suction pressures, or diffusion pressure deficits, and this is convenient
when we are thinking of the passage of water from soils to
roots. The diffusion pressure deficit of a soil's water at the
permanent wilting point (cf. fig. 39, p. 191) is about
15 atm. and at field capacity about 0·1 atm.

Root systems deprived of their tops rarely develop a suction pressure of more than 2 atm. It therefore appears that
active absorption can only occur from soils with plenty of
water not far removed from their field capacity. The
evaporating power of the air, expressed as a suction pressure, is of the order of 1000 atm. Not all the immense
difference from soil suction pressures is available to promote

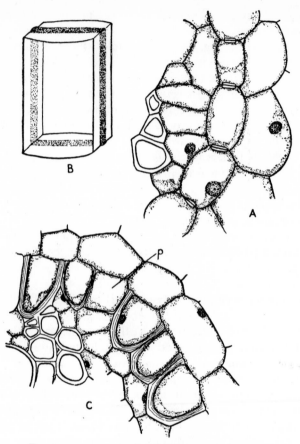

FIG. 43. ENDODERMIS AND ADJOINING CELLS IN A ROOT

A. Part of an endodermal cylinder in the young stage showing the cutin bands on the radial walls forcing water to pass through the protoplasts; from the absorbing region of the root
B. Diagram of a single cell to show the arrangement of the band
C. Old stage, the majority of the cells having formed thick impervious deposits on their inner and radial walls. A thin-walled passage cell is shown opposite the protoxylem. Highly magnified

passive absorption, and the value at the leaf evaporating surfaces is less than 100 atm. This is probably due to a layer of 'fixed' water molecules at the leaf surface. Even so, the evaporating, and hence the lifting, pressure available during passive absorption greatly exceeds the suction pressure of the soil even at the wilting point. It may also exceed the maximum suction pressure that can appear in the leaf cells; hence absorption and loss continue after the plant has wilted.

It must be remembered that the suction pressure of the cell is not the osmotic pressure of its contents, but the difference between the osmotic pressure and the wall pressure. So long as there is no transpiration going on and absorption is wholly active, the suction pressures of the root cells may be regarded as a cause of water uptake. When transpiration is rapid and uptake becomes passive the cause of absorption is the transpiration pull and the suction pressures of the individual cells become adjusted to it and are no longer the primary cause of water uptake.

THE MOVEMENT OF WATER INSIDE THE PLANT

The Passage from Root to Leaf. When a root is fully turgid, a certain amount of water is passed from the living cells into the dead vessels (fig. 44 x) embedded among them, owing to a pressure the origin of which is uncertain. This *root pressure* may cause water to rise some way up the vessels; but it is fitful and, even at its best, too small to drive the water to the tops of tall trees. It appears to be responsible for guttation, the excretion of drops of fluid water from the hydathodes of seedlings and some adult plants in humid atmospheres; and it probably assists the recovery of a wilted plant when transpiration slackens. As already mentioned, it seems that water is dragged up the stem by forces acting in the leaf and, except when transpiration is prevented, it is not lifted by any pushing

from below. The conditions under which water exhibits
its tensile strength are described in the following para-
graphs, and it is because they are so strikingly fulfilled in
the conducting tissues of plants that water is dragged
through them rather than pushed.

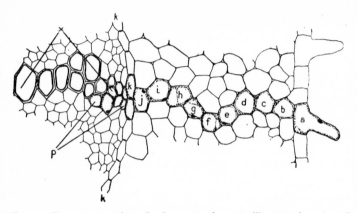

FIG. 44. Transverse section of a fragment of root to illustrate the entry of
water and passage from the root hair (*a*) towards the conducting vessels (*x*)
at the centre. Protoplasm shown in a single series of cells only. *b–j*. cells of
the cortex; *k*. cells of the endodermis; *p*. parenchyma within the endodermis;
x. xylem vessels. Diagrammatic. (M.S.)

When water evaporates from the walls of the leaf mesophyll in transpiration, they are no longer saturated, and so
draw water from the adjacent protoplasm which in turn
takes it from the vacuole and adjoining cells. The movement thus started works back to the xylem vessels in the
veins and, owing to the tensile strength of the water within
them, liquid columns are dragged up from the root. We
may, indeed, think of the water in the plant as being continuous from the cell walls of the mesophyll to those of the
root hair, and even linking up without any break with the
water of the soil. The movement started by evaporation in
the leaf will, therefore, draw a cohering column up from

the soil right through the plant. The lifting of the water is opposed by its own weight, or hydrostatic head, and by the suction pressure of the soil. These combine to bring the water into a state of tension, which is increased immediately it begins to move by frictional resistance, especially in passing through the walls and semi-permeable membranes of the root cortex (fig. 43). In spite of this hydrostatic

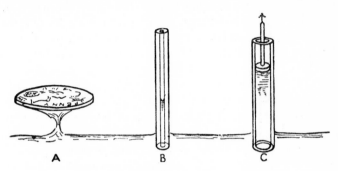

FIG. 45. THE ABILITY OF WATER TO COHERE

A. Water dropping away from a metal disk raised from its surface (height of the column much exaggerated)
B. Water hanging in a capillary tube
C. Water being drawn up a wide tube owing to its adhesion to a thoroughly wetted surface

tension across them, the living cells in all parts of the plant are kept turgid by their own suction pressures, which become adjusted to the tension by small losses or gains of water. The tendency of a cell suction pressure is to immobilize water in that particular cell.

The Tensile Strength of Water. If a penny is held horizontally in water and then lifted from it, the water follows it for a very short distance, but almost immediately runs in from the edges and drops away (fig. 45). If a very narrow tube, the sides of which have been thoroughly wetted, is dipped into water, the liquid rises in the tube, being dragged up by its own surface tension. Once it has been raised, it remains hanging from the walls of the tube, and does not run in towards the centre and finally drop back as from a flat disk. This is because the water molecules adhere to the glass and to one another, and can only be separated by the exercise of considerable force. In water, as in other liquids, the molecules will slide round one another very readily, so that the material easily changes its shape. This is quite a different matter from pulling the molecules apart, and when change of shape is prevented by the presence of solid walls, such as those of a glass tube, the tensile strength of the liquid becomes apparent. By suitable means, much greater columns of water can be raised than those due to surface tension, and, provided that there is no grease or air film to hinder contact with the glass, the water will always hang in the tube. This can be shown with a tube, such as in fig. 46, which is partly filled with water, and then boiled until all air is driven out and the sides of the tube thoroughly wetted. If it is then sealed off, the water run into the long arm, and the tube brought into the position illustrated, the water column remains hanging from the sides of the tube, even though the lower end becomes a vacuum when the steam has cooled.

Fig. 46

The Transpiration Stream. Careful measurements have shown that in order to rupture such a column of water by a direct pull a strain of over 4500 lb to the square inch (300 atm.) is necessary, and the presence of dissolved substances does not reduce this appreciably. It follows that water columns can hang in narrow tubes for a considerable height without rupturing, and, if suitable means are employed, may even be dragged up them. This is what happens to the water hanging in the vessels between the mesophyll cells in the leaf and the parenchymatous cells of the root; it is dragged up against gravity and the resistance offered by the walls of the narrow vessels. The tension in water moving up stems in this way has been measured and does not exceed 300 lb to the square inch, a very small fraction of the strain which the water columns are capable of bearing without rupture. The energy which initiates the movement is the latent heat of vaporization of water, absorbed during evaporation from the mesophyll cells. As already described, this causes an increase of tension which works back to the cells adjoining the xylem vessels. Water is then drawn in from the vessels; and, instead of breaking free from those that lie behind, the absorbed molecules drag the water columns up behind them.

The Path of Conduction. In small plants and woody twigs it can easily be shown that water passes up the stem through the xylem (**exp. 62**). In the trunks and larger branches of trees, the greater part of the structure consists of woody tissue, but not all of this carries water at any one time. The central, or *heart-wood*, which usually becomes dark owing to the slow accumulation of stains, has its cavities filled with air, although, at first, water passed through its vessels. Sooner or later, and particularly in autumn, the water columns break, and once they are severed the air gap becomes larger and larger, never closing up again. The loss of conducting material is made good in the spring by the formation of new xylem elements outside the old (fig. 47), and water passes through these until they are replaced in their turn. The comparatively narrow band of water-conducting tissue is called *sap-wood*.

Even in angiosperms, the xylem does not consist exclusively of vessels, but often contains in addition many tracheids; and in many woody plants, such as the pine-trees, the xylem is composed of tracheids entirely, so that

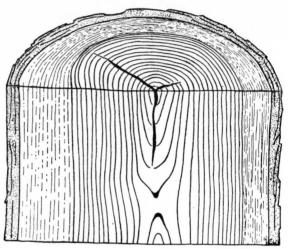

FIG. 47. A PIECE OF BLACKTHORN STEM SHOWING THE HEART-WOOD AND SAP-WOOD

The annual rings of the heart-wood are indicated by continuous lines; those of the spring wood by broken lines; bark is shaded with dots

it might be thought that their many cross walls would oppose insuperable obstacles to the dragging up of water. This does not, in fact, happen, principally because the tracheidal walls are perforated by many pits, where there is only the very thin and very easily penetrated middle lamella between the two cavities. The pits linking the tracheids are of the bordered type, and the middle lamella, having a thickened *torus* in *Pinus*, acts as a sort of valve. In fig. 48, the unshaded tracheid at the centre has formed a bubble of air, which has stretched until it has filled the

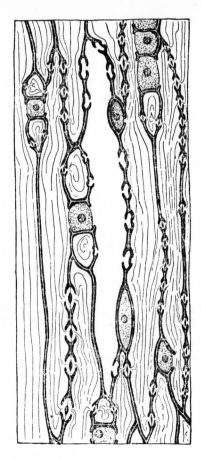

FIG. 48. LONGITUDINAL SECTION OF WOOD OF *Pinus*

illustrating the passage of water from one tracheid to another.
The direction of the flow is indicated by thin lines. The central
tracheid without such lines is supposed to be occupied by air only.
The membranes of the bordered pits adhere to the water surface
and are dragged aside by it. When there is water on both sides the
membranes lie freely in the centres of the pits. (Diagrammatic)

whole cavity of the cell. The water in the surrounding tracheids is part of the transpiration stream, and hence under tension. The pit membranes are thoroughly wet, and when the water retreats they cling to its surface and are dragged to one side of the pit, thus closing its opening. In this way, the air-bubble becomes enclosed within thickened walls, which it does not penetrate at all easily, and the flow of water continues all round the blocked tracheid.

XEROPHYTES

Plants differ very much in the type of soil and climate which they can inhabit, and the nature of the water supply is one of the most important factors influencing their distribution. Those plants which can grow in particularly dry situations are called *xerophytes*, and, as might be expected, they possess certain characters, which enable them to endure such special habitats.

Drought Evaders. Many dry regions, such as the semi-deserts of Russia and America, have a short rainy period followed by a long time of complete drought. As soon as the ground is moistened by the rains large numbers of quickly growing plants appear. Their life is very short, however; they do not grow to a large size and, before the ground has dried up, they have formed seed and died down again. The dry seed lies inactive in the ground until the next rainy season. Bulbous plants behave similarly; but the subterranean bulbs do not dry out like seeds, but depend on protective coverings as well as the overlying soil to keep their internal tissues moist.

Partial Evaders. Some plants remain above ground; but reduce their exposure by having little or no leafage (brooms, acacias, etc.) or at least to the extent of being deciduous in the dry season.

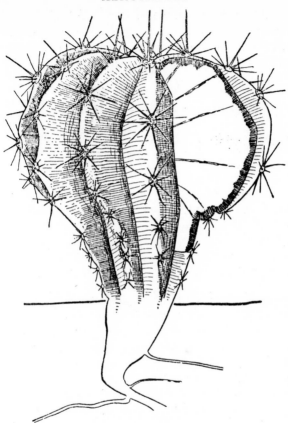

FIG. 49. *Echinocactus*, A DESERT SUCCULENT
General view of a young plant with a segment cut away on the
right-hand side. The dark shading represents the green assimilating tissue. The centre is occupied by a compact colourless tissue
penetrated by the vascular bundles which run towards the groups
of spines situated on the ridges. Somewhat reduced

Succulents do not change their appearance during
drought and owe their survival to their exceptional powers
of retaining their internal moisture. The rate of transpiration of an *Opuntia*, an extreme type of succulent, was found

to be only a thirtieth of that from a thin leaf of equal surface area. Such succulents have compact tissues with limited intercellular spaces and a very low ratio of surface to bulk. Their epidermis is pierced by relatively few

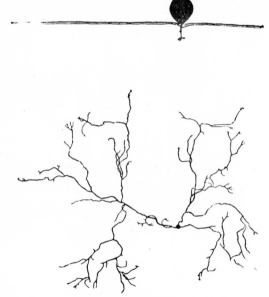

FIG. 50. ROOT SYSTEM OF *Echinocactus wislizeni*
Vertical extension above, horizontal extension below
(After Cannon, modified)

stomata which, unlike most stomata, are said to open only at night. Their actual absorption of water is not more efficient than that of mesophytes; contrary to what might be expected, they are usually shallow rooted (fig. 50) and, when the dry season sets in, uptake of water comes to a stop and their existence depends upon the slowness with which they lose the water they already contain. To illustrate this, a giant cactus was kept in a laboratory without

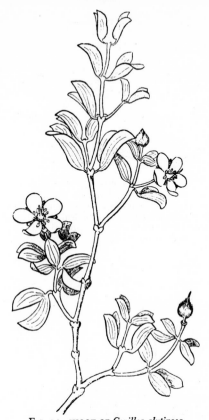

FIG. 51. SHOOT OF *Covillea glutinosa*

An extreme xerophyte, about natural size.
The plant is an evergreen shrub with low
much-branched stems and yellow flowers.
It is called the 'creosote bush' on account of
the scent of its resin. (After Gray)

once being watered, and after six years it had only lost
one-third of the moisture it originally contained. Plants
of this type are characteristic of the semi-deserts of America,
but are not found in their driest parts, or in the Sahara,

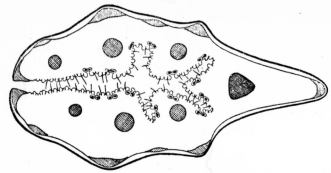

FIG. 52. SECTION ACROSS THE LEAF OF *Festuca*
in the position assumed in a dry atmosphere. The stomata, shown by pairs
of black dots enclosed in circles, are in the upper surface and become
enclosed in a long narrow cavity when the leaf folds. In damp air the leaf
opens out flat, and the stomata are then exposed. Vascular bundles cross-
hatched; fibres in single-line shading. (M.S.)

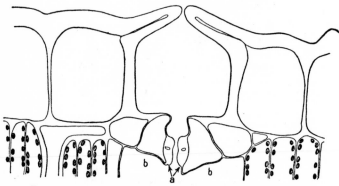

FIG. 53. STOMA AND SURROUNDING CELLS FROM A LEAF OF *Hakea*
a. guard cells; *b.* supporting cells. Chloroplasts shown in the assimilating
cells. Note also the thick cuticle of the epidermis and its folds overlapping
the stoma. Highly magnified. (M.S.)

where there are fewer short rainy periods. The succulent
plants of salt marshes differ completely from the desert
succulents in having less protected surfaces and very fast,
instead of very slow, rates of transpiration.

Drought Endurers. Drought endurers are quite different in their appearance (fig. 51), but are distinguished still more sharply by their rate of transpiration, which is usually very high. Their leaves often possess protected stomata and thickened cuticles (figs. 52 and 53), which, at first sight, suggests that their transpiration rate is likely to be slower

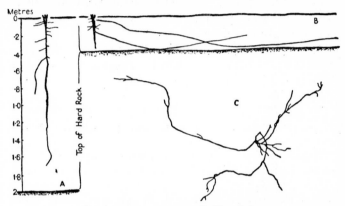

FIG. 54. ROOT SYSTEMS OF *Covillea glutinosa*

A. plant growing in deep soil; B. plant growing in shallow soil; C. horizontal extension of plant growing in shallow soil, scale rather smaller than A and B. (After Cannon, modified)

than that of mesophytes. Actually, such modifications are not of much importance during normal transpiration when the stomata are fully open; but after wilting has occurred they may be of great effect in stopping still further losses of water and complete drying up.

If the soil is porous, plants of this type send down roots to great depths (fig. 54), and absorb the subsoil water, raising it by their unusually powerful transpiration. During the digging of the Suez Canal, roots of acacias were found at a depth of 40 feet; but desert soils are often too hard for roots to penetrate far, and then very few plants are able to survive at all. A notable exception is the 'creosote bush'

(*Covillea glutinosa*) (*see* fig. 51) of North American deserts, which during the long droughts dries up almost completely, the merest traces of water remaining in the protoplasmic colloids. Most plants are unable to recover from desiccation such as this, but *Covillea* has the power, and it is to this special property of its protoplasm, rather than to structural modifications, that it owes its survival under such conditions. This is probably true of all those xerophytes which are really drought enduring.

There are thus several kinds of plants able to exist in dry places, and they can be classified according to the way in which they fit the conditions as follows:

Class	*Special characteristics*
1. Drought evaders	Pass through drought as seeds or bulbs.
2. Partial evaders	Reduced leaf surface.
3. Succulents	Slow water loss in transpiration.
4. Drought endurers:	
(*a*) Deep-rooted	Rapid transpiration; water raised from great depths.
(*b*) Shallow-rooted	Protoplasm able to recover from almost complete drying.

TRANSLOCATION

Many of the simpler substances, such as sugars, amino-acids, and inorganic materials entering from the soil, are able to move about inside the fabric of complex plants. Apart from this property, it would be impossible for such elaborate structures to develop, since the necessary substances would not come together and react. Movements of this sort are all included under the name *translocation*, whatever their direction or the nature of the moving substance.

The Direction of Translocation. While it is true that

substances spread eventually in all directions within a plant, main streams of relatively rapid movement may be recognized (fig. 55).

The general rule seems to be that substances pass from regions where they are plentiful, such as the point at which they are formed, or at which they enter the plant, towards those where they are scarce, the scarcity usually resulting from their conversion to other compounds. Products of assimilation tend to pass from leaves into the stems and along them towards growing points and storage organs. By the use of $^{14}CO_2$ it has been possible to trace where the assimilates of a selected leaf go. Young leaves which are still growing do not export photosynthetic products and may even receive them from mature leaves lower down the stem. Exchange between mature leaves is very limited and the bulk of their products usually passes down into the roots. Having undergone conversion into other products these, including their ^{14}C label, may then pass up into the above-ground organs again. As a plant ages the pattern of transport may be modified. Up to its maturity only the lower leaves of a plant may pass their products to the roots; but once fruit formation begins ever increasing numbers of leaves pass their products up to the fruits and eventually even the lower leaves are doing so. The passage of assimilates up or down the stem is frequently localized in a very narrow vertical column. This is why it is that, if the leaves are removed from one side of a swede top, the fleshy root below will be stunted on that side.

The Path of Transport. For many years there has been a notion that organic materials travelled along the phloem strands, principally in the sieve-tubes. This was mainly based on the detection of sugars and proteins in the sieve-tubes by microchemical tests, and the fact that when the phloem was cut away or killed, leaving the wood intact,

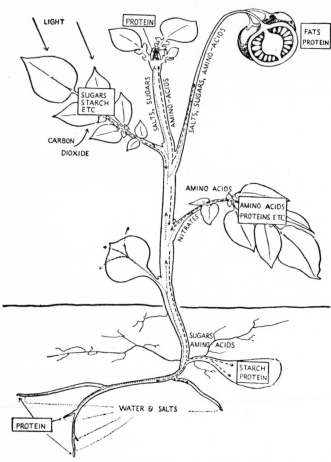

Fig. 55. Diagram of a plant to show the sites of the principal syntheses and paths of translocation during the period of active growth. Substances synthesized are shown in rectangles; the broken lines represent the principal routes of amino acid and sugar movements, and the dotted lines water and salt movements. Synthetic condensations are shown going on in leaves, storage tuber, seeds, and growing points; uptake of water and salts occurs in the roots

translocation of these substances stopped. The evidence was not satisfactory, because the microchemical tests could not show actual movements, and in killing the phloem there was always the risk that some injury had been done to the xylem, or that decomposition products of the dead phloem injured or blocked it. The latter difficulty has never been completely overcome, but continuous careful experiments have reduced the uncertainty to smaller and smaller proportions, so that it is now difficult to disbelieve that the phloem forms the normal path of translocation of sugar and nitrogenous compounds, and also, one might add, of inorganic phosphate and potassium re-exported from the leaves.

Recently confirmation has come from a more delicate method. Aphids are able to insert their stylets into the conducting strands of the young stems they infest to obtain the sugars. The stylets can be shown microscopically to be tapping the phloem and if the aphids are brushed off, the stylets remain in position and a sucrose solution exudes from them until the exudate has exceeded many thousandfold the volume and sucrose content of a single cell.

The phloem is the path of transport from the leaf whether the assimilates are moving downward to the roots or upwards to fruits. The passage of nitrates and other ions obtained from the soil by the roots is in the transpiration stream in the xylem. Some organic materials, but only in relatively small quantities, may also be carried up in it.

The Materials Transported. Sucrose is the principal carbohydrate transported in the phloem, and has been identified in the sap exuded by phloem. This is true even in plants like Jerusalem artichoke which forms fructosans rather than sucrose as a photosynthetic product in its leaves. The closely related annual sunflower can be grafted on to the artichoke. Reciprocal grafts as shown in fig. 56 have been allowed to photosynthesize $^{14}CO_2$ through a selected leaf and to translocate the assimilates down to the root. It was then found that about 90 per cent. of the

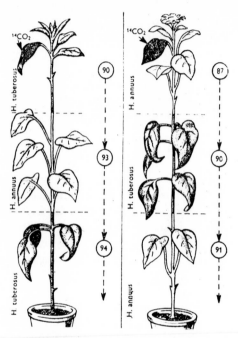

FIG. 56. For explanation, see text. Figures in circles give percentage of sucrose in the translocated assimilates

translocated assimilates (as indicated by the ^{14}C label) was always sucrose whatever sort of leaf had done the photosynthesis. In experiments feeding $^{14}CO_2$ to rhubarb leaves, it was found that labelled amino acids were also rapidly formed and translocated through the veins. They probably represent the main nitrogenous compounds translocated.

The Rate of Movement. The rate of translocation is

surprisingly fast. The rate of sucrose movements in the phloem of cotton plants was calculated to be about 40,000 times faster than the rate of its diffusion in water, or about as fast as the rate to be expected if the sucrose molecules had been in the state of a gas. The radio-activity of ^{14}C-labelled assimilates advances along the conducting strands at rates of the order of 100 cm per hour.

Phloem Respiration. The conducting cells of the phloem, unlike those of the xylem, retain their living contents and it has often been shown that if these cells are killed as, for example, by local heating, translocation is brought to a stop. The phloem tissues show exceptionally fast rates of respiration, faster than those of the tissues adjoining them. Respiratory poisons, such as dilute cyanide, or those like dinitrophenol which inhibit phosphorylation, also inhibit translocation. It has also been shown that enriching leaves with ATP accelerates the movement of assimilates towards the roots. It has, therefore, been suggested that the energy needed to accelerate translocated solutes above their own spontaneous diffusion rates is supplied by the respiration of the phloem cells; but it is not at all clear yet how this might be done.

The structure of the sieve tubes and other phloem cells is known in good detail which is being still further improved with the help of the electron microscope. It is not, however, possible to relate this structure to the movements of of the contained fluid as can be done for the xylem.

EXPERIMENTAL WORK

Exp. 53. WATER LOSS OCCURS THROUGH THE STOMATA

Cut two leaves of equal size having thick cuticles and stomata on the lower surface only. Grease the upper surface of one and the lower surface of the other; close the cut end of the petiole by means of rubber tubing and a piece of glass rod, and then weigh each to the nearest centigram. The leaves should be suspended in such a way that no grease is wiped off on to the balance. Weigh again next day. The leaf with its lower surface free will show a reduced weight owing to loss of water; and, if kept for some time, will become completely shrivelled, while the other is still fresh looking.

India rubber (*Ficus elastica*) leaves are very suitable for this experiment; also those of cherry laurel.

Exp. 54. COBALT CHLORIDE METHOD OF MEASURING THE WATER EVAPORATED. EFFECT OF STOMATA

Lay a strip of blue cobalt chloride paper (p. 317) on a small sheet of glass. Put a leaf, large enough to overlap the paper and having stomata on one side only, on top. Make a joint round the edge of the leaf with plasticine; lay a second strip of cobalt chloride paper inside the plasticine ring, and press another piece of glass down firmly on top. The cobalt chloride strips should then be enclosed in separate chambers on either side of the leaf. The emission of water vapour is indicated by the cobalt chloride paper turning pink. On which side of the leaf does this occur the faster?

The leaves of most deciduous trees are suitable for this purpose.

Exp. 55. THE POTOMETER

Assemble a potometer of the type shown in fig. 57. The container A should be a bottle of 200–300 ml capacity able to stand firmly, fitted with a rubber cork with two holes. The tube B should be of narrow bore and calibrated in tenths of a millilitre. Suitable measuring pipettes can be obtained ready graduated.

a. Uptake of Water by the Shoot. Fit a woody shoot with 20–30 leaves, and which has been standing in water overnight, into the second hole in the cork; fill the bottle to the brim and press the cork in tightly, avoiding any air

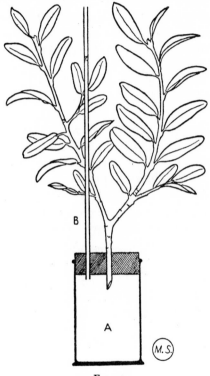

FIG. 57

bubbles in A. The excess water will rise in the tube B; if this is not sufficient, run further water down the inner side of the tube from a pipette. Note the time taken for a definite loss of water as shown by the drop in the measuring tube; confirm the first value. This shows the rate at which water is being taken into the shoot from the apparatus. Any considerable change of temperature will cause serious error in this experiment. How? Readings should, therefore, be limited to short intervals of time and the apparatus be protected from draughts.

b. Loss of Water from the Shoot. Stand the above apparatus on a good pair of scales, sensitive to about half a gram. Weigh it and leave it to stand for half an hour or longer with the weights still on the pan. At the end of the period, the scales will no longer balance owing to the loss of water from the shoot. How much has been lost?

Sometimes the simultaneous loss and gain of water by the shoot are equal, but by no means invariably. After a little practice, readings of water absorption may be taken while the apparatus is standing on the balance, and simultaneous values for absorption and loss thus obtained.

Exp. 56. Raising of Water by Transpiration and Evaporation

a. Suction Due to Transpiration. Cut a twig of cherry laurel, lilac, or other woody plant, such that the stump is 6–9 mm in diameter, and 3–4 cm long below the bottom leaf. It should have about two dozen leaves. Grease the sides of the stump, taking care not to block the cut end, and push it immediately into a piece of pressure tubing (fig. 58 A) attached to a length of glass tubing B about 45 cm long. Fill the entire length, taking care to remove all air bubbles, by running water down the side of the tube from a pipette. Close with one finger, invert, and stand the lower end of the tube in a small vessel containing mercury. Clamp in position as shown in fig. 58.

As water is transpired from the leaves, mercury will be drawn up the vertical tube. When it has reached a certain height, air will be drawn into the tube through the air spaces of the stem and leaves, and further ascent stopped.

b. Suction Due to Evaporation. Take a porous pot (fig. 58, D), 7–8 cm long, and join it to a vertical tube E by means of a rubber cork. Fill both with water, excluding all air, and clamp into position with the lower end of the tube dipping into mercury. As water is evaporated from the surface of the pot mercury will rise in the vertical tube.

Exp. 57. OSMOTIC PRESSURE

Coat the upper half of a parchment paper shell (*see* fig. 59) with paraffin wax to render it impermeable, and fit it with a wire or glass rod so that it can be suspended in a beaker. Soak the shell and then pour into it 25 ml of a molar solution of cane sugar, or an equal amount of 'golden syrup' diluted with two volumes of water. Suspend it in the beaker, and add water to the latter until the liquids are at the same level inside and outside the membrane. All the unwaxed part of the membrane should be immersed. Allow to stand for 24 hours or longer, and then pour the solution in the shell into a narrow measuring cylinder. The volume will have increased to 35–40 ml. A length of nylon foil tubing has been found a good substitute for the parchment thimble.

Exp. 58. PLASMOLYSIS

a. Cut a few sections from a fresh beetroot, and place in a watch-glass of water. Mount and examine under the microscope; the cells will appear full of sap. Immerse a section in a molar solution of sucrose, and leave for 5–10 minutes, then mount in the same medium and examine microscopically. Many of the cells will be plasmolysed, owing to the shrinking of their protoplasts as water passes out into the strong sugar solution.

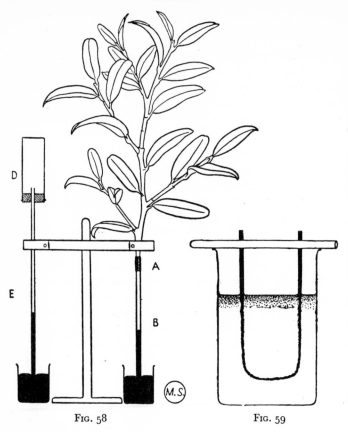

FIG. 58   FIG. 59

b. Immerse similar sections in 5 per cent. glycerine. Plasmolysis will again take place, but after a time, 15 minutes or longer, the protoplasts will return to their normal position.

Glycerine slowly penetrates the protoplasts, and so increases the internal concentration of osmotically active substances. As this happens, water re-enters the cell and extends the protoplasm again.

To avoid the necessity for section-cutting, filaments of *Spirogyra*, or other algae with conspicuous chloroplasts embedded in the cytoplasm, may be used.

Exp. 59. SUCTION PRESSURE. THE STRIP METHOD

Make a wall of plasticine, about 3 mm deep, round the edges of two microscope slides. Lay the slides upon a sheet of squared (millimetre) paper. Fill one of the chambers with a 3 M calcium chloride solution, and the other with distilled water. Cut strips from the large petals of one of the species mentioned below, about 6 cm long and 0·4 to 1·0 cm wide. Measure the length and breadth accurately on the squared paper, and then immerse a strip in each of the liquids. Cover with another slide to prevent evaporation, and measure the length and width again after an hour, and if possible after longer intervals.

The suction pressure of the strong solution will be greater than that of the petal, which will lose water and shrink (probably 3–5 mm). In water, owing to its greater suction pressure, the petal will expand about 3 mm.

Ray florets of marguerite or other composites, and petals of *Begonia* or *Amaryllis* give good results.

Exp. 60. MEASUREMENT OF SUCTION PRESSURE

Make up a molar solution of cane sugar by dissolving 85·5 g in 250 ml of distilled water. From this prepare M/2, M/4, and M/8 solutions by successive dilutions, and put about 100 ml of each into appropriately labelled, wide-necked bottles. Cut a block from a potato with a cork borer, and cut it into slices 3 or 4 mm thick. In this way, prepare four lots of disks, each between 8 and 10 g in weight. Dry the cut surfaces with blotting-paper, but do not apply pressure. Weigh each lot, and put one into each bottle. After 24–48 hours, take out the disks, dry their surfaces as before, and weigh again. Some sets will show a gain in weight, owing to the uptake of water, and others a loss. Which set shows least change? In this, the suction pressure of the solution is most nearly equal to that of the tissue. The osmotic pressure of a molecular solution of sucrose = 34·5 atm.

Exp. 61. Turgor

a. Split a fresh young bean stem, or dandelion-flower stalk, longitudinally into four strips. Note that the strips curve outwards, owing to the expansion of the inner cells when they are released from the compression of the intact stalk. Immerse pieces in M/2 calcium chloride solution. The curvature will be reduced or even reversed. Why?

b. Cut a piece about 4 inches long from the stalk of a rhubarb leaf. Push a cork-borer, of about ¼ to ⅜ inch diameter, through the middle of the piece from end to end. Carefully push the tissue out of the cork-borer without breaking it, and immerse it and the outer part in water for about half an hour. Then try to fit the centre piece back into the hole from which it came. What has happened, and what is the explanation?

Exp. 62. The Path of Conduction

Uproot a young plant of balsam (*Impatiens*) in which the stem is less than a quarter of an inch thick in the lower internodes. Wash the soil away from the roots, and stand at once in a beaker containing about an inch of water-soluble eosin, or red ink. Allow to stand for 1 hour, then lift the plant out of the eosin, and wash the roots under a tap.

The xylem strands of the roots, stem, and leaves will be picked out in bright red, and will be readily visible to the naked eye owing to the translucency of the tissues, and the position of the strands near the surface. Trace the course of the eosin from the roots to the minute strands of a leaf. If the experiment is carried on for a longer period the leaf mesophyll also becomes injected.

Cut a transverse section of an internode, and mount under a microscope. It can then easily be seen that only the xylem vessels are stained, unless the experiment has been carried on a long time, when the dye will also have travelled into some of the adjacent cells. Wild balsams may be found as garden weeds in suitable condition during the summer months, and cultivated balsams can be raised without difficulty from seed from April onwards. Twigs of Portugal laurel (*Prunus lusitanica*) may also be used if sections are cut.

Exp. 63. Migration of the Absorbing Zone

A box with one backwardly sloping glass side is required (fig. 60). The joints need not be watertight, so it is easily constructed. Line the glass side with a sheet of blotting-paper, and pack the rest of the box with a mixture of moist sand and sawdust to hold it in position. Insert a row of soaked seeds between the blotting-paper and the glass near the top. Water as required, and keep under observation. When root hairs appear, mark their position

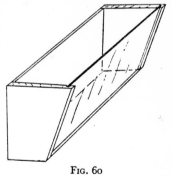

Fig. 60

with a pointer of gummed paper on the glass. Note how the subsequent growth of the roots involves the exploration of new layers of 'soil' by the constantly renewed zones of root hairs. A mixed sowing of barley grains, sunflower seeds, mustard, and cress is convenient.

Exp. 64. Effect of Aeration on Root-hair Development

Stretch a piece of muslin tightly over the top of each of two beakers, or small earthenware dishes, and secure in position with string or strong rubber bands. The muslin must not sag in the centre. Fill one vessel right up to the muslin and the other to within about 2 cm of it. Place soaked seeds (barley grains, etc.) on each, and cover with inverted jam-jars, or a bell-jar, to prevent the seeds from drying up. When the seeds germinate and send roots down into the water, abundant root hairs will form in the moist air between the muslin and the water surface, but not under the standing water.

PLATE VI

BARLEY PLANTS SIX WEEKS OLD GROWN IN WATER CULTURE

The two end plants received all the essential elements; the others lacked those shown. From a class experiment

Photograph by A. A. Kempin

−Mg   −Ca   −Fe   −K   −P   −N

VIII

NUTRITION

PLANT NUTRIENTS

FOODS are those substances from which an organism derives transformable energy and material for maintenance and growth. Animals, parasites, and saprophytes must absorb these from their surroundings; but green plants, as described in earlier chapters, can synthesize their own foods, carbohydrates, fats, and proteins, starting from simple inorganic materials. Carbon dioxide and the salts absorbed from the soil are not foods; but they are called the raw materials of plant food and, frequently also, plant nutrients.

Elements Essential for Growth. All sorts of elements find their way into plants from the soil, occasionally even silver and gold. Not all are essential: some may even be harmful, and others immaterial. Which are essential can be decided by growing the plants in pure sand, watered with suitable solutions. This method is called 'sand culture', but many plants can be grown merely by allowing their roots to enter the desired solution without any solid basis to assist its aeration. Sometimes it is necessary to blow air through such solutions to get a satisfactory root development. In 'water cultures' of this kind, many cereals will grow and ripen a good yield of grain, provided that the six elements, calcium, magnesium, potassium, iron, phosphorus, and sulphur are present, in addition to nitrogen. Together with carbon from the air, and oxygen and hydrogen from soil or other water, these make up the ten elements which are necessary to the growth of all green plants. Many fungi and bacteria can dispense with calcium, and all plants can do without iodine and sodium which are essential to animals. Besides the ten main elements, a number of others, the 'trace elements', are needed by plants in minute amounts. Even if these are not absolutely essential, their complete absence has profound effects upon growth.

Deficiency Signs. With a little practice, it is easy to tell by simple inspection when a plant is suffering for lack of one of the principal nutrient elements. These signs are best studied and noted with water-cultures, as described in **exp. 66,** p. 241. Some of the more obvious are as follows. Lack of *iron* causes the young leaves to be cream-coloured or perfectly white, owing to a failure to develop chlorophyll. Iron is not a constituent of the chlorophyll molecule, but apparently a catalyst in its formation. The first two or three leaves of an iron-starved plant are green, due to the iron present in the seed. Lack of colour (*chlorosis*) due to *magnesium* deficiency develops more slowly owing to the more abundant magnesium reserves in the seed. *Calcium* deficiency leads to death of the nuclei in the meristems, and the growth of both shoot and root is brought to an early stop. In acute calcium starvation, the plant never develops beyond the seedling stage. *Potassium* starvation causes the older leaves to yellow and die prematurely, since the small amounts of potassium that are available migrate continuously to the newly forming tissues. The plant goes on growing at the tip and dying away behind. Signs of *phosphate* deficiency are not quite so obvious. There is a general stunting of the plant, often an abnormal development of red pigments, and slow ripening.

Sources of Plant Nutrients in the Soil. There are three main sources in the soil from which roots can extract nutrients; the soil solution, the exchangeable ions, and the readily decomposed materials. The exchangeable ions are those loosely held at the surface of the soil's colloidal particles of clay and humus, notably the 'exchangeable bases', such as calcium and potassium. These three categories are not sharply separated from one another, and, if ions are removed from the soil solution, they are replaced, at least in part, from the solid materials. Most ions are not very easily washed out of a soil, because they are held more or less strongly by adsorption; nitrate ions are the only important exception. These are not adsorbed, and may be leached out much more readily by rainfall or by watering than, for example, ammonium ions.

Lateral movement of ions in the soil is, therefore, very restricted and, just as with water (p. 195), efficient uptake depends on continuous growth of the root system into fresh soil layers. The abundant root hairs grow into very intimate contact with the soil particles and their surface films of moisture (fig. 40, p. 197). Ions are taken up from the soil solution and, possibly, where contact is close enough, by direct exchange from the particle surfaces; the root gains potassium, calcium, or other adsorbed ions and loses hydrions, or even potassium ions, in exchange. Plant species differ considerably in their powers of extracting nutrients from soils. The amount of phosphate in the soil solution usually remains within the range of 1 to 3 parts per million; but different plants obtain widely varying amounts of phosphate from a given soil. It therefore appears that they cannot be solely dependent upon the phosphate in solution. Roots undoubtedly increase the acidity at their surfaces by means of the carbon dioxide which they are constantly excreting into the bathing fluid. This is quite enough to increase the solubility of the soil phosphates and carbonates, which are mainly compounds with calcium. Iron and aluminium phosphates are, on other hand, insoluble in acid media, and if iron and aluminium are present in quantity, the acidity range in which the soil phosphates are soluble may become very narrow.

As a result of the still largely unexplained differences in their foraging powers, different plant species growing on a single soil contain very different proportions of the various nutrient ions. In consequence, they also show wide differences in the minimum amount of a particular nutrient in the soil that will maintain healthy growth. On the other hand, the relative amounts of nutrient elements found in the leaves of a plant are related to, though not identical with, their proportions in the soil. If the content of a particular element falls to a dangerously low level, it may be possible to remedy this by increasing the amount available in the soil. This may be better effected by controlling the availability, for example by changing soil acidity, than merely by adding more nutrient. It is, for example, useless to add iron salts to very calcareous soils to remedy an iron deficiency: the iron becomes too insoluble, as carbonates and phosphates, to be absorbed. The solubility of phosphates may be artificially increased by adding sulphur to the soil in which the sulphur is oxidized by soil micro-organisms to sulphuric acid. It will be clear from the foregoing that soil conditions must be carefully studied to ensure the best results from the artificial application of fertilizers. In difficult conditions it may even be more rewarding to spray fertilizer solutions direct upon the foliage, or, with fruit trees, inject them into the trunk.

The Uptake of Nutrient Salts. The entry of nutrient salts into a plant is entirely independent of the simultaneous entry of water. They are two separate processes due to quite different causes. While the uptake of water may be due to osmotic pressure, to say that the uptake of salts is by 'osmosis' is nonsense.

At the extreme dilutions which are found in soil solutions, salts exist entirely as dissociated ions, and it is in this form that they pass into root cells. The two ions of a salt are not necessarily taken into the same extent; thus, from a dilute solution of calcium chloride, pea roots absorbed calcium ions five times as fast as chloride ions; and runner beans took up chloride faster than calcium. Such a separation of dissociated ions can only happen if others are supplied to keep the balance between positive and negative charges; and in the pea experiment it was found that magnesium and potassium ions had passed out of the roots to become associated with the chloride left behind. From a solution of ammonium sulphate, ammonium ions are absorbed much more rapidly than sulphate ions. Their place in the external solution is taken by hydrions, and the solution soon becomes strongly acid.

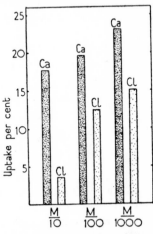

FIG. 61. Diagram to show the percentage uptake of Ca^{2+} and Cl^{-} ions from solutions of various concentrations. The excess uptake of calcium is greatest in the strongest solution

Ions may, to some extent, enter plant tissues as a result of their own diffusion pressure; but this does not seem to be the whole, or even the most important part, of the story. Actively growing root tips take up ions rapidly against their diffusion gradient: in a simple solution they are able to reduce the external concentration of nutrient ions virtually to zero, at the same time accumulating quite high concentrations in free solution in their cell vacuoles. They can only do this in the presence of oxygen. If aerobic respiration is stopped by the removal of oxygen, or by the application of a respiratory inhibitor, salt accumulation is completely stopped too. The temperature coefficient of salt uptake also follows that of respiration closely, and is higher than that of diffusion of salts in solution. It seems, in fact, that some part of the energy made available by

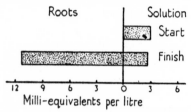

Fig. 62. Diagram to illustrate the accumulation of Br⁻ ions (initially absent) in barley roots

respiration is utilized to move the nutrients into the root cells. A very small part would suffice; it has been calculated to be no more than 1 per cent. The simplest conception of the connexion between respiration and salt uptake is that ions are taken up by an acceptor continually regenerated by respiration, and afterwards released into the vacuole or elsewhere. Concerning the identity of such an acceptor, or the means by which it moves the ions against their concentration gradients, virtually nothing is yet known.

Physiological Balance. If a young seedling is grown in pure water, its development soon comes to an end owing to starvation of the necessary mineral elements; but if it is supplied with a single salt, such as potassium sulphate, it dies even sooner. Neither potassium nor sulphate ions would ordinarily be considered poisonous to the plant, and both are, in fact, essential to its growth. The harmful effect can be much reduced by adding a second salt, especially if it contains a divalent metal, such as calcium or magnesium; but the best growth is only to be secured if all the essential elements are present in suitable proportions, or in other words are physiologically balanced. The proportions can usually be varied within moderate limits without causing much alteration in growth; but any large increment of a single substance, without corresponding increases of the others, is sure to have a harmful effect. In making culture solutions for plants it has, in fact, been found more important to balance the different constituents correctly than to fix on any absolute amount for each.

Selection and Antagonism. The relative amounts of the minerals found in plants are not identical with those available in the soil. It is clear, therefore, that different ions must be absorbed to different extents; or, in other words, that some sorting occurs. This is due to causes not yet properly understood; but some factors such as ready solubility, low electric charge (univalent rather than divalent or trivalent), and rapid consumption within the tissue, are known to favour uptake.

In a mixed solution, the presence of a second salt may restrict, or antagonize, the uptake of the ions of the first. Thus, in a solution of mixed chlorides the uptake of potassium is antagonized by the presence of rubidium or calcium; but not by the presence of sodium. This might be due to competition between potassium and rubidium, or calcium, for an acceptor which did not bind sodium. The harmful effects of poisons may also sometimes be prevented by the presence of an antagonist in the solution.

Roles of the Nutrient Elements. The parts played by *carbon*, *hydrogen*, and *oxygen* are described under the headings of photosynthesis and respiration, and the significance of *nitrogen* in Chapter IV. Among the metals, *magnesium* is an essential part of the chlorophyll molecule, probably binding it to a carrier protein. It similarly connects the prosthetic group of the enzyme, carboxylase (p. 100), to its protein. *Iron* is also important in the formation of cell catalysts, especially the cytochromes and their oxidase (p. 104), whose power of transporting electrons is associated with valency changes between ferrous and ferric iron. *Calcium* has obscure functions in the nucleus, and is needed for the healthy development of stem and root apices. It occurs in calcium pectate, which is an important constituent of the middle lamella, binding together the cells of a tissue. Calcium is almost as important to plants by securing good soil tilth as by its direct actions inside the plant itself. *Potassium* is not a constituent of any important plant substance; but appears to influence the efficiency of many of its synthetic reactions, such as the building of starch and proteins, probably through effects on the building and activity of some of the enzymes concerned. It can be partially replaced by rubidium, but not by sodium, in these activities. Potassium is an abundant constituent of the cell sap and so plays a part in its osmotic behaviour. Together with calcium, it has profound effects on the condition of cell membranes: within the usual concentration ranges, potassium tends to make them more permeable, and calcium to make them less permeable.

Among the non-metals, *phosphorus*, in the form of ortho-phosphate ions, plays an outstanding part as a metabolic catalyst. Some account of its activities has already been given on pp. 61 and 97. Phosphate ions are also present in the cell saps of plants in sufficient concentration to be important osmotically. *Sulphur* occurs in much smaller quantities in cells; but is a constituent of the side chain of the amino acid, cysteine, and is, therefore, commonly present in proteins as the thiol, —SH, grouping. Many enzymes of very diverse kinds are only active so long as their thiol groups are free to react with their substrates.

Trace Elements. These occur in plant protoplasm in exceedingly small amounts. The ratio of their concentration to that of carbon is of the order of one to a hundred thousand, or one to a million: even sulphur is likely to be a thousand times more abundant than a trace element. At higher concentrations, many trace elements are poisonous; and their indiscriminate application, as, for example, in fertilizers, may do harm. On account of the exceedingly small amounts required it is likely that their functions are mainly catalytic. Some are known to be, like magnesium, constituents of enzymes; e.g. *copper* forms the prosthetic group of polyphenol and ascorbic oxidases, and manganese occurs in the enzyme arginase. *Manganese* also seems to be important for some oxidations; and is needed as an activator of peptidases and carboxylases; that is to say, it increases the efficiency of these enzymes though not included in their molecular structure. *Zinc*, another trace element, is an activator of the same enzymes. *Molybdenum* is an essential catalyst in the biological fixation of nitrogen (pp. 141 and 143); and *boron* is necessary for efficient uptake and utilization of calcium. All these elements may have other important functions at present unknown.

Trace element deficiencies may occur in plants growing naturally in soils: the very small amounts needed may be present but unavailable, or may be used up by soil microorganisms. The demonstration of the essentiality of a trace element requires very refined methods of water culture with very specially purified salts and special containers.

EXPERIMENTAL WORK

Exp. 65. PRESENCE OF MINERAL SUBSTANCES IN ASH

a. Ashing. Weigh out about 5 g of air-dried plant material; the species is unimportant. Transfer to a crucible or vitreosil dish and ignite, preferably in a fume chamber. Heat the residue to a dull redness (a greater heat will drive off potassium) for 3 or 4 hours. Allow to cool in a desiccator.

b. Detection of Metals. If possible, a systematic analysis of the ash should be carried out. If this cannot be done, the presence of some of the important metals may be shown as follows:

(1) *Potassium.* Take up a little of the ash on a looped platinum wire, and hold in the violet flame of a bunsen burner. The pale-violet flame of potassium will be easily detected. Dissolve a little of the ash in dilute HCl, filter and add a few drops of sodium cobaltinitrite reagent (p. 318). A yellow precipitation shows the presence of potassium ions.

(2) *Calcium.* Moisten the platinum wire with concentrated HCl, and take up a further quantity of the ash. On entering the bunsen flame it will now give the brick-red flame of calcium.

(3) *Iron.* Dissolve a small quantity of the ash in dilute nitric acid and filter. To a portion of the filtrate add potassium ferrocyanide. A dark-blue colour, ferric ferrocyanide, will be formed.

(4) *Magnesium.* To 2 or 3 ml of the solution of the ash, add a drop of Magneson II reagent prepared as on p. 317. Add 5 N sodium hydroxide until the mixture becomes alkaline. If magnesium is present in the ash, the purple colour of the reagent will turn to a bright blue. The test is highly sensitive.

c. Detection of Non-metals.

(5) *Phosphorus.* To a further quantity of the filtrate from **b** (3), add nitric acid and ammonium molybdate. A canary yellow precipitate of ammonium phospho-molybdate will be formed.

(6) *Sulphur*. Make a strong solution of the ash in concentrated hydrochloric acid. Decant off the liquid from the insoluble residue, dilute to about three times the volume, and filter. Divide the filtrate between two test-tubes and to one add $BaCl_2$. A white turbidity of $BaSO_4$ will be formed. The amount of sulphur in plant ash is small, but by viewing the two tubes against a dark background the formation of $BaSO_4$ will easily be seen.

Exp. 66. WATER CULTURES

a. Common glass bottles holding about 500 ml of solution and stoppered by corks having a hole about half an inch in diameter are required. Each bottle should be fitted with a covering cylinder of dark-brown paper, which can be slid on and off. Immediately before use, the bottle should be thoroughly washed with boiling water, and the cork well scalded and then allowed to dry. The seedling will afterwards be fitted into the hole in the cork by a plug of clean cotton-wool, with the seed just below the cork. It is important to see that this plug and the cork are kept scrupulously dry, and away from the culture solution. If the seedling gets damp at this point, it will probably damp off, becoming a prey to fungal attacks. If the cotton-wool becomes wet at any time, it should be removed and a new plug put in its place.

Barley is one of the best plants to grow in water culture, and should be started not later in the year than the middle of April. Seeds should be germinated upon damp sawdust, or better upon a sheet of cork floating upon water and drilled with small holes to allow the passage of the roots. The cork should be coated with paraffin wax. When the seedlings have well-developed first leaves—after about ten days—they should be transferred to the bottles, and fixed into the corks as previously explained, the bottles having been filled with their solutions to within an inch of the corks, so that the roots alone enter the liquid (*see* Plate VI).

The following solution gives good results with barley, and should be renewed every third week. If growth is vigorous water will eventually be lost rapidly by transpiration, and distilled water should be added from time to time.

$CaSO_4.2H_2O$	0·25	g
$CaH_4(PO_4)_2.H_2O$	0·25	,,
$MgSO_4.7H_2O$	0·25	,,
NaCl	0·08	,,
KNO_3	0·70	,,
$FeCl_3.6H_2O$	0·005	,,

Make up to 1 litre.

For cultures lacking various elements substitute as follows:

Potassium: replace KNO_3 by 0·59 g $NaNO_3$

Calcium: replace $\begin{cases} CaSO_4.2H_2O \text{ by 0·20 g } K_2SO_4 \\ CaH_4(PO_4)_2.H_2O \text{ by 0·71 g} \\ \qquad\qquad\qquad Na_2HPO_4.12H_2O \end{cases}$

Iron: omit $FeCl_3.6H_2O$

Nitrogen: replace KNO_3 by 0·52 g KCl

Phosphorus: replace $CaH_4(PO_4)_2.H_2O$ by 0·16 g $Ca(NO_3)_2$

Sulphur: replace $\begin{cases} CaSO_4.2H_2O \text{ by 0·16 g } CaCl_2 \\ MgSO_4.7H_2O \text{ by 0·21 g } MgCl_2 \end{cases}$

b. Duckweed, *Lemna minor*, is a convenient plant for water-culture experiments. The solution may be placed in jam-jars, or other wide-mouthed receptacles, and each 'sown' with ten fronds. Growth can be measured by counting the number of fronds once a week for 5 or 6 weeks. Root lengths will also show interesting differences.

IX

GROWTH

THE GROWTH OF UNICELLULAR PLANTS

ALL plants, the simplest as well as the most intricate, are slowly changing the whole time they are alive. They do not come into existence in a mature form, remaining unchanged for the whole of their lives, but show a gradual and regular development leading up to maturity and reproduction. In free-living single cells, the life-history may be very simple, starting with a small cell formed by the division of a large mother cell, the daughter increasing its size until it has reached that of its parent, and then dividing in its turn. Even in unicellular plants, however, this simple cycle may be varied; pairs of cells may conjugate, or the organism may form resistant walls, and go into a state of inertia, suspending the normal development, perhaps for long periods. The different phases of development are determined very largely by the inherent nature of the plant, but they are also affected by external factors. Thus lack of moisture leads to the formation of resting spores, and the intensity of light often has a strong influence on the frequency of reproduction. The cells in a *Spirogyra* filament were found to divide more rapidly when they were subjected to a stronger light, though their individual growth was considerably reduced; with *Protosiphon* the result was just the reverse.

The Growth of a Colony. If a few yeast cells are put into an aerated sugar solution, containing, in addition, the other elements necessary for growth, development sets in at once. As soon as each cell has reached a certain size (about 10 μ in diameter), it buds off a daughter cell (fig. 63) and so increases the total number of individuals present in the solution. Under favourable conditions, this would

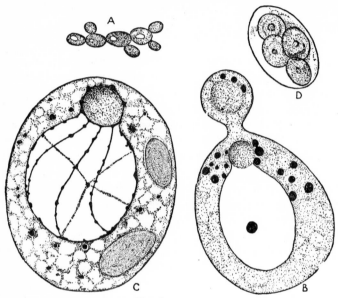

FIG. 63. YEAST

A. Cells budding and forming chains, × 200
B. Single cell forming bud
C. Diagram of the structure of an individual cell
D. Formation of spores inside mother cell; this takes place under unfavourable conditions and a resting stage follows.

(B and C after Wager and Penistone; D after Curtis)

happen about once in every hour, and this period would then be called the *generation time*. The other cells present will also behave in a similar fashion; but the divisions will not all be simultaneous, because, when first put into the solution, the cells were not all at the same stage of development, and there will also be small individual differences between them. On the average, however, the total number of cells in the solution would be doubled at the end of each succeeding generation time. Assuming this to be an hour, each original cell in the culture, by the end of the day, would have given rise to 16·5 millions, and, at the end of a second day, to 281·5 billions. This unrestricted development could only go on as long as there was sufficient sugar and other materials available, and, in a limited environment, such as a culture flask, a deficiency would soon set in. The rate of growth of the colony would then slow down as more and more of the cells were forced into an inert condition, and a correspondingly smaller number continued to divide. In actual practice, the growth of a yeast colony is retarded even before a deficiency of nutrients becomes felt, and this is due to the accumulation of alcohol, which the yeast itself produces. In a concentration of about 15 per cent. this brings all activity to a standstill, and it may slow down growth considerably at much lower values.

There are thus two phases in the growth of a colony of free cells: (1) the phase of *unrestricted growth*, in which all the cells are dividing at more or less equal intervals, and (2) the *senescent* phase, in which for one reason or another increasing numbers of the cells become inactive. If the cells are inactive when first introduced into the culture, there is also an *initial lag phase* during which they come to their full activity.

HIGHER PLANTS

Soon after the seedling of a normal green plant has spread its leaves in the air, it is able to photosynthesize, and thereafter lives and grows by the material it assimilates. The further growth that follows is distinguished by two important characters; it continues, though at varying rates, all through the life of the plant, and is restricted to certain growing regions, the meristems. Contrasting with this is the growth of animals which is completed in youth, and occurs more uniformly, the whole animal keeping more or less the same proportions throughout life.

The stages of growth shown by rapidly dividing cells and those slightly older have been described on p. 166, and these phases are found whether the meristem is young, as in a newly formed radicle, or old as at the tip of a well-developed root or stem. The cells which have become vacuolated are usually unable to divide even though they are still alive; and, once they have reached a certain size, they do not increase or multiply any further. As a final stage, many of the cells lose their protoplasmic contents altogether, and consist only of the walls formed by them. These represent so much inert matter which has not even the power of *rejuvenation*, or of the resumption of meristematic qualities which is sometimes shown by adult parenchymatous cells.

The primary meristems of stems and roots give rise to the growth in length of these organs, but their growth in thickness is usually due to the activity of rejuvenated meristems, or *cambia*, which arise in the young parenchyma. The development of the daughter cells of cambia is similar to the development of cells in the primary tissues, and, for the greater part of the plant's life, the two processes are going on simultaneously, with the result that it grows in height and girth.

Correlation and Inhibition. All complex plants consist of large numbers of individual cells; but they differ from simple colonies, because the cells are no longer independent of one another, and are even linked by the protoplasmic fibrils which pass through their walls (*see* fig. 38). The effects which individual cells within higher plants exercise upon other cells of the same plant are very complex and only slightly explored at present; the following are common examples shown by the bean plant

If the root is cut away from the stem, cells near the cut surface start to divide, and eventually form new roots. In other words, the removal of the original root has taken away some influence, or *inhibition*, which prevented these cells from forming other roots while it was present.

A bean stem usually develops by means of an apical bud, and so grows into a single tall stem, though lateral buds are also formed in the axils of the leaves, remaining dormant as long as the tip of the stalk is intact. If the young leaves near the tip are removed, even though the growing point is not damaged, the dormant axillary buds begin to develop, and form side shoots, whose further growth may be stopped again as the terminal bud produces new leaves in place of those cut away. It seems, therefore, that these leaves exercise some effect upon the cells of the side buds, which prevents their development.

Growth Regulators. The effect of the young leaves upon cells in other parts of the plant is exercised through growth regulators, i.e. substances which either promote or retard the growth of certain cells. Growth regulators are effective in very minute concentrations and may be produced in other parts besides young leaves. They may exercise their effect either upon the cells in which they are produced or only upon others at a distance. Substances which control a physiological function at a site remote from their place of production are called *hormones. The auxins* are the best known plant hormones. They affect not one but many aspects of growth and appear to be entirely non-specific; i.e. the growth hormone obtained from one species is the same as the hormone got from another. The single auxin, identified as β-indolylacetic acid, has been found capable of producing a most astonishing range of growth effects. It is now manufactured artificially and its effects on a plant can be measured quantitatively with fair accuracy. It is

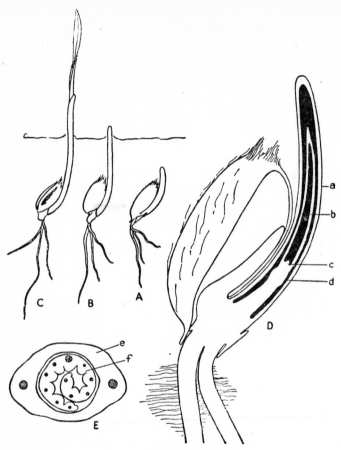

FIG. 64. COLEOPTILE OF WHEAT

A, B, C, stages in the germination of a wheat grain, showing the emergence of
the coleoptile (A); coleoptile breaking through the soil surface (B); and the
first leaf emerging from the coleoptile (C). D, enlarged section of A. *a*, coleoptile; *b*, first leaf; *c*, stem apex; *d*, node. E, transverse section of the sprout.
e, coleoptile; *f*, the first leaf, vascular tissue shaded. (E after Percival)

extremely active; 1 mg of the crystalline substance suitably applied will cause a 10° curvature in 30 million oat coleoptiles, or will start the development of a hundred thousand roots. The natural rate of formation in an actively growing stem is probably less than a millionth of a milligram per hour.

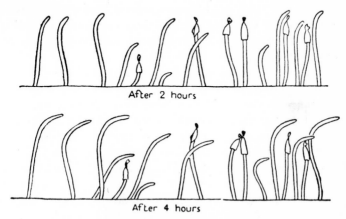

After 2 hours

After 4 hours

FIG. 65. COLEOPTILES OF OAT

grown in the dark and then subjected to a lateral beam of light. Marked curvature is shown by those with uncovered tips. Those with tinfoil caps show much slighter curvatures

The quantitative study of plant hormones began with the investigation of curvatures which are due to unequal growth rates on the two sides of an organ. The coleoptiles (*see* fig. 64) of grass and cereal seedlings, especially of oats, are highly sensitive and suitable. The region of most rapid elongation and hence of curvature is some distance down the tubular coleoptile (fig. 65); but the auxin is synthesized almost wholly in the solid tip. The most accurate method of assaying the minute amounts of auxin, with which growth studies are concerned, is still the *Avena* test. The auxin, dissolved in agar blocks, is applied laterally to oat coleoptiles, from which the tips have been removed; and the angle of curvature induced after a given time is measured. To obtain reproducible results, the variety, the conditions, and the time of growth, as well as all details of the actual experiment, must be rigidly standardized. It was the development and stringent application of the *Avena* test that brought about the great advance in present knowledge of the plant growth substances. Other methods, useful though not quite so exacting or so precise, have been developed since.

Auxins are produced, probably from precursors received from other parts, in the meristematic tips of stems, including the young leaves, and in root apices. From these positions they travel into the elongating and other zones farther back. The auxin reaching the elongating zone of stems from their own apices increases the rate of elongation; but in roots the rate is retarded. This is what happens naturally; but, if the amount of auxin is varied artificially, it is found that very low concentrations of auxin accelerate elongation even in roots; whereas higher ones retard even in stems. The responses of the two organs do not coincide in the same concentration range of auxin (fig. 66); but why is not known.

It has now been shown that the auxin, β-indolylacetic acid, affects other aspects of growth besides the lengthening of cells during vacuolation. The most important of these are as follows.

The suppression of side buds. Most stems show marked apical dominance; that is to say lateral buds in the axils of leaves, having developed to the dormant stage, do not grow on beyond it, unless the terminal bud is injured or removed. This effect depends on the production of auxin by the apical bud. If it is removed, side shoots begin to develop; but the application of auxin in lanoline paste to the cut tip stops the development, just as if the terminal bud were still there. This effect has been used to delay the sprouting of potatoes in store; but in practice it has been found convenient to gas the potatoes with the artificial hormone, MeNA (α-naphthylacetic acid methyl ester), which vaporizes, rather than use β-indolylacetic acid.

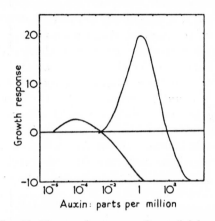

FIG. 66. The growth responses of roots (left-hand curve) and stems (right-hand curve) to varying concentrations of auxin. (After Audus, modified)

The initiation of roots on roots or stems. It has long been known that cuttings (p. 259) will not root unless they have actively growing leaves or buds upon them. This is probably due to the leaves' production of auxin which travels down the stem towards the cut surface. The formation of roots at the basal end may be induced by soaking in dilute solutions of auxin; but this is also likely to pass up into the buds of the cutting and prevent their development after roots have been formed. The synthetic growth substance, γ-indolylbutyric acid, is just as effective in promoting root formation and does not travel readily in the stem, so is more useful in practice. Many other things are also, of course, necessary for the successful striking of cuttings, and, if they are not also attended to, the hormone will be without effect.

The initiation of cambia in woody stems has been shown to be associated with a wave of auxin production. Wound cambia that cause the callusing at cut surfaces are also stimulated by auxin.

The development of fleshy fruits is normally determined by the growth of the seeds. Lop-sided apples are sometimes due to the failure of some seeds to develop; and a similar unequal development of the fleshy receptacle of strawberries has been brought about by removing some of the pips: growth could be restored by local application of auxin. The effective auxin in normal fruits appears to be produced in the endosperms of the seeds. The setting and growth of seedless tomatoes has been achieved on a greenhouse scale by spraying the flowers with auxin solutions.

The delay of leaf fall and fruit drop, due to late differentiation of the abscission layers, is also associated with the presence of auxin.

Comparatively high, but by ordinary standards still quite dilute, concentrations of auxins inhibit growth (fig. 66). It has been found that there are wide differences between species in the dosage needed to stop growth. The grasses, cereals, and potatoes are highly resistant, while many common weeds are highly susceptible. Readily manufactured artificial growth substances have therefore come into use as more or less selective weed-killers. One of the most commonly used is 2,4D (2,4-dichlorophenoxyacetic acid) which is not so readily destroyed in the soil as natural auxins.

The gibberellins, like the auxins, promote elongation of cells particularly in primary stems. Although first discovered in the fungus *Gibberella* they are now known to be formed generally in the higher plants. They can also have numerous effects upon growth; but, cell-elongation apart, these differ from the effects of auxin. They promote germination and the breaking of dormancy; they bring on the premature flowering of biennial plants; they can convert dwarf varieties (e.g. dwarf peas) into tall ones and increase leaf growth, more especially in monocotyledons. None of these effects are promoted by auxins, and gibberellins do not share the capacity of auxins to suppress side buds, inhibit root elongation, initiate the formation of side roots, etc., as set out on p. 250. Gibberellic acid is a tetracyclic lactonic carboxy acid with little structural resemblance to β-indolyl acetic acid.

Kinetin (6-furfurylaminopurine) may be regarded as a nucleic acid derivative and has been extracted from vascular tissues, malt, etc., and also synthesized. It is not yet certain that it occurs in plants precisely in the form extracted and other adenine (amino purine) derivatives show similar properties. It causes a very striking acceleration of cell division in some tissue cultures provided that auxins are also present; it assists the initiation of shoots, and retards the senescence of leaves, possibly by assisting the mobilization of amino acids.

Attempts to elucidate the modes and the primary sites of action of the plant growth factors have so far met with very meagre success. It is, however, now clear that the known substances and, perhaps, others yet undiscovered interact with one another in complex ways to produce the final correlations and controls observed.

The Measurement of Growth. The processes responsible for growth are exceedingly numerous and complex; and, as described above, they occur in a number of disconnected positions in the plant. It is even rather difficult to frame a precise definition of what is understood by the term growth, though in practice one accepts any permanent increase in size as showing its occurrence.

The basis of all vital activity is the active protoplasm of the living cells, so that growth might be defined ideally as increase of active protoplasm; but this would not coincide with the usual use of the term which includes the formation of inert matter in the woody and other tissues. Moreover, in actual practice, it is still impossible to measure the amount of active protoplasm in a complex plant, and, in deciding the rate at which growth is going on, some simpler standard is necessary. The oldest plan was to measure the increase in length of the plant's main axis, but this had serious disadvantages. It entirely disregarded growth in thickness, which is not necessarily proportional to growth in length, and it would also make plants grown in darkness appear to be growing faster than those kept in light, although actually they are losing matter instead of gaining it. With young organs the rate of elongation may be an adequate expression of their growth. An experiment (**exp. 68**) illustrating its dependence on temperature is described on p. 279. Another method is to measure the rate at which plants increase the amount of their solid material, or *dry weight*. This has the great disadvantage that drying kills the plant, so that only one determination can be made with an individual, and large numbers have to be taken to obtain successive values. There is, perhaps, no ideal method of measuring growth, and the unit chosen must depend upon the particular purpose of the investigation.

The Grand Period of Growth. Expressed in general terms, the vegetative growth of most plants shows three phases, starting slowly, becoming gradually faster, and finally slowing down again. These three phases cover the whole of the vegetative history of an annual plant, and together are called its *grand period of growth*. In a perennial plant the story is repeated annually with periods of dormancy between the repetitions.

Various attempts have been made to determine the annual growth cycle more precisely by weighing the dry matter formed at regular intervals. Fig. 67 A shows the average weight each week of samples from a set of maize plants all of which were grown together; similar curves

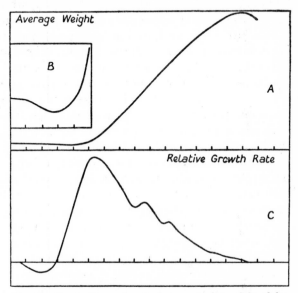

FIG. 67. Graphs illustrating the increase in dry weight of the maize plant. B shows the initial phase of A with the vertical scale enlarged. The divisions of the horizontal axis are weeks. (C after Briggs, Kidd, and West)

have now been constructed for many other annual plants, and all of them show the same S-shape. It should be noticed (fig. 67 B) that during germination, i.e. at the beginning of the curve, the seedling is actually losing weight as shown by the curve's initial dip. After this, for a short time while the plant is still very young, its weight may increase uniformly, like a sum of money at continuous compound interest when the rate of interest is unchanged. This would imply that all the cells in the plant were growing and dividing at equal rates, and is only likely to be true as long as the greater part of it is meristematic; and it is, in fact, found that the *relative growth rate*, corresponding with the rate of interest, is not uniform, but varies continually throughout the life of the plant. The relative growth rate is defined as the increase of weight in unit time per gram of material already formed, and is usually calculated for weekly periods, the average of the weights at the beginning and end of the week being taken as 'the amount of material already formed'. The curve showing the relative growth rate of maize throughout its life-history is set out in fig. 67 c.

As long as the seedling is losing weight, the rate is negative, and it does not suddenly leap to its full value when the seedling becomes autotrophic, but climbs to it comparatively slowly. There is thus an initial period, when the young plant is growing slowly, the full relative growth rate only being attained after about 5 weeks. When this maximum has been reached, it is not maintained for long, a decline setting in almost immediately, so that growth becomes slower and slower until finally it ceases with the 'ripening' of the plant.

The fall in relative growth rate is mainly due to the multiplication of cells which are unable to divide, so that, although the meristems may continue to form new cells at a more or less uniform rate, the growth of the whole plant becomes progressively slower.

Leaf Area and Growth. The main process contributing to the increase of day weight is photosynthesis. The leaf is the organ of photosynthesis and its surface area is the simplest measure of its capacity for the process. The amount of photosynthesis also depends on the efficiency of the leaves, which can be expressed as the *net assimilation rate*, i.e. the plant's rate of increase of dry weight per unit leaf area. This is the full assimilation rate less the plant's losses due to respiration, leaf shedding, or other causes.

It has been found that the net assimilation rate varies with the age of the plant, increasing to a maximum about the time of flowering and then falling away again. The differences between different sorts of plants and also of similar plants under different nutrient treatments are not very great, however. There is also little correlation between the net assimilation rate and the final dry weight of different varieties of species such as sugar-beet or potatoes.

Leaf area is more liable to variation both in size and duration. It can, for example, be much reduced by late germination at the beginning of the growing season. Liberal supplies of soil nitrogen increase leaf area at any time during the life of the plant; phosphates increase it in the early stages and potassium in the later stages by delaying senescence.

It has been shown, for example, that the final dry weights of mangold plants grown under a very wide range of fertilizer treatments was closely correlated with their leaf area and scarcely at all with their net assimilation rate. It seems that the differences in the growth rates of plants are due much more to the different amounts of leaf produced than to different photosynthetic efficiencies.

External Conditions affecting Growth and Yield. It is usually impossible to find out the quantitative effect of external conditions upon the rate of growth during any given week because the rate is affected not only by the conditions during that week, but also by others that have gone before. For instance, a dry spell in spring retards the whole development of most annuals whatever the subsequent weather may be like. It is more often possible, however, to decide the effect of such conditions upon the final yield of the plants at the end of their life, this quantity being as it were a summary of growth, since it is affected by every condition that has any influence upon the stages leading up to it. The final weight of the plant may be called its yield, but often, and especially with agricultural crops, the weight of some particular part of it is taken; thus the yield of corn is the weight of grain secured, while that of sugar-beet is the weight of sucrose extracted from the root.

An interesting example of this kind has been worked out with wheat. Records of wheat yields have been kept for many years for individual districts and even for single fields, and, by comparing these figures with the weather records, the effect of external conditions upon yield can be decided.

The English climate is found to be on the average too wet for wheat, so that every inch of rain above the average reduces the wheat crop. The amount of the reduction depends, however, upon the time of year at which the rain falls, the greatest damage being due to rain in January and July, and the least to rain in May. In a certain Hertfordshire field, the harvest is, on the average, reduced by as much as a bushel and a half per acre by every inch of January rain above the average for the month; but in East Anglia, where the soil is lighter and the average rainfall lower, much less harm is caused.

Yield is also affected by the amount of nutrient material in the soil, and the quantitative effect of each substance depends not only on its own concentration, but also upon the concentrations of the other essential materials. Thus, additions of potassium salts to a soil will not increase its fertility if nitrogen is deficient, and the extent to which potassium can profitably be added is decided by the available quantities of nitrogen and other essentials. In general terms, it may be said that if a single nutrient, or other factor of the environment, is increased by equal steps without altering any others, the increase in yield becomes less with each increase of the factor.

VEGETATIVE PROPAGATION

Pieces of stem or root cut from their parent plant and fixed in moist soil are able to regenerate new organs, and grow into independent plants. Since this does not involve any specialized cells or organs, it is called *vegetative propagation* to distinguish it from *sexual reproduction*, involving the fusion of special cells (gametes), and *asexual reproduction*, in which a single special reproductive cell or group of cells is formed without a prior fusion. Sexual reproduction in higher plants leads to the formation of an embryo inside a seed, asexual reproduction occurs in the formation of the spores, i.e. pollen, and megaspores, and various kinds of vegetative propagation occur also.

Propagation by means of 'cuttings' is frequently used by gardeners to preserve choice varieties. In this way stems, roots, and even leaves (figs. 68 and 69) can be made the basis of new plants, which show all the characters of the original, since there is no mixing of strains as in sexual reproduction. It is said that continuous vegetative propagation sometimes eventually causes loss of vigour, and greater susceptibility to disease, a well-known instance being that of the garden hollyhock (*Althea rosea*), which was cultivated for many years from cuttings. The plants thus produced were very liable to the attacks of the rust, *Puccinia malvacearum*, which even threatened to extinguish the species entirely until reproduction by seed was resorted to. Seedling hollyhocks and the adult plants into which they grow generally appear much more resistant to the attack of the fungus than plants produced from cuttings, but there are, on the other hand, numerous species which have been kept in cultivation for many plant generations by vegetative means alone, and which still show no sign of deterioration.

Natural vegetative reproduction may be brought about by organs which have become swollen owing to the precipitation within them of large quantities of reserve substances; thus potato tubers and crocus corms are swollen segments of stem containing starch. In other plants, organs

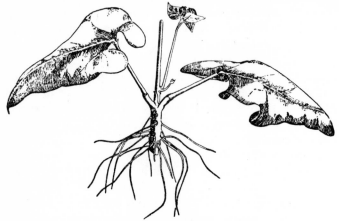

FIG. 68. A CUTTING OF *Phaseolus multiflorus*

i.e. a piece of stem cut away at top and bottom and kept standing in water. A cluster of young roots has been formed, bursting through the swollen tissues at the lower end of the piece of stem. The axillary shoot has also developed owing to the cutting away of the leader

showing no obvious swelling may be effective, thus the underground stems of twitch grass (*Agropyrum repens*) may give rise to new plants from any node, and bramble (*Rubus fruticosus*) stems may root and form new plantlets wherever they touch the ground.

Very often this method of reproduction is associated with a previous period of dormancy and so affords a second means of hibernation. The principal physiological difference between dormant seeds and vegetative organs in a similar condition is that the latter do not show the dryness characteristic of seeds, but other differences exist also. As

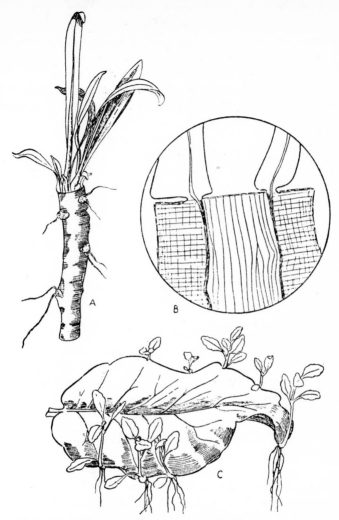

FIG. 69. ROOT AND LEAF CUTTINGS

A, a piece of *Anchusa italica* root, which has been planted in damp soil. A cluster of leaves has been produced at the upper end. B, enlarged vertical section showing the origin of the new leaves from the cambium shown by dark shading; wood, vertical shading; cortex, etc., cross hatched. C, leaf of *Bryophyllum calycinum* which has been kept on damp fibre. Young plantlets are forming at the notches round the edge of the leaf.

(A and C somewhat reduced)

an example, the dormancy and rejuvenation of a potato tuber are described below, and may be compared with those of a seed of the same species described on p. 273.

The tuber is usually formed at the tip of an underground stem, though almost any side shoot can be forced into

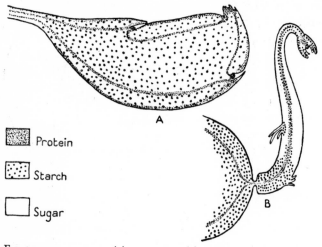

Protein

Starch

Sugar

FIG. 70 POTATO TUBER (A) AND SPROUT (B) SHOWING THE DISTRIBUTION OF RESERVES

Shading as in fig. 72 for comparison. (After de Vries, modified)

tuber form by keeping it in darkness and enclosing it in a moist atmosphere. Simultaneously with the swelling, starch is laid down in all the cells, and, by the time the tuber is mature, numerous large grains are contained in each of them, and form the bulk of the organ's dry weight. Fats, which are the principal reserve of the seed, are almost entirely absent from the tuber, and proteins are limited to the strip of cambium and phloem and to the corky skin (fig. 70); a trace of amino acid may also be present. In the autumn, sugars are very scarce or entirely absent; but as the tuber lies in the ground, or in storage, they gradually appear in the tissues immediately behind the 'eyes', or groups of buds. In spring, the tuber germinates by the development of one or more buds, which first give rise to stems, roots being formed soon afterwards from their lower segments. The apex of the young stem shows an abundant formation of protein (fig. 70 B), and behind this there is a starch region, replaced in its turn by a sugar region, and another region of starch at the base. These tissues and reserves are formed at the expense of the starch in the tuber, which disappears first of all at the centre, the potato even becoming hollow, while there is still a large amount of starch in the outer cells. The evacuation goes on long after the young sprouts have started to assimilate, and even to a late stage of the plant's life, when many young tubers are in course of formation.

THE REPRODUCTIVE PHASE

Sooner or later vegetative development is interrupted by the onset of a reproductive phase in which seeds or other special bodies are formed. The time at which this takes place depends upon a large variety of factors, many of them internal or inherent in the plant. The majority of plants in temperate regions set their seed at the end of the summer after a period of active vegetative growth, but there are many perennials which flower before their leaves unfold for the year, and thus commence their reproduction at the beginning of the active season. Differences such as this must depend upon the different natures of the plants, and how they are brought about is beyond our present knowledge.

The onset of flowering is, however, also considerably influenced by external conditions, and particularly by those experienced in the early stages of germination. Plants cannot flower and form fruits without carbohydrate reserves, and their accumulation is a necessary prerequisite for flowering: plants which flower early in the growing season do so at the expense of reserves accumulated the previous year. These, though necessary, do not initiate flowering, which is probably brought on by the accumulation of a flowering hormone, or florigen. The change from a vegetative to a reproductive stage starts long before it becomes visible as flowering; it begins when the meristem ceases to form leaf primordia and begins to form flower primordia instead; and it may be the role of the hormone to cause this change when its concentration in the meristems has become great enough. The onset of flowering, and possibly therefore the production of the hormone, are influenced particularly by temperature and by light in the earliest stages of development.

Vernalization. This has been described as a technique by which flower production is accelerated. It has been effected especially by chilling soaked seeds and cereal grains to about 2° C. The seed must be saturated, but not moist enough to put out its radicle and start germinating. The usual period of treatment for cereals is about 40 to 50 days. Some subtropical plants, such as cotton, millet, and soya, have been vernalized by warming the soaked seed for 15 to 20 days at 20° C. 'Winter' rye usually forms about twenty-five leaves before it begins flowering, whereas the quick-flowering spring variety usually flowers after it has formed about seven leaves. By suitable vernalization the winter variety can also be made to flower after forming seven leaves, but not sooner. It appears that the cold treatment at this early stage favours the formation of the vernalizing substance. Conversely, the effect may be destroyed by subsequently depriving the plant of oxygen for a while, and by other means which, perhaps, cause destruction of the hormone previously formed.

Photoperiodism. The length of the light and alternating dark periods in which a plant grows may have a very pronounced effect on its time of flowering. Some plants come into flower early when receiving short days—12 hours or less of daylight—but others when they receive long days with 14 hours or more of illumination. Others are day-neutral, that is to say they appear unaffected by such variations. The most sensitive stage is when the first leaves are being unfolded; and, if the day length later changes, as is usual in high latitudes, this is not likely to undo the effect already established. With winter rye, short days during the early seedling stages are an effective alternative method of vernalization.

Hyoscyamus niger (henbane) has two varieties, an annual and a biennial. It has been found possible to make biennial plants flower in their first years by grafting upon them shoots of plants that flower in their first year. These need not necessarily be from other henbane plants, but other annuals of the same family, such as tobacco and petunia, which will form graft unions with henbane, will also induce its early flowering. When such a graft is made, flower primordia may appear upon the henbane after a few days. It is not essential to have a complete shoot of the annual: a young leaf of *Nicotiana sylvestris*, grafted upon biennial henbane, caused flowering in the first year under long days, the conditions needed by the *Nicotiana*. It has also been recorded that the angiosperm parasites, broomrape and dodder, flower only when their hosts flower. Dodder is itself day-neutral; but on *Calendula*, a long-day plant, it flowers with long days; and on *Cosmos*, a short-day plant, it flowers only with short days.

These observations suggest that a flower-determining hormone is formed in young green leaves under suitable conditions, and is transported thence, if necessary through a graft-union, to the shoot meristems. Further, the hypothetical hormone appears to be non-specific since leaves of one species can determine flower formation in another.

It is useful to compare the idea of a flowering hormone with that of a growth hormone. At least one growth hormone, β-indolylacetic acid, is a tangible substance that has been extracted from plants, analysed and synthesized; and the identical actions of the natural and synthetic compounds have been demonstrated over a wide field. Against this, the flowering hormone is an unidentified substance whose existence is inferred from certain aspects of plant behaviour. Its existence is at present a useful hypothesis, whereas the existence of the auxin is an ascertained fact. The study of the auxins was, however, begun in precisely the same way; their occurrence was first deduced from the growth reactions of plants, and finally confirmed by extraction and identification. It remains to be seen whether it will be possible to prove the existence of a flowering hormone with the same finality.

THE FORMATION OF FRUITS AND SEEDS

The development of the seed begins with the fertilization of the ovule, but knowledge of the physiology of these early stages is very meagre. Fertilization may be regarded as starting three separate growth cycles, each of which follows its own characteristic course; the growth of the fruit, that of the embryo, and that of the endosperm. In cereal grains, there is only a small amount of fruit tissue developed, which soon dries up; but in the fleshy fruits large quantities of tissues are formed; barley grains and apples afford convenient examples.

Barley grains take about three weeks to develop, passing through stages called milky, doughy, ripe, and dead ripe respectively. The adjectives refer to the state of the endosperm which becomes progressively harder as it fills up with starch. By the time the endosperm is doughy, the external tissues of the grain are beginning to turn from green to yellow because their chlorophyll is breaking down. The photosynthesis carried on by the young grains in the early stages is said to contribute a good deal of their starch, which accumulates even if the leaves are removed. In the ripe stages the outer (fruit) tissues are dry and the endosperm also loses moisture and becomes hard. The grain as a whole may be separated from the parent plant and lie loose in the ear. By the time it is dead ripe, the fruit and endosperm tissues have passed through all the stages of development (p. 81) from embryonic to senescent; but the development of the embryo itself has been arrested at the first stage by dormancy. During the earlier stages, not only starch, the principal reserve, accumulates in the endosperm; but also reserve proteins, especially in its outermost, or aleurone, layer. Protoplasmic proteins, including many enzymes, are laid down in the embryo which also forms cellulose walls, but contains very little sugar and no starch. Much carbohydrate is also used in forming the fibre or outside protective layers of the fruit. At first, the respiration rate is very fast; but it slows down as ripening proceeds, and at dead ripeness can scarcely be measured.

In fleshy fruits, the conspicuous development is that of the fruit wall itself. An apple takes a whole season, from April or May to August or September, according to variety, to pass through the successive stages. It grows by cell division until it is about the size of a walnut, when it contains about a hundred million cells. This takes three or four weeks; then vacuolation with rapid accumulation of sugars, particularly fructose, sets in. There is also considerable accumulation of malic acid, making the tissue very sour. When vacuolation is complete, the apple has attained its full size and begins to ripen. Acids diminish, sugars go on accumulating, respiration gradually slows down, and the apple develops aroma and flavour. At this stage, the climacteric, the respiration rate suddenly increases again (*see* p. 83) and, at about the same time, an abscission layer is developed in the stalk, and the ripe, or overripe, i.e. senescent, fruit falls from the tree. Inside the fruit wall, the seeds (pips) have passed through a development very similar to that of the barley grain; the fruit itself is senescent, but the embryos of the seeds have become dormant.

Dormancy of Seeds. When the building up of the seed is complete, germination in some species follows at once; but much more frequently there is a period of dormancy, even if the external conditions favour active development. During this period, respiration and all other activities are reduced almost to a standstill. The state of the protoplasts becomes much more static than at any other time, and they tend to lose their normal characteristic of continuous change. It is impossible to say whether activity stops entirely; but it is known that it may be reduced to an extreme slowness without destroying the ability of the seeds to germinate afterwards. This has been done experimentally by drying them as thoroughly as possible, keeping them in a vacuum for years, or subjecting them to a temperature of $-250°$ C, and after any of these treatments they have still been able to germinate.

Sensational claims have sometimes been made as to the length of time for which dormant seeds retain their ability to germinate. Actually this period varies very much in different species, and, particularly among water plants, may be very short, often only a few weeks. Grains of wheat have never been found to survive for more than sixteen years in spite of fraudulent stories about living seeds from the granaries of Herculaneum or from Egyptian tombs. Hard-coated seeds of leguminous species, such as *Cassia bicapsularis*, may germinate after considerably longer periods; but the extreme examples are afforded by *Nelumbium* whose seeds have been known to germinate after 237 years and probably longer.

The great majority of dormant seeds are characterized by their dryness, having only about 10 to 20 per cent. of water instead of the 80 to 90 per cent. which is present in more active tissues. 'Wet dormancy', although less frequent, is not, however, unknown even in thin-walled seeds, where there is no doubt that the water penetrates to the interior. It is found especially among seeds falling into mud, or in forest soils, where abundant carbon dioxide is being liberated by the soil bacteria, the carbon dioxide acting as a narcotic. *Oenothera biennis*, *Rumex crispus*, and other seeds have been found to germinate after sixty years' storage deep in wet sand.

Wet dormancy also occurs in the buds of winter twigs, tubers, and other perennating organs. Although the dormancy may sometimes be broken by various treatments, such as heating, chilling, etherization, or a variety of other treatments, their mode of action and the causes of the dormancy are still very uncertain.

Causes of Seed Dormancy. External conditions sometimes prevent seeds from germinating, and so keep them dormant until there is a change. Dormancy frequently arises, on the other hand, from internal causes, three of which may be named. *Incomplete development of the embryo* is frequent in such common species as Lesser Celandine (*Ranunculus ficaria*) and Wood Anemone (*Anemone nemorosa*). In such instances, although the seed is to all external appearances ripe when it is shed from the parent plant, the embryo itself is only partially differentiated, and undergoes further development while the seed is lying in the ground. *After-ripening* is characteristic of Juniper and other species in which the embryo is apparently complete at the time of seed dispersal, but still unable to germinate. During the further period of maturation which is necessary in such seeds, various internal changes are going on, especially an increasing activity of the enzymes. Finally, *impermeable seed-coats* may also be a cause of dormancy by preventing the access of water, or even of air, to the embryo.

GERMINATION

Dry seeds are very hygroscopic, and the first event in germination is the uptake of large quantities of water, which is imbibed into the protoplast, or passes into the cell vacuole. In doing this the seeds, which at first are more or less wrinkled and shrunken in appearance, increase their size and become turgid, stretching out the folds in the seed coat. At the same time the total weight of the seed is increased by that of the water, which now forms a high proportion of the whole (**exp. 75**). The suction pressure of the seeds is very high until their colloids are saturated, and if the testa is tight round the internal tissues, or inelastic, the swelling of the colloids which takes place during the imbibition will cause it to burst. This actually happens in some seeds; but in the majority the testa is sufficiently loose or elastic to allow the colloids to complete their swelling without breaking it. Indehiscent fruits containing a single seed often have hard shells and are rarely ruptured by such swelling, since the dry seed occupies only a fraction of the space inside them.

As soon as the seed tissues have become saturated, the embryo starts into renewed growth inside them and, although no new solids are entering the seed, its own materials undergo extensive transformations. As the embryonic cells divide and grow, the space occupied by them becomes much greater, and this enlargement does not come to an early stop like the swelling of the original colloids, but may continue more or less indefinitely. The pressure developed by the growth of the young cells may be very considerable, though not so great as might be supposed at first sight. The growth of the embryo of a hazel-nut (*Corylus avellana*) was found to cause a distending pressure of 50 lb per sq. in., but the dry shell of the fruit could resist 120 lb to the square inch before breaking. The resistance of the wall dropped very considerably when it was thoroughly wetted, however, and it could then withstand no more than 45 lb to the square inch, and was easily ruptured by the growth of the embryo.

The resistance to splitting offered by the seed coat or fruit wall varies enormously, from the thin membranes of peas to the woody shells of coco-nuts or of *Canna indica*, whose seeds have even, upon occasion, been used as shot. In coco-nuts rupture occurs at special weak points, the 'plugs', but there are other seeds like those of *Canna* in which germination is completely held up until the walls have rotted.

In almost all seeds, the first organ to emerge from the split in the testa is the *radicle*, or embryonic root, and, since it is positively geotropic, it turns over and grows downwards no matter at what angle it first appears. The young shoot soon follows the radicle, and taking the opposite direction makes its way above ground, where it develops chlorophyll and commences active assimilation. The apex of an adult stem is not suited to penetrating soil like the apex of a root, and special organs are sometimes formed, which enable the young stem to grow to the surface. The coleoptile of the Gramineae, which is morphologically the first leaf, forms a hollow tube, which is furnished with a solid tip, and is about five centimetres long (*see* fig. 64). The first normal leaf grows inside this special organ and emerges near the tip, when it has approached the surface of the ground. If the seed is planted at a depth greater than 5 or 6 cm, the leaf remains curled up when it leaves the coleoptile until it reaches the light. It can be made to uncurl underground by planting the seed close to the glass side of a well-illuminated box, and when this is done it can no longer penetrate the soil but becomes twisted and folded as it uncurls (fig. 71).

The shoots of many other plants, such as peas and beans, are curled over when they first leave the seed, so that only the back of the hook and not the actual apex is pressed against the soil. Here again, if the underground stem is illuminated, its emergence becomes uncertain due to the fact that the bend straightens out into the upright position, which it normally assumes only on leaving the soil.

FIG. 71. Deeply planted wheat seedling germinating in soil against the side of an illuminated glass box. The light has caused the first leaf to appear from the coleoptile and unfold, with the result that it has become crumpled by the resistance of the soil

The Biochemistry of Germination.

The changes just described involve the expenditure of energy, and this is supplied by respiration, which is very rapid during germination and the early growth of the seedling. Sugars are consequently decomposed, and although the volume of the seedling increases, its weight is reduced by that of the carbon dioxide, which escapes into the atmosphere. Grains of wheat and maize may lose as much as half their total dry weight during this period, which for wheat is no more than 6 days. In both these grains the reserve carbohydrates are in the form of starch, and fatty seeds generally lose a much smaller fraction of their weight (in sunflowers, for example about one-tenth), associated with the fact that fats release more energy per unit weight of material oxidized.

Whether the seeds have starchy or fatty reserves, the loss in weight is always due to loss of carbon, hydrogen, and oxygen; nitrogen is just as plentiful after germination as before, since it is not oxidized during respiration. The mineral elements are also unaltered in quantity, and ash from a sample of seedlings is just the same as ash from a sample of the ungerminated seed. This does not mean that these elements are inactive in the changes going on, and the compounds in which they exist undergo, in fact, numerous transformations. The biochemical changes which go on during germination may in very general outline be described as follows.

Starch and fats disappear from the storage tissues, becoming converted into sugars, some of which are broken down by respiration. Another fraction of the sugar formed in the storage tissues travels into the growing cells of the embryo, and is built up into new cell material, especially the cellulose of the newly formed walls, or is again precipitated as starch or respired in the embryo.

Fig. 72 shows these changes in a potato seed and its seedling, the original reserve being fat, which forms a quarter of the total weight of the seed. Starch is entirely absent in the dry state, although it is present in small quantities in most fatty seeds. As soon as water has been absorbed, the oil droplets in the endosperm begin to disappear; and when the young root is thrust out through the testa, a regular arrangement of the principal reserve materials can be discovered. Nearest the seed, fat is still the main accumulation, but farther along it is replaced by starch, and near the tip this may in turn be replaced by sugars.

While these changes have been going on, the insoluble proteins present in the endosperm have been converted into forms soluble in salt solutions and water. The various products of protein hydrolysis, peptones, polypeptides, and amino acids, appear simultaneously as a result of the activity of the proteases, which, in common with other

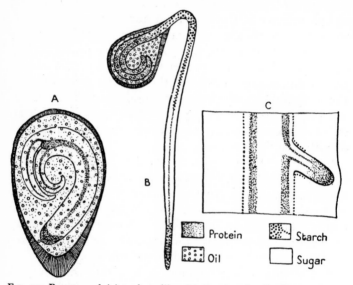

FIG. 72. Potato seed (A) and seedling (B) showing the distribution of the principal reserves; C, longitudinal section of a piece of root showing the origin of a lateral rootlet. (A and B redrawn after de Vries)

enzyme activities, increases markedly at this time. The amino acids, and perhaps other soluble forms, are trans-located towards the growing points of the embryo, and there give rise to the proteins of the new tissues, which consist very largely of the conjugated nucleoproteins. The distribution of these various substances in a castor-oil (*Ricinus communis*) seed about to germinate is shown in fig. 73; in a dry seed, peptones, polypeptides, and amino acids are absent.

When the radicle has emerged, proteins are always

abundant in the meristem, remaining plentiful in this position as long as the root lives; the meristems of lateral roots show similar accumulations, even while they are penetrating the parent cortex (fig. 72 c). In slightly older roots, a regular succession of reserves can be made out in

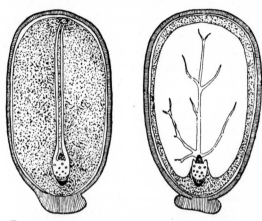

FIG. 73. SOAKED CASTOR-OIL SEED READY TO GERMINATE
Showing the distribution of proteins and related substances. Left in plane at right angles to the cotyledons; right parallel to cotyledons. Tissues with nucleoproteins in full black; soluble proteins, dot shading; peptones and polypeptides, circles; amino acids, white

passing from the tip backwards. The root-cap cells are always full of starch, while the elongating region and the older parts of the root contain sugars. The arrangement of the nitrogenous substances within the protein region at the tip of the young radicle is probably similar to that shown in the embryo of *Ricinus*—that is to say, nucleo-proteins predominate at the tip immediately behind the root-cap, and are followed by proteins, peptones, and amino acids in that order.

Most of the mineral elements present as compounds in the reserve tissues show a rather similar behaviour to that of nitrogen and carbon. Their insoluble compounds be-come converted, that is to say, into soluble forms which are translocated into the embryonic meristems, and there form fresh compounds in the growing tissues. The best-known example is phosphorus, which is present in the dry seed as lecithin, phytin, and various insoluble organic phosphates. During germination, these substances break down, and the comparatively soluble inorganic phosphates appear temporarily in their place, and pass by degrees into the embryo. In the meristems, they give rise to nucleic acid, an organic phosphorus compound, which unites with simple proteins to form nucleoproteins. Potassium differs from phosphorus and the majority of other elements by existing in the plant always in soluble forms, whatever the stage of development.

EXTERNAL CONDITIONS AFFECTING GERMINATION

When maturation of the seed is complete, certain external conditions are necessary for its further development, the most important of which are a supply of moisture and oxygen, a suitable temperature, and certain conditions of light. Some seeds may also have other special require-ments; the seeds of orchids, for example, will not ger-minate unless a symbiotic fungus is present, without which the embryo remains undifferentiated. The seeds of para-sites like broomrape (*Orobanche* spp.) only develop in con-tact with the roots of host plants, which the seedlings promptly invade.

The role of moisture in germination has been described on p. 270, and those of the other principal factors are as follows:

Oxygen Supply. In the absence of oxygen, seeds can only respire anaerobically, and do not germinate (*see* p. 100). This occurs, for example, when they are completely immersed in water, which very greatly reduces the access of oxygen, and it is for this reason that seeds are unable to germinate in waterlogged soils or in soils that are too compact.

Dry seed-coats are surprisingly impervious to gases, and the testas of dry peas and beans are air-tight even at the micropyle. This has been shown by closing the end of a barometer tube with a piece of testa and enclosing the whole in a dry atmosphere. Under these conditions, a column of mercury was maintained at atmospheric level, showing that a vacuum had been obtained, and that no air penetrated the closing membrane. As soon as the atmosphere round it was moistened, the testa began to take up water; and, at the same time, the mercury column began to fall, showing that air was passing through the membrane. Peas and beans, and perhaps many other seeds, are thus hermetically sealed when dry, and one important and rather unexpected effect of the absorption of moisture is to render the seed-coats permeable to gases, including oxygen.

Temperature. Germination will only occur within a limited range of temperatures, but the actual extremes vary a good deal in different species. On the whole, plants of cool and temperate regions have a lower range of germination temperatures than those of warmer countries, the following being characteristic examples:

	Germination temperatures	
	Minimum	Maximum
Wheat (Temperate) . . .	0–5° C	31–37° C
Maize (Sub-tropical) . . .	5–10° C	44–50° C

Above the maximum temperatures, soaked seeds are killed, probably on account of heat coagulation of their proteins and enzymes.

Temperatures within the possible range are not all equally good for the purpose, as can be seen by measuring the rates of germination which they allow. This rate can be regarded as inversely proportional to the time taken to reach some definite stage of development, such as the first appearance of the radicle, and when this is ascertained it is found that the best or 'optimum' temperature is somewhere about the middle of the range. The position of the optimum is, however, very indeterminate and depends largely upon the stage of development which is taken as a standard; thus maize germinated at 35° C puts out its radicle very rapidly, but further growth is very slow, and the seedlings may lag behind others germinated at 15° C. The unfavourable effect of rather high temperatures upon the later stages of germination is probably due to coagulation of the seedling enzymes, occurring more slowly than at temperatures above the maximum. Temperature also exercises a marked effect upon the rate at which water enters the seed, the higher the temperature the faster being the rate of absorption.

Light. The reasons why oxygen, heat, and moisture affect germination are not hard to understand, but the action of light is much less obvious. In the first place, seeds have very different reactions towards it, and may be classified roughly as *light* and *dark seeds*, the former needing to receive a certain amount of light before they can germinate, while the germination of the latter is hindered or prevented by it.

Common species possessing 'light seeds' are the Purple Loosestrife (*Lythrum salicaria*), Willow Herb (*Epilobium hirsutum*), and the buttercup *Ranunculus sceleratus*. If seeds of any of these are kept entirely in the dark, they will not germinate, although a flash lasting no longer than a second will enable many of them to do so. In some species, a temperature above 30° C will have the same effect as exposure to light, and removal of the testa may also bring about germination, so it seems that the action of light may be to make the testa permeable to oxygen and water.

'Dark seeds' are found in *Nigella*, and their germination can be brought about in light, either by removing the seed coats or by exposing them to an unusually low temperature. The explanation of these curious facts has not yet been discovered.

EXPERIMENTAL WORK

Exp. 67. The Growth of Ephemerals

The principal features of vegetative growth may be observed by growing quick-developing 'ephemerals', such as Chickweed (*Stellaria media*) or Speedwell (*Veronica* spp.), in pans of fine soil. Ripe seeds collected early in the season should be sown, not too thickly, and covered with a thin layer of soil and sand, and kept well watered.

Secondary thickening is very slight in these species, so that a fairly accurate estimate of growth may be made by measuring the length of important organs. Determine (*a*) the weekly increase of length of the main stalk, or stalks, and (*b*) the length of individual internodes. The latter series of measurements will show where growth is most rapid. Is the rate of growth fast or slow at the onset of flowering?

If seeds of the above plants cannot be obtained, similar observations may be made, over rather longer periods of time, with peas or beans germinated and grown in flower-pots.

Exp. 68. The Effect of Temperature upon Root Growth

Since the increase in length of a pea radicle is only about $\frac{1}{2}$ mm per h the apparatus uses a convenient measuring

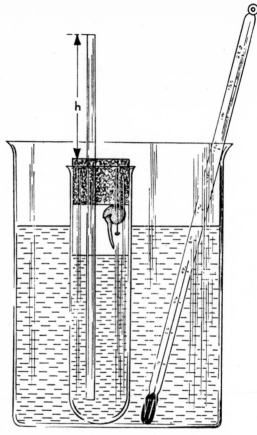

Fig. 74

system to 'magnify' the increase in root length. Quite a considerable downward movement of the glass rod will only slightly raise the water level in the specimen tube. The technique for measuring the change in root length is to depress the glass rod carefully until the water level rises to the point where the meniscus just 'jumps' on to the end of the radicle. This is quite easy to see. At this exact point measure the length of glass rod remaining above the cork (h). Raise the rod and repeat the procedure, taking the average of three readings at any one time. Finally raise the rod to lower the water away from the root. After about 20 minutes take another measurement and repeat at intervals until a steady growth rate is attained for a given temperature. Raise the temperature of the water by 10° C; leave the system for about 15 to 30 minutes to come to equilibrium and make a new series of measurements at the higher temperature.

It can easily be shown that the multiplication factor involved is R^2/r^2 where R = internal radius of specimen tube and r = radius of glass rod. The length grown by the root between two readings is therefore $(h_2 - h_1)r^2/R^2$. Calculate the actual growth rate of the root for each temperature (mm/hour) and also the increase in rate of growth caused by the increase in temperature:

$$Q_{10} = \frac{\text{rate at } (t+10)° \text{ C}}{\text{rate at } t° \text{ C}}.$$

Exp. 69. AUXIN AND COLEOPTILE GROWTH

To grow coleoptiles.

Soak wheat grains in water for about 2 hours, then sow them thickly on top of blotting paper in a polythene bowl as shown on the next page. (If seeds are sterilized in bleaching powder solution, 3 per cent. available chlorine, for 10 minutes, or in 'Milton' for 30 minutes, prior to soaking, this helps to check fungal growth on the seedlings.)

Germinate 4 days at 20° C, until the coleoptiles are 20–30 mm long.

Preparation of test. Select a batch of fairly uniform, straight coleoptiles and cut them off at the base. Align them on a moist slide with apices all facing the same way and against one edge of the slide. With a simple cutter, as shown in the diagram, several segments each 10 mm in length can be cut at a distance 3 mm from the apex of the coleoptile.

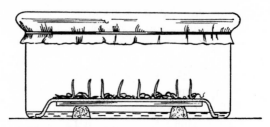

FIG. 75a. A bowl for germinating wheat grains

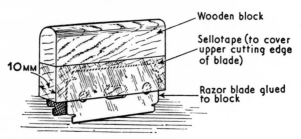

FIG. 75b. Cutter for making 10-mm segments of coleoptile

Place five coleoptile cylinders into each of six 2 inch by 1 inch specimen tubes containing 5 ml of one of the following solutions:

Water, 100 mg/l., 10 mg/l., 1 mg/l., 0·1 mg/l., and 0·01 mg/l. indolylacetic acid.

Incubate the segments in darkness at 25° C for 6–24 hours, according to convenience, and then measure the final lengths of the segments.

Plot the mean length per segment against the logarithm of the concentration of indolylacetic acid.

N.B. The increase in segment length is due solely to cell extension.

Exp. 70. AUXIN AND ROOT GROWTH

Soak cress seeds 2–4 hours in water and then plant them out into Petri dishes containing a wet filter paper. Sow about 100 seeds in each dish. Germinate at 25° C for 24 hours. Then select seedlings with radicles of a uniform length (about 5 mm) and place ten seedlings into five fresh dishes containing a filter paper and, respectively, 5 ml of water, 0·1 mg/l., 0·01 mg/l., 0·001 mg/l., or 0·0001 mg/l. indolylacetic acid.

After 24 hours' incubation measure the final lengths of the radicles, discarding any seedling whose radicle has grown up out of the solution.

Plot the mean final length against the log concentration of indolylacetic acid on the same graph as that showing coleoptile growth from the previous experiment.

Note the differences in response between coleoptiles (shoot tissue) and roots, particularly within the range 0·01 mg/l. to 10 mg/l. indolylacetic acid.

Exp. 71. THE EFFECT OF GIBBERELLIC ACID ON STEM ELONGATION

Plant six seeds of the dwarf pea variety Meteor in a 6-inch pot. After germination, select the four most uniform seedlings and remove the others. When the seedlings have 3–4 leaves two of them are treated with gibberellic acid (G.A.) whilst the other plants are controls.

One drop of a solution of 5 mg G.A. in 100 ml water should be applied to the apex of each of the two experimental seedlings and the treatment renewed every 4–5 days. Measure the height of each seedling initially and at convenient intervals for about 3 weeks; also count the number of leaves (or internodes) per plant. Are the treated seedlings taller because they have longer internodes, more internodes or both?

If a tall variety of pea, e.g. Pilot, is used, the G.A. will have very little effect.

Exp. 72. Auxins and Apical Dominance

Plant six seeds of dwarf French bean in a 6-inch pot. When the plants have their first pair of leaves fully expanded cut off the shoots from four of them, about 1 inch above the first leaves. On the cut stump of two of these place a 'blob' of plain hydrous lanolin, on the other two put hydrous lanolin containing indolylacetic acid (*see under* Reagents, p. 316). This auxin in lanolin should be renewed every few days. Note the rate of development of lateral buds in the three pairs of plants.

Exp. 73. Polarity

(a) **In shoots.** Collect young shoots of willow just before bud-break in early spring. Cut six 6-inch lengths of twig from the centre of last year's growth. From two of these carefully remove a quarter inch ring of bark from the centre of the twig. Since the 'bark' will come away at the cambium this is an effective way of removing a ring of phloem tissue, thus interrupting a normally continuous channel of supply.

Stand all six pieces of twig in about 0·5 inches of water in a beaker but place two of the untreated ones upside-down, i.e. with their buds pointing towards the water. Stand the beaker under a bell-jar whose sides are lined with wet blotting paper. After a week or two, note the numbers and position of the lateral roots and also those buds which begin to elongate first.

If all the buds are first removed from a piece of twig,

few, or no, roots will develop. However, if a little indolyl-acetic acid in lanolin (*see* p. 316) is placed on the morpho-logically upper end of the twig, root formation will be stimulated.

(**b**) **In roots.** From a stout tap root of dandelion cut pieces approximately 3 inches long and 3–5 mm wide. The morphologically upper end should have a horizontal, transverse cut whereas the lower end should be cut slant-ing (for later identification).

Plant the lengths of root in a 6-inch pot half of them the right way up and half of them upside-down, i.e. with the slanting cut uppermost. The surface of the root should be just covered with soil. Water well and cover the pot with a glass plate or polythene bag. Keep the soil moist and, when some of the pieces of root begin to form leaves, empty the pot and record the position of new shoots and roots on all the root cuttings. In the inverted pieces shoots will still have formed at the morphologically upper end of the root cutting in spite of the fact that it was under 3 inches of soil.

Exp. 74. RESERVE SUBSTANCES IN MATURE SEEDS

Cut half a dozen thin slices of castor-oil, lupin (preferably *Lupinus pilosus*), and bean seeds. It will be necessary to strip away the hard testa of the castor-oil seeds before cutting. Place the sections in nine separate watch-glasses, three of each species, and test each seed for

(*a*) starch by adding iodine solution;
(*b*) cellulose by adding chlor-zinc-iodine;
(*c*) fats by adding Sudan III.

Lay the watch-glasses in a regular order upon a sheet of white paper and notice the comparative intensities of the colours produced indicating roughly the amount of material present. The results will be as follows:

				Castor-oil	Lupin	Bean
Starch	.	.	.	None	None	Much
Cellulose	.	.	.	Little	Much	Little
Fats	.	.	.	Much	Little	None

Test the same seeds for sugars with Fehling's solution (*see* **exp. 1**).

Exp. 75. Uptake of Water by Seeds

a. Count out ten dry peas and weigh them to the nearest centigram. Then determine their volume by dropping them gently into a narrow measuring cylinder containing sufficient water to cover them, and noting the rise in level of the water. Allow the seeds to soak for 24 hours and then measure their volume again. Dry their surfaces gently with blotting-paper, or filter-paper, and then weigh. Both weight and volume will have increased owing to the up-take of water.

b. Weigh five seeds of *Canna indica* to the nearest centi-gram and then leave in a beaker of water for a week. Carefully dry the surfaces with blotting-paper and weigh again. There will be little or no increase of weight. File a hole in the testa of each seed and soak for 1 or 2 days longer. On weighing once more, there will be a marked increase due to the absorption of water through the hole in the impervious testa.

For other experiments on germination see **exp. 48** (The Effect of High Temperatures), p. 186, and **exp. 29** (Loss of Weight during Germination), p. 115.

Exp. 76. The Effect of Light on Seedling Development

Sow half a dozen oat seeds near the bottom of a glass box

with about 6 inches of fine soil above them. Place the seeds against one side of the box so that light will easily reach them, and place in a bright window with the box sloping gently backwards. This will ensure that the seedling shoots grow close against the glass. Set up a second lot of seeds but keep them in the dark. The first set will grow as shown in fig. 71, but the second set will reach the surface without difficulty.

Carry out a similar experiment with peas.

X

IRRITABILITY

THE NATURE OF IRRITABILITY

THE preceding chapters have described the various processes which lead to the synthesis of living protoplasm and so to the formation of the tissues and organs which together make a plant. The mature protoplast is not by any means an inert body, but is, on the contrary, characterized by its great physical and chemical activity, and one way in which this becomes apparent is through its ability to respond to changes of heat, light, pressure, moisture, and many other outside influences. The responses thus evoked are very varied according to their cause and the state of the protoplasm at the time of the change. Light alone has many different effects, being deadly to some protoplasts, such as those of *Bacillus tuberculosis*, and causing alterations in the rate of growth of nearly all plant organs. In addition, it effects further internal changes, such as the movements of chloroplasts, and prevents etiolation.

During photosynthesis, light is taken up quantitatively, and is therefore called one of the *conditioning factors* of the process. In other processes, such as the bending of a stem towards a source of light, only a fraction of the energy used up is supplied by the light, which merely sets in train a long series of reactions in the protoplasts, these finally giving rise to the visible bending. When acting in this way, light is said to be a *stimulus*, and the protoplasm is said to *respond* in virtue of its *irritability*. Irritability is thus another name for the extreme reactiveness of protoplasm, which makes it always liable to change by influences from without, in addition to the many changes it undergoes spontaneously.

The energy imparted by the stimulus is often only a small fraction of that used up in the response, the remainder being supplied by the protoplasm itself. For this reason, the plant's behaviour is sometimes likened to the action of a trigger, by which a small initial squeeze releases a very large amount of energy from the exploding cartridge. In the cartridge, the amount of energy obtained from the explosion is not increased by increasing the pressure on the trigger, so there is no constant relation between the two; all that is required is that a certain minimum force should be applied, anything in excess of that amount having no further effect. Plant responses often differ in this respect, since it has been found, where measurements have been made, that the amount of response is often proportional to the amount of stimulus. Trigger action cannot, therefore, be used as a name to describe the process.

The Internal Sequence. The visible response does not necessarily occur at the point where the stimulus first affects the plant, and hence it seems likely that some form of internal conduction occurs. There are thus three stages to be considered:

1. Induction ('Stimulation', 'Excitation') at the point acted upon by the stimulus.
2. Conduction, if any.
3. Response at the same point or some other.

The stimulation usually begins as a physical act, such as the absorption of light by an appropriate pigment in phototropism, which is then followed by physiological changes in the stimulated cells. At the other end of the sequence, the primary response is not usually the finish of the story, but is followed by secondary 'after effects' of varying degrees of importance.

Each of these stages is well illustrated by the rapid movements which occur in *Mimosa* leaves when the leaf-tip is cut or slightly burnt. When the stimulus is applied to a leaf-tip, the leaflets close together in pairs, usually starting with those nearest to the affected tip, the closure being due to changes in shape of the swollen pulvini at the base of each leaflet. When the bottom pair has closed, the response often occurs along other axes, and then starts from the bottom and works upwards, as the stimulating effect is conducted along them.

In the meantime, usually while the pinnae of the first axis are closing, the main leaf-stalk has dropped, the pulvinus at its base acting as hinge (fig. 76). These changes occur in a few seconds, but are not the full extent of the response, since the stalk and leaflets eventually return to their original position ('after effects') without any further external stimulus. The recovery movements take a much longer period than the original drooping, but both parts of the response use up energy, which is released from the protoplasm as a result of the stimulus.

The three stages are thus: (1) induction due to wounding at the leaf-tip, causing unknown changes in the affected cells, (2) rapid conduction along the leaf axes carrying stimuli to the various pulvini, and (3) response, consisting of a contraction of the lower sides of the pulvini, followed by a slow return to their original condition.

GEOTROPISM

Many of the known responses of plants have not yet been studied in detail, but a good example of one that has is given by the response of plant organs to gravity. This force exercises a mechanical drag on all parts of plants and produces visible effects in almost all of them, though these responses may sometimes be masked by the action of more powerful influences. The drag of gravity acts in a single

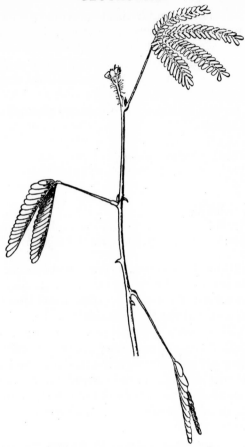

FIG. 76. A YOUNG PLANT OF *Mimosa pudica*
The top leaf is in the normal position, but the others
have responded to a mechanical stimulus. The pulvini
can be seen at the hinge positions. About natural size

direction only, and the response of the plant is a curvature which must bear some definite relation to the direction
of the pull. Responses of this kind are called *tropisms*, and
any tropism induced by gravity is named *geotropism*. The

direction of the responsive turning is different in different organs; it may be towards the centre of the earth (*positive geotropism*), away from it (*negative geotropism*), or obliquely to the vertical (*plagiogeotropism*): if the angle formed with the vertical is a right angle, the special term *diageotropism* is sometimes used.

The following list shows the usual responses of the various organs of plants:

1. Positively geotropic   primary roots.
2. Negatively geotropic   primary stems, aerating roots (mangroves), coleoptiles, most hypocotyls, fungal sporophores.
3. Plagiogeotropic   secondary roots, lateral stems.
4. Diageotropic   many dorsiventral leaves, rhizomes.
5. No response   tertiary roots, fungal hyphae.

These terms describe results and do not imply different plant órgans. It is easier to suppose that all geotropic responses consist of two components, one positive and one negative, and that the visible result is the balance between the two. This seems to be supported by the observation that wheat roots, for example, are not usually strictly positively geotropic, but slightly plagiogeotropic and that the angle they adopt from the vertical can be changed by changes of acidity and supply of growth regulators. If the roots are placed vertically they actually perform a negative curvature to bring them to their normal position.

The actual position taken up by a plant organ may well be the result of more than one type of response, and it is not always possible to deduce its reaction to gravity by simple inspection.

It has been shown for some species that the diageotropism of the rhizome is induced by light. In darkness, the positive component of their geotropism is weakened and the rhizomes grow upright. The position assumed by leaves is largely influenced by their epinasty—that is to say by the tendency of the upper surfaces, especially the upper surface of the petiole, to grow faster than the lower. This has been shown to be associated with a higher concentration of auxin on the upper than on the lower side.

It must also be remembered that the normal response may change during the life-history of the organ, a striking example being afforded by the hypocotyl of *Adoxa moschatellina*, which exhibits all three responses in turn. Upon germination, the hypocotyl comes above ground owing to its negative geotropism; but shortly after it takes on a positive reaction, bending right over and again penetrating the ground. When it has become embedded in the soil it changes once more, becoming diageotropic, and so forms a rhizome which grows parallel with the surface of the ground.

It has been shown for some species that the diageotropism of the rhizome is induced by light. In darkness, the positive component of their geotropism is weakened and the rhizomes grow upright.

Geotropic Response in Primary Roots. The behaviour of primary roots under gravitational stimulus was one of the first plant responses to be studied, and its simpler features can easily be examined experimentally (**exp. 77**). If a young root is placed at an angle to the vertical, its tip curves, as further growth takes place, sufficiently to bring it back into the plumb line. The older part of the root undergoes no visible change, curvature being restricted to the elongating region just behind the apex (fig. 77), and resulting from the greater increase of the cells on the upper side. The cells on the lower side also increase their length, but not to so great an extent as those on the upper.

If a root is placed for a short time at an angle to the vertical, and is then rotated and allowed to lie for an equal time at some other angle on the opposite side of the vertical, it will receive two unequal stimuli, and will eventually curve in the direction of the greater, if it is returned to a rest position. The amount of stimulus is proportional to the sine of the angle by which the root is deflected from

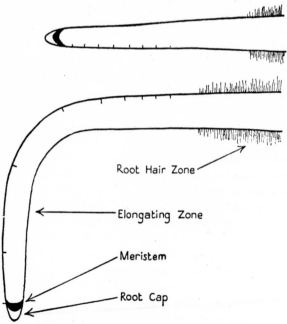

Root Hair Zone

Elongating Zone

Meristem

Root Cap

FIG. 77. GEOTROPIC CURVATURE OF A BEAN ROOT
showing that response occurs in the elongating region.
Diagrammatic. (M.S.)

the vertical, and it has been shown that the amount of induction or stimulation, but not necessarily the amount of response, is proportional to the same quantity. Thus geotropic stimulation is greatest when the root is placed horizontally (sine = 1) and nil when it is placed vertically (sine = 0).

The root does not sag inertly under its own weight, and this becomes apparent if it is first stimulated and then placed in a vertical direction before any response is visible. It does not then continue to grow in the vertical direction, but first forms a bend in the direction of the stimulation and only returns to the vertical in response to the second stimulation which results. The bending will also occur against a resistance, such as that of a viscous liquid, and work is, therefore, done, the necessary energy being released during respiration. It is, perhaps, due to this fact that there is no response in the absence of oxygen (**exp. 78**).

The Clinostat. A root may be equally stimulated on both sides by placing it at two equal angles for equal times, and then no curvature will result. The simplest way of securing a balance of stimuli is to place the plant upon a disk which is rotating slowly in the vertical plane; it then rests for an equal period in every angle to the vertical and, in the course of a single rotation, each side of the root is stimulated equally. A machine which secures this result is called a *clinostat* (fig. 78) and is of great service in studying geotropic responses. With an intermittent clinostat, i.e. one which can be stopped in any desired position for a known time, any amount of stimulus can be applied and its effects studied during a subsequent period of rotation.

Geotropic Induction in Roots. Although all parts of a root are subject to the geotropic pull of gravity, a limited region is specially 'sensitive' to its action. If the first 2 mm from the tip of a broad-bean root is cut off, care being taken that the cut is accurately transverse, only a very slight curvature takes place when the root is placed in a horizontal position, even although the region which normally responds, i.e. the elongating zone, is still intact (*see* fig. 79 A). After a comparatively lengthy period, usually

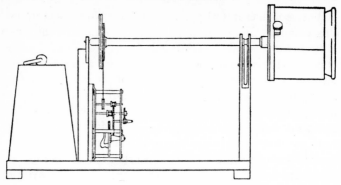

FIG. 78. A SIMPLE TYPE OF CLINOSTAT

The pot with the plant growing in it is clamped into the cubical box, which is made to rotate slowly by the clockwork. Two different speeds of rotation can be obtained by means of the two gear wheels on the spindle. (After Darwin)

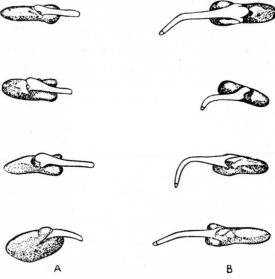

A   B

FIG. 79. GEOTROPIC RESPONSE OF DECAPITATED BEAN ROOTS

A. without tips; B. with tips replaced (drawn from a photograph by Snow)

more than 2 days, the tip of the stump itself becomes
sensitive owing to internal changes in its cells. It is possible
to dispense with the cutting if a root is fixed to a disk,
rotated at high speed about a
horizontal axis, with 2 mm of its
tip on one side of the axis of rotation and the rest of the root on the
other (fig. 80). Centrifugal force
then operates in opposite directions on the tip and the region
of curvature; but the direction of
curvature is that to be expected
if the tip is the region of induction.

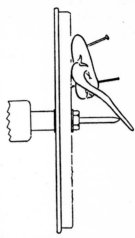

The first physical effect in the
induction of geotropism may well
be the movement within the tip
cells of statoliths, i.e. particles of
greater density than the general
protoplasm. Starch grains and
mitochondria have both been
suggested as possible, but in spite

FIG. 80. Clinostat experiment
showing that geotropic induction occurs in the root tip. For
explanation see text

of a good deal of investigation and various different pro-
posals, it is still uncertain what special effect such movements have upon the protoplasm of meristematic cells.

Geotropic Response in Primary Stems. The curvatures produced in primary stems are in the opposite direction to those produced in roots, that is to say, away from
the earth's centre. The region of bending is, usually, similar
to that in roots, being limited to the young elongating
region behind the apex. The actual movement is rather
more complicated, however, and results in the stem apex
being carried beyond the upright position (fig. 81), to
which it finally returns. The whole movement, to and fro,

is the result of the single original stimulus, since it is carried out even if the plant is subsequently kept upon a clinostat. Geotropic response in stems is not entirely limited to the elongating zone of young and tender organs. Some woody twigs, particularly those of the Lombardy Poplar (*Populus nigra* var. *pyramidalis*), are able to carry out curvatures, and

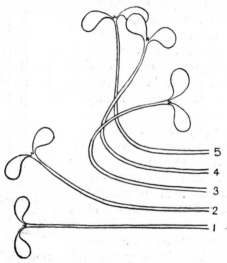

FIG. 81. DIAGRAM OF THE GEOTROPIC CURVATURE OF A YOUNG SHOOT
1, stem laid horizontal; 2–5, stages of response. (M.S.)

a more important instance is given by the nodes of grasses, cereals, carnations, etc. These retain their power of response long after the internodes on either side of them have lost it, and the result is that the stems of such plants which have been beaten down by the wind or rain return to the vertical position from a point near their base instead of only at the tip. Examples of this bending can frequently be seen in a field of young corn after bad weather, and a closer examination will show that the under surface of the node responsible for the recovery has become much

longer than the upper, which may even have been compressed by the sharpness of the bend
(fig. 82). If bending is prevented by
slipping a glass tube round a horizontal stem, the rapid growth of the
lower side causes it to form a swelling
(cf. fig. 87, **exp. 80**). If the plant were
rotated on a clinostat, the swelling
would make a frill all round the node.

Conduction. It has been explained
that geotropic induction is normally
greatest in a very short region at the
apex, and that response occurs in the
elongating region extending for some
distance behind it. It would seem,
therefore, that the stimulus must be
transmitted for a certain distance
along the root or stem. The sensitive
tips of bean and other roots have been
removed by an accurate transverse
cut, and then lightly replaced with a
thin film of water or gelatine separating them from the stump. After
being placed horizontally for about
24 hours, a large proportion curved
down in a similar manner to that of
normal roots (fig. 79). It is interesting
to note that the stumps of maize

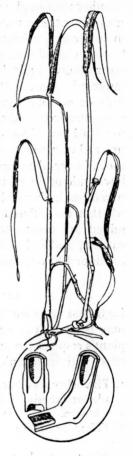

FIG. 82. YOUNG WHEAT PLANT

The stalk on the right has been knocked down and has returned to the upright position by the bending of its lower nodes. Other stalks in normal
condition. Inset in circle is an enlarged view of nodes split down the centre.
That on the left has remained vertical, that on the right shows curvature
from the horizontal to the vertical position. Note the thickening of the lower
side of the leaf sheath and the outgrowth of the stem

roots, similarly treated, carried out their usual curvature whether the tips placed upon them were of roots or coleoptiles. Since the stimulus can travel through a short aqueous discontinuity, a hormone seems the most likely agent. It has been found that, when primary roots and stems are laid horizontally, auxin becomes more concentrated on their lower sides than on the upper, though there appears to be little or no total increase of hormone production. These concentrations tend to accelerate the growth of stems and to retard that of roots (cf. fig. 66, p. 251), and thus to cause upward curvatures of stems and downward curvatures of roots. In cereal and grass stems, the renewed growth on the lower side of the node is associated with renewed production of auxin. Nevertheless, some doubt has been expressed whether the differences of auxin concentrations as determined are great enough to produce the observed curvatures, and isolated roots, apparently devoid of auxin, continued to respond when suitably stimulated.

LIGHT AND PLANTS

Light has so many different effects upon plants, that it may be as well to summarize them before describing the plant's responses in any detail: the following list gives each effect with its technical name.

1. Photochemical reaction of photosynthesis — —

2. Chlorophyll formation — —

3. Effects upon form — Prevention of etiolation; production of rosette form.

4. Effects upon development — Germination, time of flowering, etc.

5. Growth reaction. — —

6. Photonasty — Responses to diffuse light, or with no definite relation to direction of light.

7. Phototaxis   Movements relative to a source of light.

8. Phototropism   Curvatures with definite relation to the direction of unilateral light.

The first step in any of the above effects is usually the absorption of light by a special pigment, rather than by the more or less translucent protoplasm as a whole.

The light growth-reaction, photonasty, phototaxis, and phototropism are usually classified as phenomena of irritability and will be described here.

Changes in the Rate of Elongation of Roots and other Organs. The rate of elongation of roots, stems, and other organs such as hypocotyls, coleoptiles, and fungal sporangiophores is often dependent upon the presence or absence of light, though some are unaffected. It is well known, for example, that shoots growing in the dark run to a much greater length than when grown normally in the light, even though they have no opportunity of synthesizing new material and so increasing the total amount of matter which they contain. The relation between light and the rate at which comparatively simple organs, such as young roots, increase their length has been carefully observed. Red light is without effect, and can be used to make measurements when white light is excluded, so that differences caused by the latter can be determined.

A root of *Sinapis* kept under red light increased its length at a steady rate, which was carefully determined (fig. 83). When a weak white light was turned on, there was no visible change for half an hour, but at the end of that time elongation became perceptibly slower, though it became rather more rapid again after a further interval. Finally it settled down to a steady rate, slightly below that which occurred when white light was absent. The initial period during which no response was visible was presumably occupied by internal induction changes, and for this reason is given the name of *induction period*, and similar intervals of greater or lesser length occur in all responses to stimulation, whatever the nature of the stimulus.

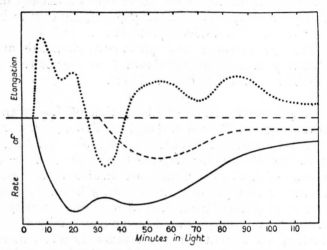

FIG. 83. Graph of the effect of light upon the elongation rates of *Sinapis* root (broken line); *Helianthus* hypocotyl (continuous line); *Phycomyces* sporangiophore (dotted line). Figures along the horizontal axis show the number of minutes in white light. (After Blaauw, modified)

The hypocotyl of a sunflower seedling (*Helianthus annuus*) was found to behave in a very similar way, the principal difference being that the induction period was much shorter, about 3 minutes instead of 30. The coleoptile of the oat (*Avena sativa*) and the sporangiophore of *Phycomyces* were also found to respond in a complicated fashion. The oscillations of the elongating rate in the fungus were even more numerous, and the final steady rate in light was actually faster instead of slower than the 'dark' rate, unless the intensity was very high. Similar results were also obtained if only a flash of light was given instead of continuous illumination, and it could then be shown that the amount of response, or change in elongation rate, was proportional to the amount of light received ($=$ intensity $\times$ duration of the flash). These complex changes are called the light growth-reaction.

PHOTONASTY

Periodic Movements of Flowers and Leaves. Many flowers open by day and close again at night, and a number of leaves exhibit similar motions in the so-called 'sleep' movements. Two causes are responsible, light and heat, both of which are present to a greater degree during the daytime than at night. It is often difficult to decide which of them is the stimulus causing any particular movement, but light is probably mainly responsible for the opening of daisy (*Bellis perennis*) heads, and wood sorrel (*Oxalis acetosella*) leaves; it also causes the closing of flowers such as evening primrose (*Oenothera*) and *Nicotiana*, and the drooping of balsam (*Impatiens*) leaves. The flower movements are most probably due to unequal growth on the two sides of the petals, while those of the leaves depend upon changes of turgor in the swollen pulvini at the hinge positions (cf. fig. 84).

PHOTOTAXIS

Free Swimming Cells. Many unicellular plants such as *Chlamydomonas*, and swarm spores, such as those of filamentous green algae, are able to move about owing to the lashing of their flagella, the direction of their motion frequently depending upon the direction of the light falling upon them. Usually they move towards the source, provided it is not too bright (**exp. 83**), and away from it if it exceeds a certain high intensity, but a few species move away from lights of even medium intensity.

The eyespots of many flagellates are red owing to the possession of carotene. It was at first supposed that the light inducing phototaxis was absorbed by the carotene; but recent experiments have shown that the action-spectra

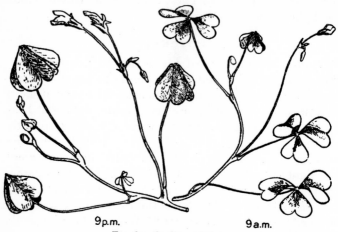

9 p.m.   9 a.m.

FIG. 84. *Oxalis corniculata*

Left, a shoot drawn at 9 p.m. with the leaflets in the 'sleep' position owing to the loss of turgor by the pulvini at their point of attachment to the petioles. Right, a shoot drawn at 9 a.m. with the leaflets elevated at the 'light' position. Somewhat reduced

of phototaxis in the **various** organisms examined are complex and various. Other pigments are apparently present and may be playing a part.

The slime fungi (Myxomycetes), which consist of naked protoplasm, and exhibit a gradual flowing motion, also move away from light sources.

Chloroplasts. In the leaves of many plants, the chloroplasts are able to take up different positions in the assimilating cells according to the brightness of the illumination. In a simple organ, such as the assimilating tissue of duckweed (*Lemna trisulca*), found just beneath the surface film of ponds, these arrangements are easily seen. In a moderate light the disk-shaped chloroplasts take up their position against the horiztonal walls, so exposing a maximum amount of surface to the light falling from above; but under very strong illumination the chloroplasts migrate to the

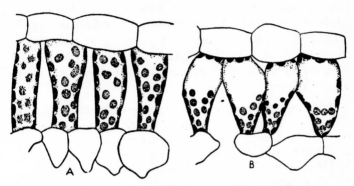

FIG. 85. PALISADE CELLS OF DWARF BEAN (*Phaseolus vulgaris*)
showing the position of the chloroplasts in diffuse daylight (A), and in parallel light falling at right angles to the leaf surface (B). × 300–400. (After Senn, modified)

vertical walls, and leave only the edges of their thickened disks pointing upwards. In darkness, the chloroplasts are scattered between the two positions, and this applies also to the chloroplasts in the palisade tissue of a complex leaf, in which there is much reflection from the cell walls. If the light is made to fall exactly at right angles to the leaf surface, and so pass straight down the length of the palisade cells, the chloroplasts tend to desert the long side walls and collect at the upper and lower ends. A very intense light has the opposite effect, and the movement is then towards the vertical walls, leaving the end ones bare. The mechanism of these movements is at present unknown, but they may be due to a streaming of the protoplasm carrying the chloroplasts with it.

PHOTOTROPISM

Just as in the case of geotropism, the curvatures which occur in response to a lateral light differ in different plants and organs, and may be classified according to their direction relative to the path of light. An organ which bends towards the source is said to be positively phototropic, while one which bends away from it is called negatively phototropic, and if a position is taken up at right angles to the path of light the organ is said to be transversely phototropic or diaphototropic. The commonest examples are as follows:

1. Positively phototropic	Primary stems; coleoptiles of grasses, etc.; sporangiophores of many fungi.
2. Negatively phototropic	Some primary roots.
3. Diaphototropic	Many leaves.
4. No response	Some roots.

Responses in Stems, Roots, and Coleoptiles. The responses of stems and roots are observed by growing seedlings under lateral illumination (**exp. 84**); like the responses of geotropism, they are limited to the young elongating zones. If the direction of the stimulus is altered, the second response occurs beyond the first, owing to the growth of the organ meanwhile and the consequent shifting of the responding region.

The coleoptile of grasses and cereals (fig. 64, p. 248) is particularly reactive to light and has proved especially useful in the study of phototropism. The response to a given light stimulus can be measured by the angle to which the coleoptile bends in a fixed time (cf. the auxin test on p. 249), and varies with the intensity of light both in its amount and direction. In low and moderate light intensities, curvature is towards the source of light up to about 3400 metre candles. There is then a reversal of reaction and, around 10,000 metre candles, the coleoptile actually bends away from the light source. There are further reversals at still higher light intensities.

Phototropic Induction. If the top 2 mm of a coleoptile are cut off, it loses its reactiveness to light even though the bending region lower down is unharmed. The light-accepting pigment must therefore be present in the tip.

An effective pigment can often be identified by comparing its light-absorption spectrum with the action spectrum of the process: for example, the wave-lengths of light most effective in photosynthesis correspond closely with those of the absorption bands of chlorophyll. The light-sensitive tip of coleoptiles (p. 248) is the only part to contain carotene. Carotene has two strong absorption bands in the blue-violet, and it has been shown that the lights most active in producing phototropic curvatures correspond closely. Nevertheless, it does not seem that carotene can be the light acceptor for phototropism, because albino mutants of barley, which have no carotene in their coleoptile tips, show strong phototropic responses. The effective light absorber seems to be a pigment of the riboflavin type. Responses by tissues which do not possess carotene are strong at wave-lengths where absorption by riboflavin is high. The relation of carotene to the action-spectrum seems to be due to its behaving as an internal light filter and thus increasing the difference of illumination between the two sides of the organ. The coleoptile is hollow (p. 248) and, when it is filled artificially with a dye, a corresponding increase of phototropic curvature can be observed.

Phototropic Conduction. When the tips of coleoptiles are shaded with tin-foil caps phototropic curving is not entirely prevented as when the tips are cut off (fig. 65, p. 249). The difference is explained by supposing that auxin, the substance which causes elongation, is formed in the tip above, but that the light absorbed may cause an unequal lateral distribution of it as it moves downwards. Direct examination has, indeed, shown that the illuminated side of the coleoptile contains less auxin in its zone of curvature than the shaded side. When the lower parts of the coleoptile are injected with a dye, to increase the difference of illumination between the two sides, curvature is increased and it appears likely that the lower concentration of auxin on the illuminated side is due to its destruction by light. Riboflavin catalyses the photolysis of auxin in aqueous solutions. It is present in all parts of the coleoptile and it or some allied pigment may well act similarly inside its cells; but this has not yet been proven.

Phototropic Responses of Leaves. Most leaves in their younger stages take up definite positions in relation to the direction of the light which they receive. These adjustments generally depend upon unequal rates of growth in the petiole, which by forming twists bring the leaf laminae into their final position. The power of elongating becomes much less or is entirely lost as the petiole grows older, and the ability to carry out these light responses goes with it. As a result of this, the leaf becomes permanently fixed in the position it has taken up, and light changes in the older stages have no visible effect. If a creeping branch of *Convolvulus*, *Calystegia*, etc. (fig. 86), is examined, it will be seen that, although the petioles arise from the stem in different ranks, they are twisted in such a way that all the laminae lie horizontally or approximately at right angles to the path of the light falling upon them.

Some plants have the opposite arrangement, their leaves being placed with their edges towards the direction of the strongest or midday light. The well-known *compass plants* (*Lactuca scariola*, etc.), which have their edges pointing due north and south, are examples of this kind.

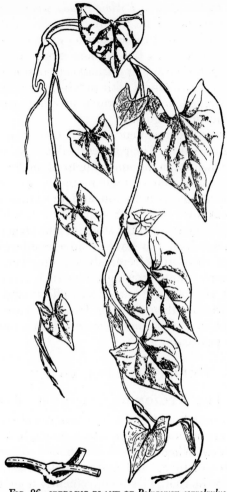

FIG. 86. SEEDLING PLANT OF *Polygonum convolvulus*

trailing over the surface of the ground. All the leaves have come into the horizontal position, regardless of their insertion on the stem, owing to the twisting of their petioles. About natural size. Insertion of one petiole shown enlarged

The leaf movements of *Robinia pseudacacia* depend upon turgor changes and are more elaborate; if the light is very strong they take up a profile position exposing only their edges to the direct rays, but in more moderate intensities they take up the customary transverse position. In this species, as in many others with pulvini, the power of response is retained in leaves which are fully grown, and frequent adjustments go on.

The biological consequences of all these leaf arrangements are interesting. Their general effect is to secure for the leaf the maximum amount of light of moderate intensity and to avoid that of high intensity. The former is effective in carbon assimilation and the latter is apt to cause a breakdown in the photosynthetic machinery, as well as a wider opening of the stomata and higher internal temperatures, which may have an adverse effect in hot or dry climates. It must be remembered, however, that the leaves of many plants growing under such conditions do not exhibit any of these directional effects and manage quite well without them. It is, in fact, very easy to credit such 'adaptations' with more biological importance than they really possess.

EXPERIMENTAL WORK

Exp. 77. The Region of Geotropic Response

Germinate some broad beans in a mixture of equal parts of silver sand and fine sawdust, which should be kept moist but not sodden. When the roots are about $\frac{3}{4}$ to 1 inch long, remove three of them, and mark equal divisions (about 2 mm) along the root. This is conveniently done by drawing out a fine thread of brunswick black between two pins and then dropping it across the root. The mark thus made adheres well when dry, and causes no damage to the tissues. By means of long wires or pins, fix the two beans to the cork of a wide-necked bottle lined with damp blotting-paper; when finally placed in position they should have their roots and flat sides horizontal. Put some water in the bottom of the bottle, insert the cork and leave over-night. By the following morning, response will be practically complete.

Measure the lengths now shown by each of the original divisions and notice that bending has occurred in the region of the greatest elongation (cf. fig. 77).

Exp. 78. OXYGEN NECESSARY FOR RESPONSE

Take one or two beans, germinated as in the previous experiment, and fix them below the cork of a wide-necked bottle by means of long pins, so that their roots and flat sides are horizontal. Clamp in this position outside the bottle for thirty minutes. Partly fill the bottle with an alkaline solution of pyrogallol, and then put in the beans, still fixed to the cork, which must fit tightly and should be painted with a thin coating of wax. The beans should be as near the liquid as possible without touching it.

The pyrogallol will rapidly absorb the oxygen above its surface, and it will be noticed that the bean roots show no curvature after a period which sufficed for marked response in **exp. 77**.

Exp. 79. REACTION TIME

Rule a horizontal straight line on a piece of cardboard, and fix the latter in a vertical position. Then fasten a young sunflower seedling to the board so that the root lies along the line. Keep under close observation, and note the time taken for the first appearance of response. This is usually a few minutes.

Exp. 80. GEOTROPIC RESPONSES OF GRASS NODES

Collect some long grass or cereal stalks with roots attached, selecting those which have prominent nodes. Prepare a

large flat cork by cutting a shallow groove across it, and
fasten a stalk horizontally with the node above the groove
by means of a piece of sheet cork or cardboard on either
side (fig. 87 A). Fix a second stalk only on the side nearest
the roots, leaving the upper end free to move. Embed the

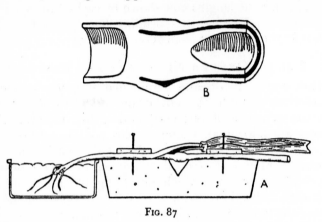

Fig. 87

roots of both in damp sawdust and keep thoroughly moist
for a week.

The second stalk being free to move above the node will
have returned to the vertical position owing to the greater
growth of the node's lower surface. If the outer leaf sheaths
are stripped away, it will be found that the unequal growth
of the fixed node has formed a swelling on its under side
(fig. 87 B).

Exp. 81. CURVATURE IN A REST POSITION
AFTER STIMULATION

Take three broad beans germinated as in **exp. 77** and lay
them on their side for 30 minutes. Mark their upper surfaces, and then plant them again in the sand and sawdust,
taking care that the roots are vertical. Examine again

after 24 hours, when it will be found that the root has curved away from the marked side, i.e. in the direction of the stimulus.

Exp. 82. The Clinostat

For construction of the apparatus see fig. 78. If a clinostat is not available, a simple one, sufficient for light weights, may be improvised from a cheap clock by removing the hands and fixing a thin rod to the 'minute' spindle. (A watch-mender will do this.) The rod should be passed through a cork and its far end supported in a hole drilled in a piece of hard wood or metal, the latter being supported by a stand. The cork may advantageously be covered with blotting-paper which can be kept moist.

a. Stimulate some broad beans as in the previous experiment, but instead of planting them in sawdust fix them to the cork with their roots parallel to the revolving rod. It is important to see that they are kept moist. After about 24 hours the roots will again have curved in the direction of the original stimulus, and the small stimuli received while revolving slowly on the clinostat will cancel one another out. This method of examining the effect of the initial stimulus is more reliable than that of **exp. 81**, since there any slight deviation from the vertical will lead to a further curvature, which may mask the primary response.

Fix a grass stalk with well-developed nodes on to a clinostat parallel to the axis of rotation. Keep it there for a week, during which period the roots must be kept moist with damp cotton-wool pinned to the clinostat. An automatic dripper can be arranged by corking a cotton-wool wick into the neck of a bottle of water and supporting it horizontally.

If the nodes are examined at the end of the experiment, they will be found to have developed a ring of tissue all round instead of on one side only as in **exp. 80**.

Exp. 83. Phototaxis

Introduce sufficient motile algae to give a green coloration into a beaker, darkened with brown paper and having a slit about ⅛ inch broad on one side. Allow to stand in a bright window. At the end of the day, strip away the paper, and the region of the slit will then be found to be coloured green by the algae which have collected there, whereas the darker sides will be free from them.

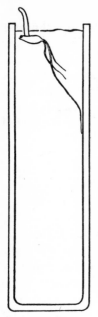

Large numbers of *Chlamydomonas* cells can usually be found in water butts or other fresh standing water during the summer. As an alternative, *Euglena* may be found in stagnant ponds in summer and autumn.

Exp. 84. Phototropism

Soak some oat grains, and plant in damp soil in a glass box (fig. 88). The soil must be crumbly and not too tightly packed and the grains should be near the surface and along one of the longer edges of the box. Place in a bright window and keep moist for a week to ten days. The coleop-

Fig. 88

tiles as they emerge will curve towards the light, and the rootlets will become visible on the darker side of the box away from the window. If a similar experiment is performed with mustard seed, the phototropic curvature of the young stems will also be observed.

Exp. 85. The Tip, the Sensitive Region of Coleoptiles

Soak about two dozen oat grains and put them to germi-nate in a pot of damp soil. The pot must be kept in the dark until the coleoptiles are half to three-quarters of an inch high (3 or 4 days). At this stage, cut the top 2 mm from about half the plants. This operation must be carried out in red light. Place a cap of dull black paper, with a slit in one side, over the pot without damaging the seedlings, and illuminate by means of an ordinary electric lamp placed about 1 foot from the slit. Turn out this light and examine the seedlings by red light, or very dull daylight, after 2 hours and again after 4 hours' illumination. The uncut coleoptiles will have curved towards the light, whereas the others will remain upright.

LIST OF SPECIAL REAGENTS AND METHODS OF PREPARATION

Alcohol. Required strengths may be obtained by diluting laboratory methylated spirits (= 95 per cent. alcohol).

Aniline chloride. Make up a saturated solution in distilled water, filter and acidify with a few drops of hydrochloric acid.

Aniline sulphate. Make up as aniline chloride, but acidify with sulphuric acid.

Auxin in lanolin. Dissolve 10 mg indolylacetic acid in a drop of alcohol and mix this thoroughly into 100 g hydrous lanolin. (If the lanolin is anhydrous, mix thoroughly with excess water, stand overnight, and decant the excess water.) The auxin in lanolin is best kept dark and cool, it will then remain effective for a few weeks.

Baryta water. N/10. Dissolve about 50 g of barium hydroxide and 15 g of barium chloride in 500 ml of boiling distilled water. Allow the solution to cool with a tube of soda lime corked into the neck of the flask. The excess barium hydroxide will crystallize out, and the clear fluid may be siphoned off into a second vessel, from which carbon dioxide has been removed, without allowing the solution to come into contact with the outer air. Its strength will be about 0·35 N. Add about a litre of freshly boiled distilled water, which has cooled under soda lime, and standardize with N/10 hydrochloric acid, using phenolphthalein.

Brom-cresol purple. Solutions in alcohol may be obtained ready for use.

Calcium chloride. Dissolves readily in water. Molar solution (M) = 111 g per l.

Caustic soda. Strong solution = 40 per cent. When dissolving in water keep well stirred, or the heat evolved may crack the vessel.

Chloral hydrate. Dissolve 160 g of chloral hydrate crystals in every 100 ml of water.

Chlor-zinc-iodine. (Schultze's Reagent.) Dissolve 110 g of zinc
in 300 ml of hydrochloric acid and evaporate to half the
volume. During the evaporation add a little extra zinc to
make sure that all the acid is neutralized. These operations
are best carried out in the open. Then dissolve 10 g of
potassium iodide in the least possible quantity of water
and add 0·15 g of iodine crystals. Mix the two solutions
and, if turbid, filter through glass wool. Keep in a tightly
stoppered bottle in the dark.

Cobalt chloride paper. Cut strips of filter-paper about 1 by 2 inches,
and dip into a 5 per cent. solution of cobalt chloride. Dry
in an oven at 100° C and keep in a desiccator.

Fehling's solution. Must be made up as two separate solutions
which are mixed immediately before use.

   Soln. A. 70 g of crystalline copper sulphate in a litre of
   distilled water.

   Soln. B. 350 g of Rochelle salt (sodium potassium tartrate)
   and 100 g of caustic soda in a litre of distilled water. Mix
   equal quantities of A and B.

Glycerine, dilute solution = 5 per cent.; prepared by making up
5 g of pure glycerine to 100 ml with distilled water.

Hydrochloric acid, N/10. Dilute 11·3 ml of concentrated acid
(sp. gr. = 1·16 at 15° C) to a litre. The resulting solution
will be roughly decinormal. For quantitative work it must
be standardized against a solution of pure sodium carbonate made up by weighing.

Iodine, solution in alcohol. Made by shaking up the crystals in
alcohol until a deep golden brown is obtained.

Iodine, in potassium iodide. Make a strong solution of potassium
iodide; add some crystals of iodine and shake up from time
to time. The solution as used should be a dark golden-
brown.

Lime-water. Shake up an excess of freshly slaked lime with
distilled water in a Winchester. Allow to stand until clear
and then siphon off the liquid into a second Winchester,
which has been freed from atmospheric carbon dioxide.
Can also be obtained from druggists.

Magneson II. Dissolve 0·1 g Magneson II, (*p*-nitrophenylazo-

1-naphthol), in 100 ml 1 per cent. sodium hydroxide and filter. The solid is readily obtainable.

Millon's reagent. 15 g of mercury are dissolved (in a fume cupboard) in 43 ml of strong nitric acid. Dilute with 80 ml of distilled water and filter after 2 hours. Can be obtained from dealers ready for use.

Nessler's reagent. Dissolve 62·5 g potassium iodide in 250 ml distilled water. Remove and set aside a few millilitres. To the rest, add about 500 ml cold saturated mercuric chloride until the precipitate of mercuric iodide no longer dissolves on stirring. Then add back the few millilitres of solution originally set aside and further mercuric chloride very cautiously until a slight permanent precipitate is formed. Then slowly add 150 g potassium hydroxide in 150 ml water and make up to 1 l. The reagent may be diluted with 5 parts of water immediately before use.

Phenol phthalein. Dissolve 1 g in 100 ml alcohol.

Phloroglucin. Make a saturated solution in alcohol and gradually add strong hydrochloric acid until precipitation begins.

Pyrogallol, alkaline solution. Dissolve 28 g of pyrogallol in 100 ml of distilled water, and 50 g of potassium hydroxide in a second 100 ml. Mix the two solutions immediately before use.

Schimper's solution. 160 g of chloral hydrate in every 100 ml of distilled water. Colour by adding a few drops of strong iodine solution.

Sodium cobaltinitrite. Dissolve 20 g cobalt nitrate and 35 g sodium nitrite in 65 ml water and 10 ml glacial acetic acid. Filter, if necessary, and keep in a cool place.

Sodium picrate paper. Dip strips of filter-paper into 1 per cent. picric acid, and allow to dry in air. Just before use moisten with 10 per cent. sodium carbonate.

arch solution. Mix 1 g of dry starch into a suspension in a little cold distilled water. Bring 200 ml of distilled water to the boil in a beaker, and pour in the suspension, stirring all the time. Continue to boil for about a minute and then allow to cool. If the solution is at all lumpy a part of it may be filtered while still hot. The filter-paper soon becomes clogged, but the clear filtrate contains sufficient starch to give a deep coloration with iodine.

Sucrose. Commercial granulated sugar is extremely pure and may be used. For a molar solution dissolve 342 g and make up to a litre.

Sudan III, alcoholic solutions may be obtained ready for use.

BIBLIOGRAPHY

THE following is a short selected list of books dealing with the physiology of plants and written in English. Up-to-date reading at an advanced level is to be found very largely in review articles in recent numbers of *Annual Review of Plant Physiology, Biological Reviews, Botanical Review, Endeavour, Nature, New Phytologist, School Science Review*, and *Science Progress*.

GENERAL

DAVSON, H., *Textbook of General Physiology*. 2nd edition. London, 1959.

FRUTON, J. S., and SIMMONDS, S., *General Biochemistry*. New York, 1958.

MEYER, B. S., ANDERSON, D. B., and BOHNING, P. H., *Introduction to Plant Physiology*. 2nd edition. New Jersey, 1960.

RUHLAND, W., *et al.*, *Encyclopedia of Plant Physiology*. Berlin, 1955.

SKENE, M., *The Biology of Flowering Plants*. London, 1924.

STEWARD, F. C., *et al.*, *Plant Physiology*. New York, 1960.

THOMAS, M., RANSON, S. L., and RICHARDSON, J. A., *Plant Physiology*. 4th edition. London, 1956.

CHAPTER I. *Material and Energy*

ARBER, A., *Water Plants*. Cambridge, 1930.

FOGG, G. E., *The Metabolism of Algae*. London, 1953.

GALE, E. F., *The Chemical Activities of Bacteria*. London, 1947.

HILL, R., and WHITTINGHAM, C. P., *Photosynthesis*. London, 1953.

LOFTFIELD, J. V. G., *The Behaviour of Stomata*. Carnegie Institute of Washington Publication 314, Washington, 1921.

RABINOWITCH, E. I., *Photosynthesis and Related Processes*. New York, 1945.

CHAPTER II
Sugars and the Plant Materials formed from them

BELL, D. J., *Introduction to Carbohydrate Biochemistry*. 3rd edition. London, 1952.

PIGMAN, W., *The Carbohydrates: Chemistry, Biochemistry, Physiology*. New York, 1957.

CHAPTER III

The Decomposition of Sugars and the Liberation of Energy

BEEVERS, H., *Respiratory Metabolism in Plants*. New York, 1960.
DAVIES, D. D., *Intermediary Metabolism in Plants*. Cambridge, 1961.
JAMES, W. O., *Plant Respiration*. Oxford, 1953.

CHAPTER IV. *Nitrogenous Compounds*

BURGES, A., *Micro-organisms in the Soil*. London, 1958.
HALLSWORTH, E. G., *Nutrition of the Legumes*. (Symposium.) New York and London, 1958.
HARLEY, J. L., *The Biology of Mycorrhiza*. London, 1959.
LLOYD F. E., *The Carnivorous Plants*. Waltham, Mass., 1942.
RUSSELL, E. J., *Soil Conditions and Plant Growth*. 8th edition by E. W. Russell. London, 1950.

CHAPTER V

Some Physical Characters of Organic Substances
and

CHAPTER VI. *Catalytic Protoplasm*

DOWNES, H. R., *The Chemistry of Living Cells*. New York, 1955.
FREY-WYSSLING, A., *Macromolecules in Cell Structure*. Harvard, 1957.
NEILANDS, J. B., STUMPF, K., and STANIER, R. Y., *Outlines of Enzyme Chemistry*. London, 1955.
PRESTON, R. D., *The Molecular Architecture of Plant Cell Walls*. London, 1952.
ROELOFSEN, P. A., *The Plant Cell-wall*. Berlin, 1959.

CHAPTER VII. *Water*

CRAFTS, A. S., CURRIER, H. B., and STOCKING, C. R., *Water in the Physiology of Plants*. Waltham, Mass., 1949.
DIXON, H. H., *Transpiration and the Ascent of Sap in Plants*. London, 1914.
—— *The Transpiration Stream*. London, 1924.
KRAMER, P. J., *Plant and Soil Water Relationships*. New York, 1949.
LEVITT, J., *Frost, Drought and Heat Resistance*. Vienna, 1958.
MAXIMOV, N. A., *The Plant in Relation to Water*. London, 1929.
WEAVER, J. E., *Root Development of Field Crops*. New York, 1926.

CHAPTER VIII. *Nutrition*

BRIGGS, G. E., HOPE, A. B., and ROBERTSON, R. N., *Electrolytes and Plant Cells*. Oxford, 1961.

HAMBIDGE, G., and others, *Hunger Signs in Crops*. Washington, 1941.

STILES, W., *Trace Elements in Plants and Animals*. 3rd edition. Cambridge, 1961.

WALLACE, T., *The Diagnosis of Mineral Deficiencies in Plants by Visual Symptoms*. London, 1951.

CHAPTERS IX AND X. *Growth and Irritability*

AUDUS, L. J., *Plant Growth Substances*. 2nd edition. London, 1959.

CROCKER, W., and BARTON, L. V., *Physiology of Seeds*. Waltham, Mass., 1953.

HINSHELWOOD, C. N., *Chemical Kinetics of the Bacterial Cell*. Oxford, 1946.

LEOPOLD, A. C., *Auxins and Plant Growth*. Berkeley and Los Angeles, 1955.

LOOMIS, W. E., and others, *Growth and Differentiation in Plants*. (Symposium.) Ames, Iowa, 1953.

MILTHORPE, F. L. (editor), *The Growth of Leaves*. (Symposium.) London, 1956.

EXPERIMENTAL

CLARKE, L. J., *Botany as an Experimental Science in Laboratory and Garden*. Oxford, 1935.

HEWITT, E. J., *Sand and Water Culture. Methods used in the Study of Plant Nutrition*. Farnham Royal, 1952.

LOOMIS, W. E., and SHULL, C. A., *Methods in Plant Physiology*. New York, 1937.

McLEAN, R. C., and COOK, W. R., *Plant Science Formulae*. London, 1941.

—— —— *Textbook of Practical Botany*. London, 1952.

MEYER, B. S., and ANDERSON, D. B., *Laboratory Plant Physiology*. Lithographed. Ann Arbor, 1935.

INDEX

The principal references are given in heavy type

REPRINTED LITHOGRAPHICALLY IN GREAT BRITAIN
AT THE UNIVERSITY PRESS, OXFORD
BY VIVIAN RIDLER
PRINTER TO THE UNIVERSITY